Cultural Geography

Human Impact on Place

A Visual Approach

Computer Design
Photocopy

Street Scene in Kathmandu, Nepal more than a year after a devastating earthquake.

Human Impact on Place

A Visual Approach

Custom Learning Solutions provided by Instructional Design Works and is intended to be used as an e-book and supplemented with embedded course material including discussions, labs, projects, and assessments.

Website: http://www.instructionaldesignworks.com
IG @life.by.ty

Tyrell Heaton, Patagonia

About the Author

Tyrell Heaton is an accomplished communications professional, geographer and freelance photojournalist with more than 20 years experience capturing images of people and places in 100 countries. He has written articles from Antarctica to Afghanistan in his quest to tell a story. Having grown up in South Dakota he found cultures the antithesis of anything he had previously experienced so he became the explorer he had dreamed about since the age of six. He traversed Russia on the Siberian Railway, learned to haggle in Chinese, completed an Ironman in Brazil, and was witness to escalated protests in Korea. Each new encounter taught him something about the world and himself to create a unique voice as a writer and keen vision as a photographer.

An avid runner, he has spoken at several marathons and sat on expert-running panels. Having coached track & field at the collegiate level for more than a decade he gained clientele ranging from Olympians to professional football (NFL) players; additionally he has trained more than 500 first-time runners through the marathon distance.

As an Emmy Award-winning journalist Ty promotes the positive effects of travel, education, exercise and an overall healthy lifestyle.

Books:

Heaton, T. (2020). *Travel Translated - How Travel Affects your Brain & The Psychology Behind Place.* Instructional Design Works, ISBN 13- 979-8630003805.

Heaton, T. (2019). *Human Geography - Perception on Place: A Visual Approach*, Instructional Design Works. ISBN 9781796605136.

Heaton, T. (2018). *World Geography - The Impact of Place on Thought: A Visual Approach*, Instructional Design Works. ISBN 13- 978-1980804024.

Human Impact on Place

A Visual Approach

Cultural geography focuses on the uneven distribution of people and human activity on the surface of the earth and on the causes and consequences of these uneven spatial patterns and cultural landscapes.

This book covers the various cultural landscapes created by humans around the globe by region and will introduce you to the systematic study of patterns and processes that have shaped human understanding, use, and alteration of the Earth's surface. Such landscapes include patterns in agriculture, urban development, populations, economics, languages, religions, and more. Used in conjunction with a cultural or human geography course, this book provides an overview of many different cultures and the opportunity to compare other cultures to your own.

Rural Argentina – Tyrell Heaton

This book is designed to help you gain insight into your own behavior by recognizing that the individual choices you make are part of a wider pattern of place and environmental choices that ultimately form the geographic patterns of the world for the future.

Objectives & Outcomes

- Analyze human interaction with the environment and how it impacts geographic patterns of the world.
- Compare human behavior within different geographies across the globe.
- Explain the tools and techniques that geographers use to examine social, cultural, and economic relationships.
- Critique suggested explanations of the uneven distribution of human activity.
- Explain significant historical and cultural events of various societies.
- Analyze various political and economic systems and their impact through exploring regions/realms of the world.
- Discuss religion, politics, language, population, agriculture, urbanization, environmental, and social problems.

Contents

Introduction......6
Geography Themes and Essential Elements.....38
Techniques of Geographic Analysis......62
Physical Geography.....76
Population Geography....97
Human Geography.....131
Political Geography.....177
Economic Geography.....213
An Urbanizing World.....244
Why Geography.....276

Geography

Introduction

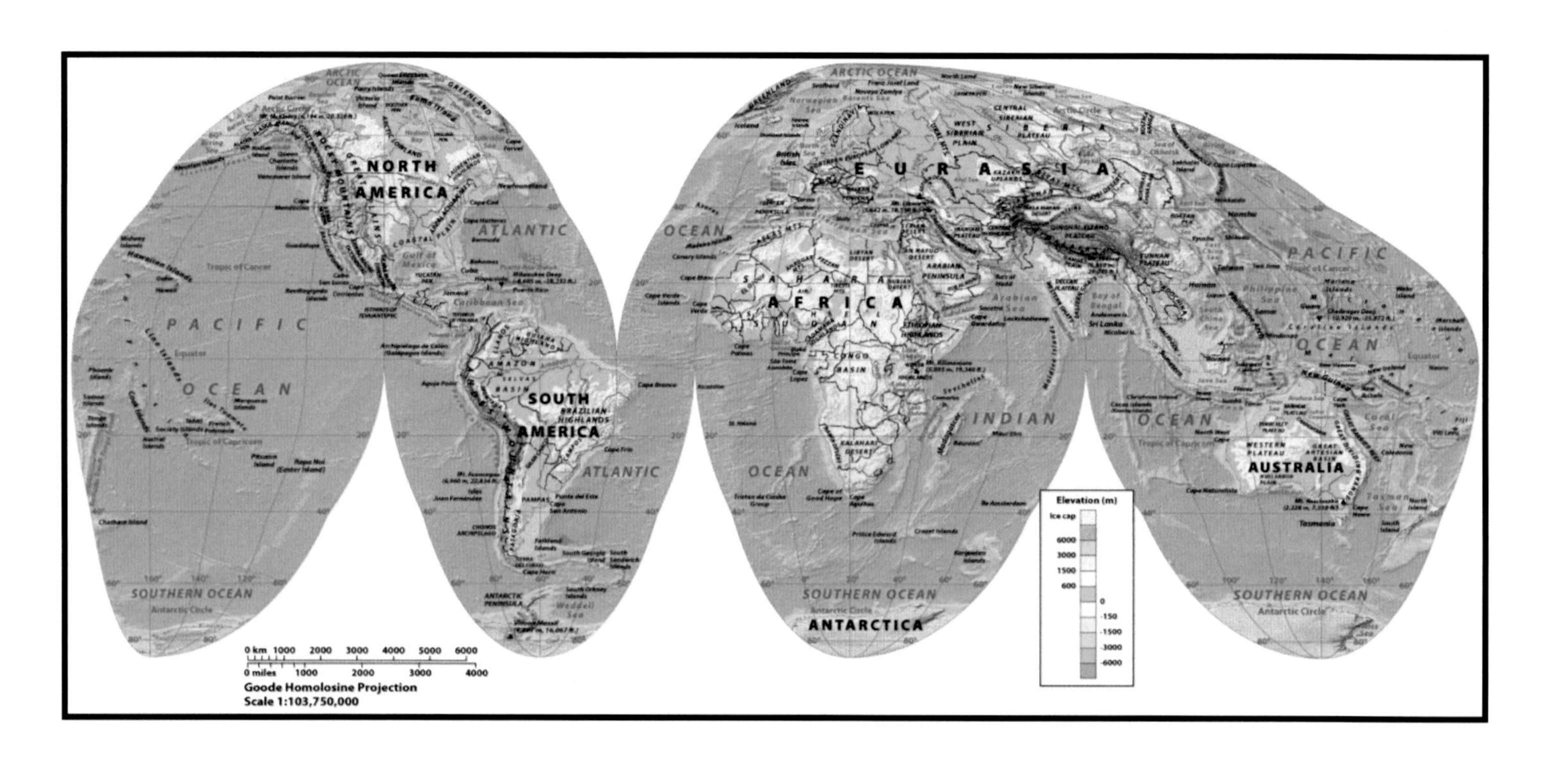
NORTH AMERICA
SOUTH AMERICA
EURASIA
AFRICA
AUSTRALIA
ANTARCTICA
PACIFIC
OCEAN
ATLANTIC
OCEAN
INDIAN
OCEAN
PACIFIC
OCEAN
SOUTHERN OCEAN
SOUTHERN OCEAN
SOUTHERN OCEAN
ARCTIC OCEAN
Elevation (m)
Ice cap
6000
3000
1500
600
0
-150
-1500
-3000
-6000
0 km 1000 2000 3000 4000 5000 6000
0 miles 1000 2000 3000 4000
Goode Homolosine Projection
Scale 1:103,750,000

Tyrell Heaton, Atlantic Ocean over the Azores

Geography

- 'To write about the earth'
- The study of **place** and **space**
- Studies the **location** and **distribution** of features on the **earth's surface**
- Studies **human activity**, the **natural environment**, and the **relationship** between the two
- Answers **where?** and **why?**
- For example:
    - ***Where is Timbuktu, Mali and why did this settlement evolve on this site?***

Classification Systems

<u>Biologists</u> → Taxonomy: kingdom, phylum, Class, order, family, genus, species

<u>Geologists</u> → Three major groups, subsidiary groups, geological time

<u>Historians</u> → Eras, ages, periods

<u>Geographers</u> → **Geographic realms and/or regions based on sets of spatial criteria**

World Geographic Realms

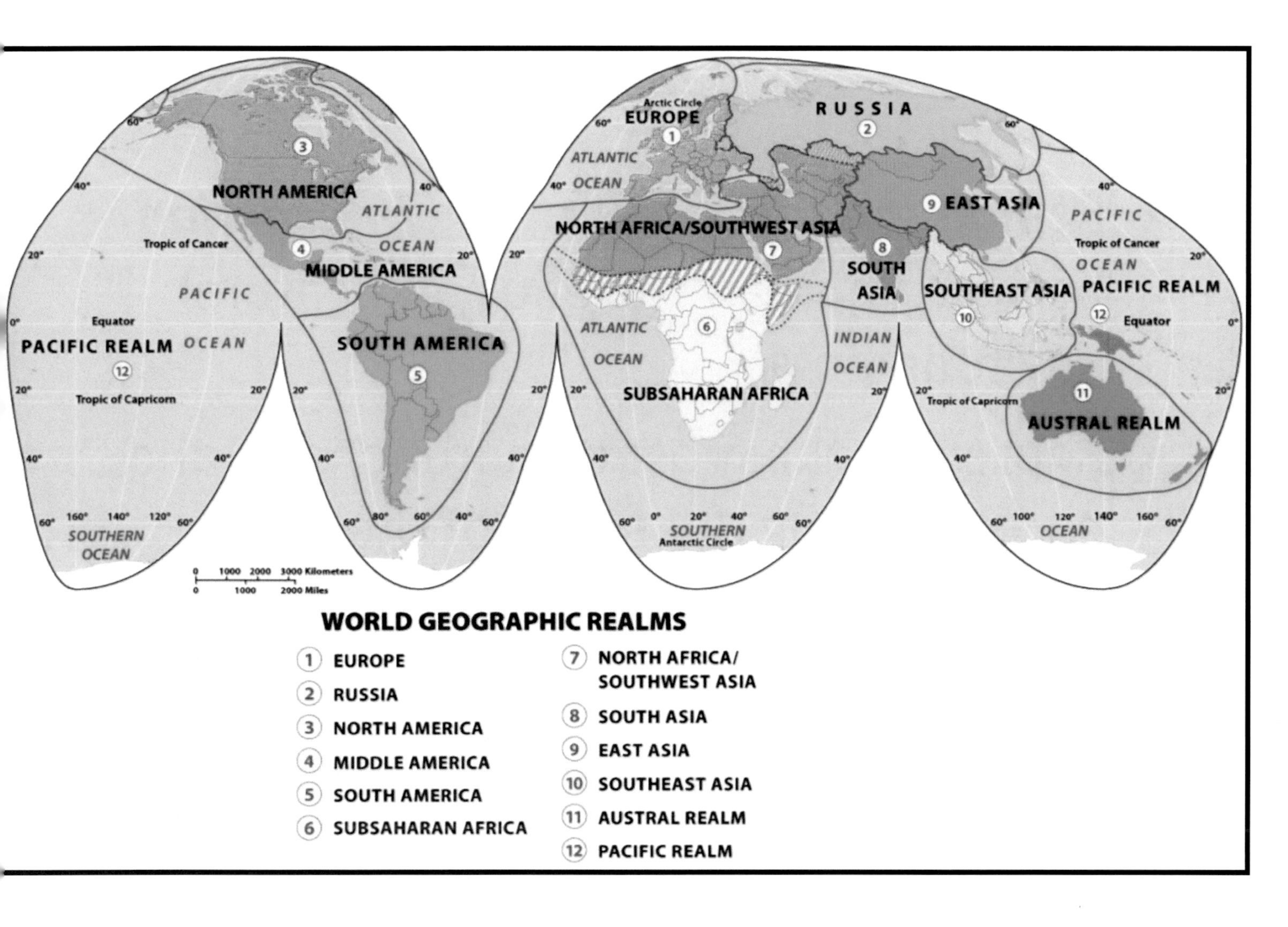

Arctic Circle
EUROPE
RUSSIA
ATLANTIC OCEAN
NORTH AMERICA
ATLANTIC OCEAN
Tropic of Cancer
MIDDLE AMERICA
PACIFIC OCEAN
Equator
PACIFIC REALM
SOUTH AMERICA
Tropic of Capricorn
SOUTHERN OCEAN
NORTH AFRICA/SOUTHWEST ASIA
EAST ASIA
PACIFIC OCEAN
SOUTH ASIA
SOUTHEAST ASIA
PACIFIC REALM
ATLANTIC OCEAN
INDIAN OCEAN
SUBSAHARAN AFRICA
AUSTRAL REALM
SOUTHERN
Antarctic Circle
OCEAN
0 1000 2000 3000 Kilometers
0 1000 2000 Miles
WORLD GEOGRAPHIC REALMS
1 EUROPE
2 RUSSIA
3 NORTH AMERICA
4 MIDDLE AMERICA
5 SOUTH AMERICA
6 SUBSAHARAN AFRICA
7 NORTH AFRICA/ SOUTHWEST ASIA
8 SOUTH ASIA
9 EAST ASIA
10 SOUTHEAST ASIA
11 AUSTRAL REALM
12 PACIFIC REALM

- Realms are based on ***spatial criteria***
- They are the ***largest geographic units*** into which the world can be divided
- Based on both ***physical*** (natural) and ***human*** (cultural) features

Geographic Realms

- Realms are the result of the ***interaction*** between human societies and natural environments
- Represent the most comprehensive and encompassing definition of the ***great clusters of humankind*** in the world today

- ***Change*** over time…
  - Would the world have been divided up the same way in 1491?

Transition Zones

- Where geographic realms meet, ***transition zones***, not sharp boundaries, mark their contact.
- This zone is an area of ***spatial change*** where peripheries of two adjacent realms or regions join.
- Zones are marked by a ***gradual shift*** (rather than a sharp break) in the characteristics that distinguish neighboring realms.

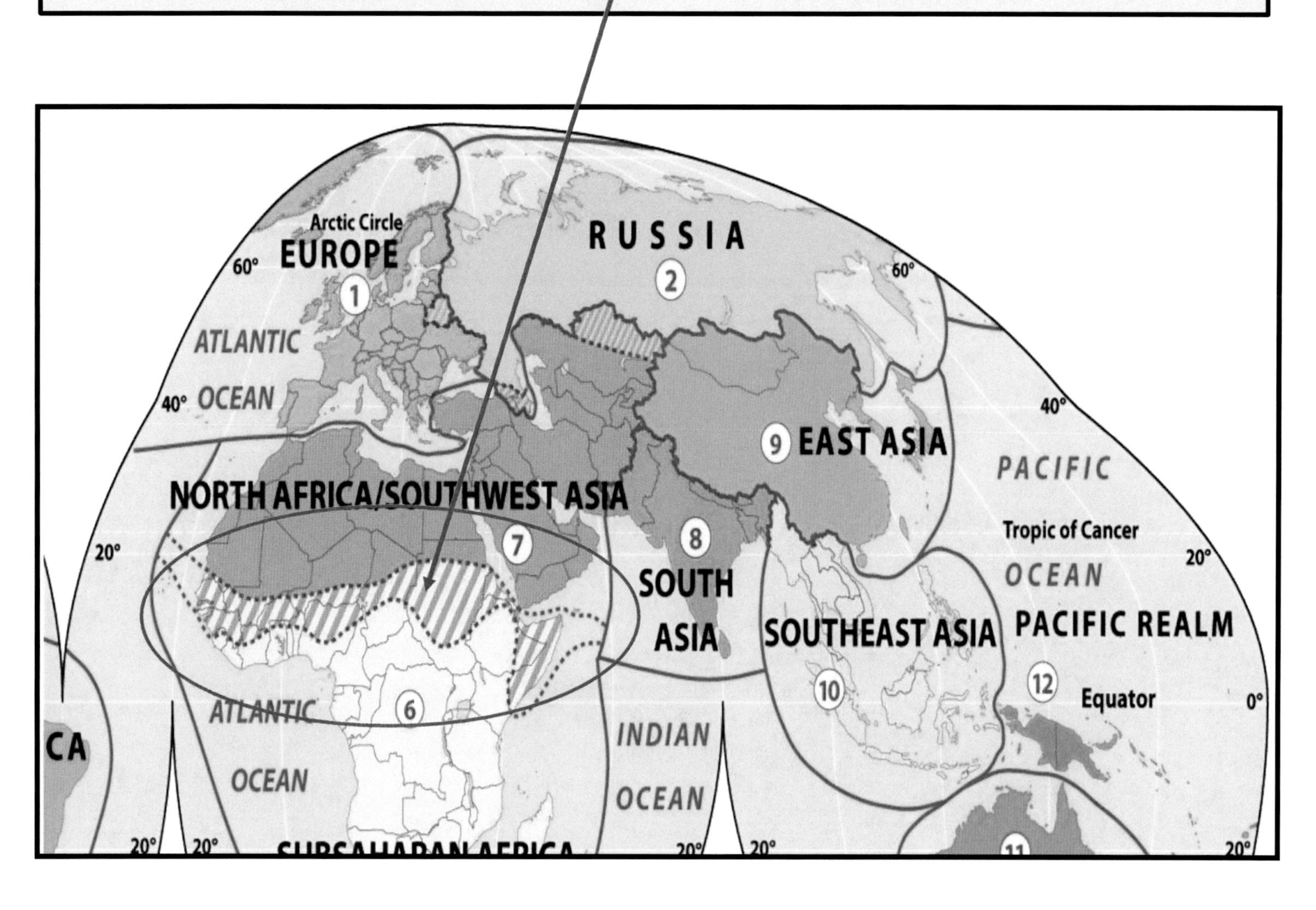

Arctic Circle
EUROPE
1
RUSSIA
2
60°
ATLANTIC
40° OCEAN
40°
9 EAST ASIA
PACIFIC
NORTH AFRICA/SOUTHWEST ASIA
7
8
SOUTH
ASIA
Tropic of Cancer
OCEAN
20°
SOUTHEAST ASIA
PACIFIC REALM
10
12
Equator
0°
6
ATLANTIC
OCEAN
INDIAN
OCEAN
CA

Geographical Classification

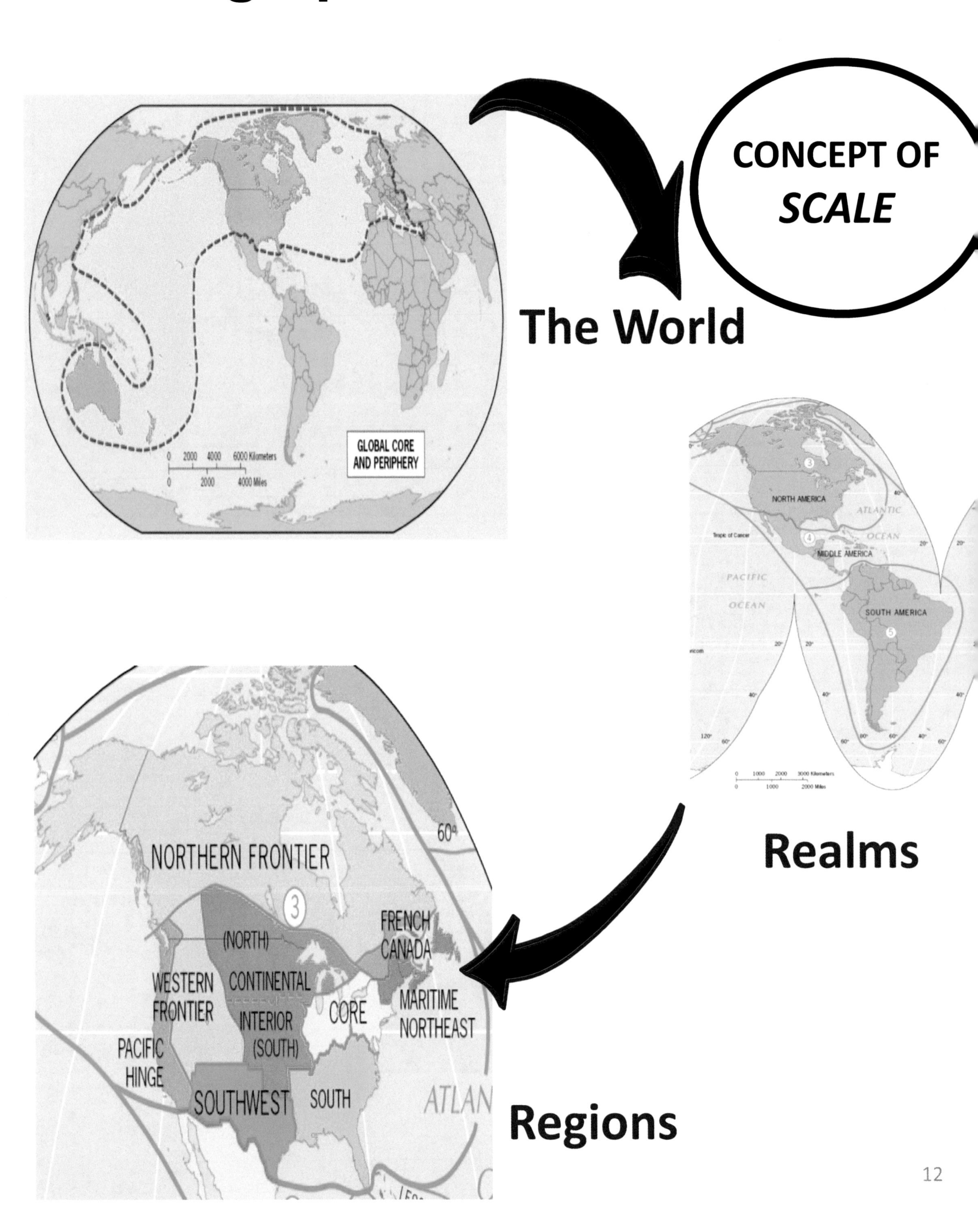

CONCEPT OF
SCALE
GLOBAL CORE
AND PERIPHERY
0 2000 4000 6000 Kilometers
0 2000 4000 Miles
The World
NORTH AMERICA
ATLANTIC
OCEAN
MIDDLE AMERICA
PACIFIC
OCEAN
SOUTH AMERICA
Realms
NORTHERN FRONTIER
(NORTH)
FRENCH
CANADA
WESTERN
FRONTIER
CONTINENTAL
INTERIOR
(SOUTH)
CORE
MARITIME
NORTHEAST
PACIFIC
HINGE
SOUTHWEST
SOUTH
Regions

Regions

- Areas of the earth's surface marked by certain **properties**
- Based on criteria **we establish**
- Criteria can be:
  - ✓ *Human* (cultural) properties
  - ✓ *Physical* (natural) characteristics
  - ✓ or both

Regions are smaller and more detailed than **realms**

Tyrell Heaton - Ulan Bator, Mongolia

Regions

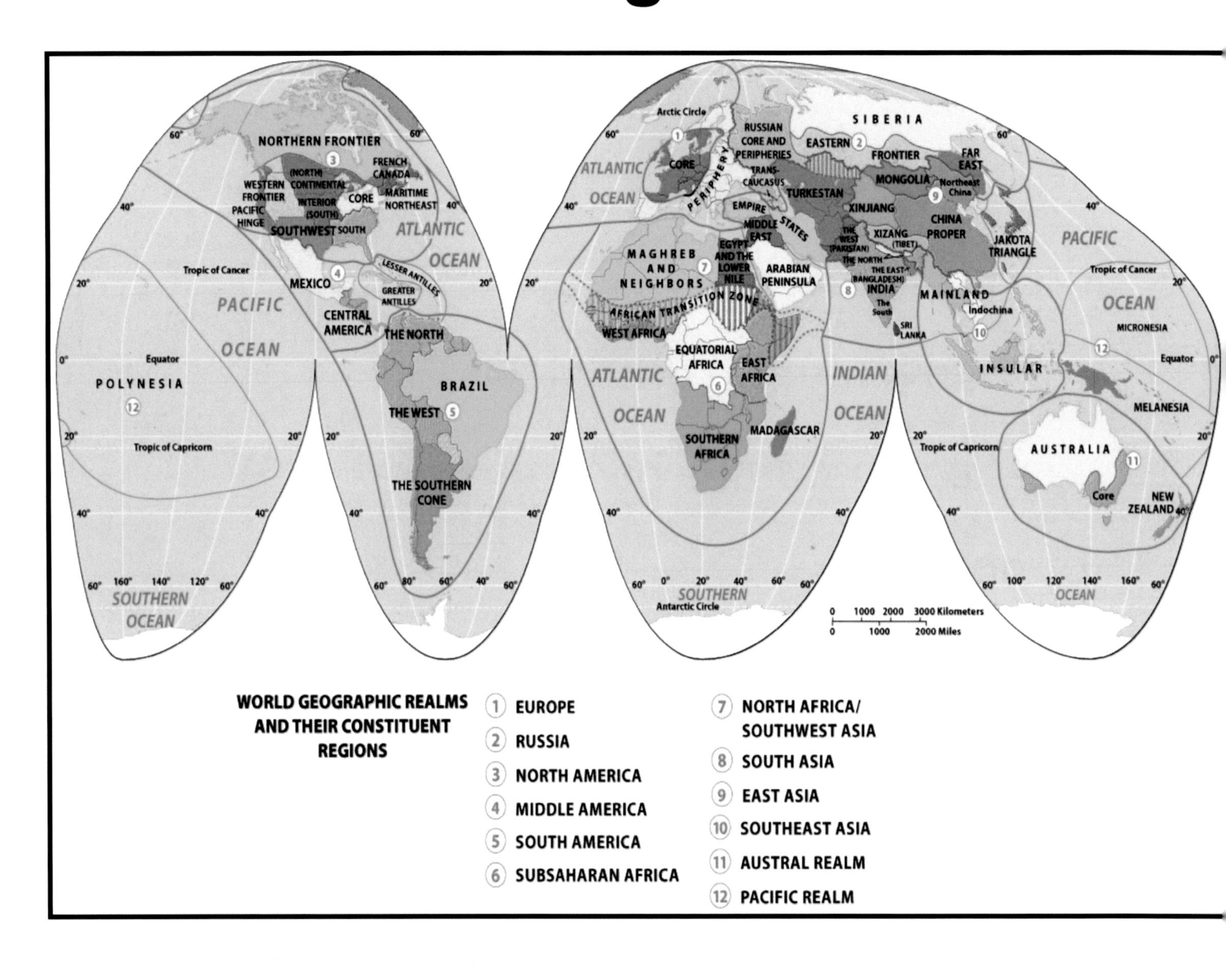
WORLD GEOGRAPHIC REALMS AND THEIR CONSTITUENT REGIONS
1 EUROPE
2 RUSSIA
3 NORTH AMERICA
4 MIDDLE AMERICA
5 SOUTH AMERICA
6 SUBSAHARAN AFRICA
7 NORTH AFRICA/ SOUTHWEST ASIA
8 SOUTH ASIA
9 EAST ASIA
10 SOUTHEAST ASIA
11 AUSTRAL REALM
12 PACIFIC REALM
NORTHERN FRONTIER
FRENCH CANADA
(NORTH) CONTINENTAL INTERIOR (SOUTH)
WESTERN FRONTIER
PACIFIC HINGE
CORE
MARITIME NORTHEAST
SOUTHWEST
SOUTH
MEXICO
CENTRAL AMERICA
LESSER ANTILLES
GREATER ANTILLES
THE NORTH
BRAZIL
THE WEST
THE SOUTHERN CONE
POLYNESIA
SIBERIA
RUSSIAN CORE AND PERIPHERIES
EASTERN
FRONTIER
FAR EAST
PERIPHERY
TRANS-CAUCASUS
TURKESTAN
MONGOLIA
Northeast China
XINJIANG
CHINA PROPER
XIZANG (TIBET)
JAKOTA TRIANGLE
EMPIRE STATES
MIDDLE EAST
MAGHREB AND NEIGHBORS
EGYPT AND THE LOWER NILE
ARABIAN PENINSULA
INDIA
The South
SRI LANKA
MAINLAND
Indochina
INSULAR
AFRICAN TRANSITION ZONE
WEST AFRICA
EQUATORIAL AFRICA
EAST AFRICA
SOUTHERN AFRICA
MADAGASCAR
MICRONESIA
MELANESIA
AUSTRALIA
Core
NEW ZEALAND
ATLANTIC OCEAN
PACIFIC OCEAN
INDIAN OCEAN
SOUTHERN OCEAN
Arctic Circle
Tropic of Cancer
Equator
Tropic of Capricorn
Antarctic Circle
0 1000 2000 3000 Kilometers
0 1000 2000 Miles

All regions have:

- An area
- Boundaries
- Location

Formal Region

- Marked by a certain degree of **homogeneity** in one or more phenomena
- Also called a ***uniform*** region or ***homogeneous*** region

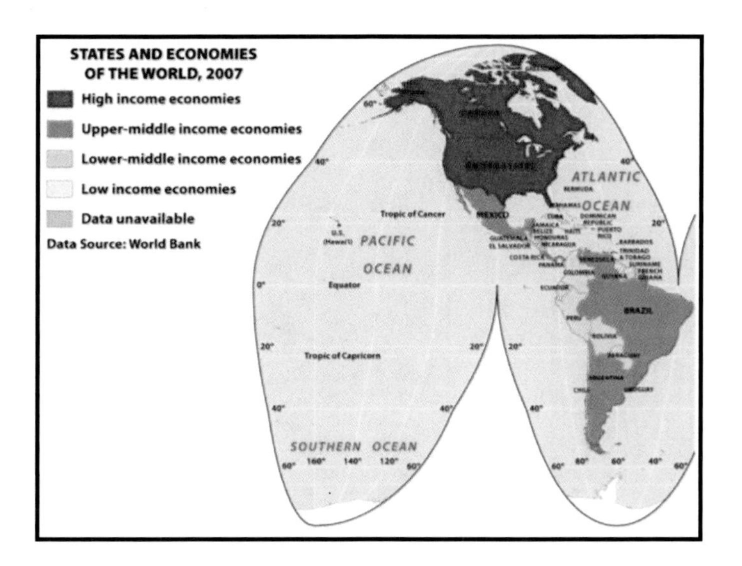

STATES AND ECONOMIES OF THE WORLD, 2007
High income economies
Upper-middle income economies
Lower-middle income economies
Low income economies
Data unavailable
Data Source: World Bank
ATLANTIC OCEAN
PACIFIC OCEAN
SOUTHERN OCEAN
Tropic of Cancer
Tropic of Capricorn
Equator
MEXICO
BRAZIL

Examples:

- English language, global spread
- Economic development, levels

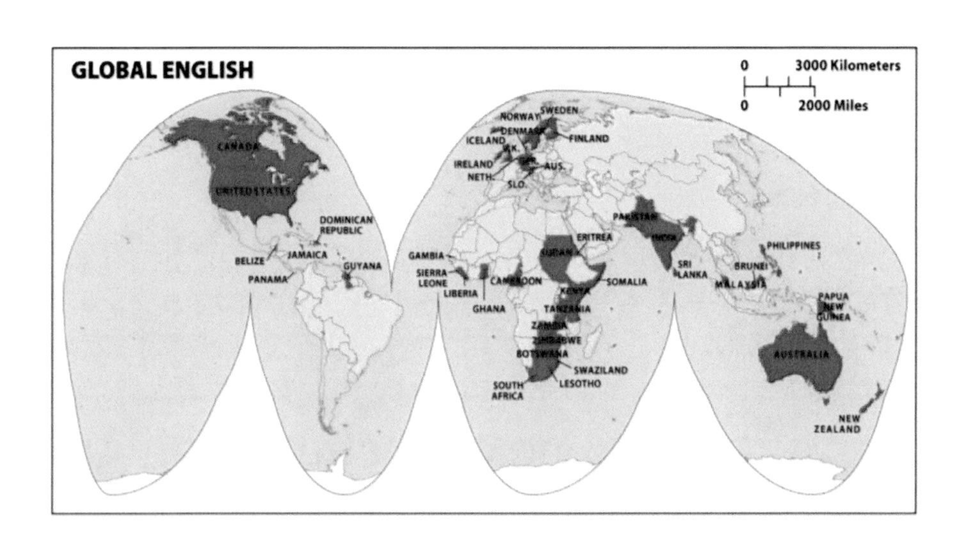

GLOBAL ENGLISH
0 3000 Kilometers
0 2000 Miles
CANADA
DOMINICAN REPUBLIC
BELIZE
JAMAICA
GUYANA
PANAMA
NORWAY
SWEDEN
ICELAND
FINLAND
IRELAND
AUS.
NETH.
SLO.
PAKISTAN
INDIA
ERITREA
GAMBIA
SIERRA LEONE
LIBERIA
GHANA
CAMEROON
SOMALIA
KENYA
TANZANIA
ZAMBIA
ZIMBABWE
BOTSWANA
SWAZILAND
LESOTHO
SOUTH AFRICA
SRI LANKA
PHILIPPINES
BRUNEI
MALAYSIA
PAPUA NEW GUINEA
AUSTRALIA
NEW ZEALAND

Functional Region

- A region marked less by its sameness than its **<u>dynamic internal structure</u>**

- A spatial system focused on a central core
- A region formed by a set of places and their functional integration
- Also called a ‘<u>nodal</u>’ region

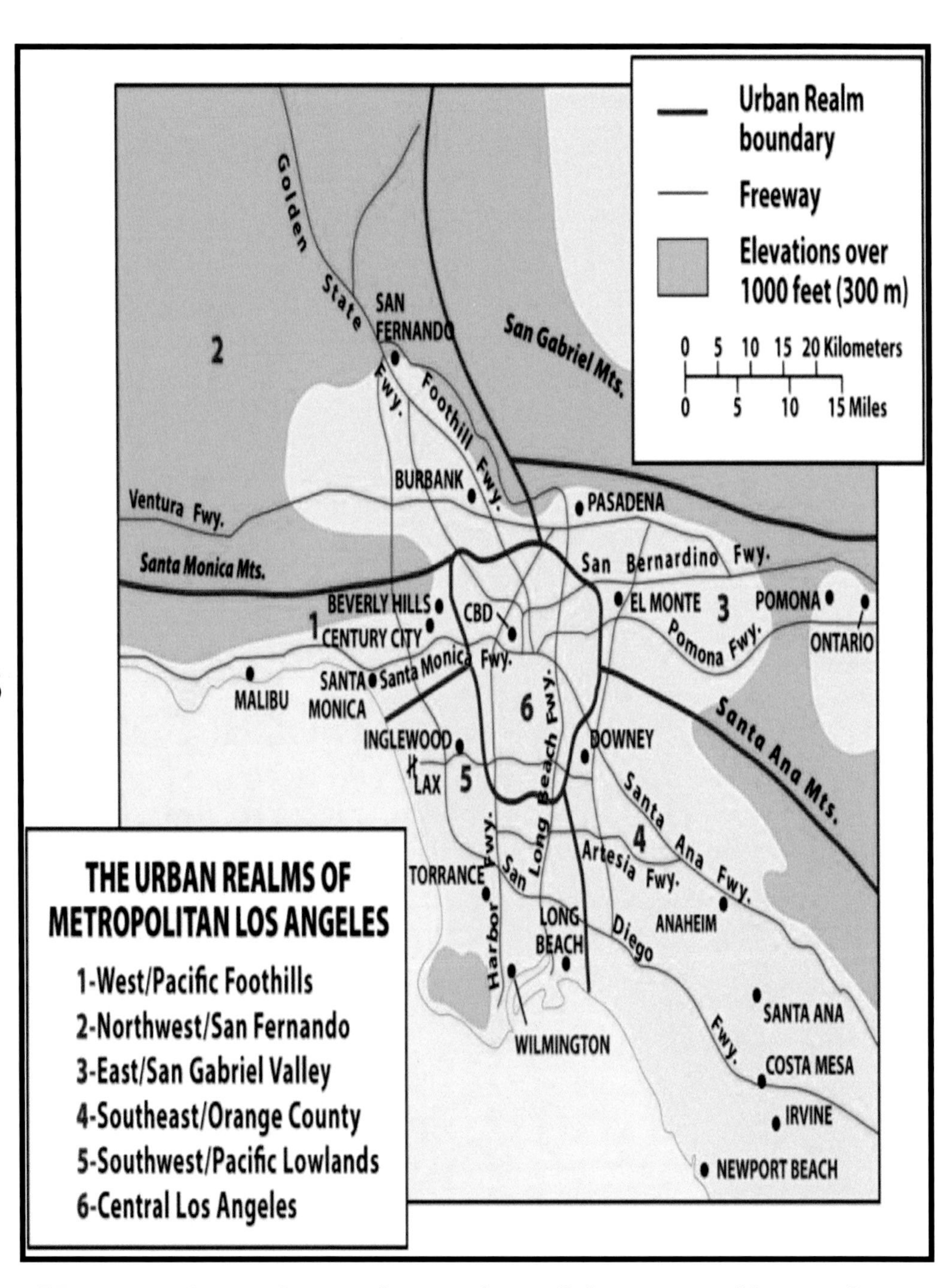

Urban Realm boundary
Freeway
Elevations over 1000 feet (300 m)
0 5 10 15 20 Kilometers
0 5 10 15 Miles
Golden State Fwy.
SAN FERNANDO
San Gabriel Mts.
Foothill Fwy.
BURBANK
Ventura Fwy.
PASADENA
Santa Monica Mts.
San Bernardino Fwy.
BEVERLY HILLS
CENTURY CITY
CBD
EL MONTE
POMONA
ONTARIO
Pomona Fwy.
MALIBU
SANTA MONICA
Santa Monica Fwy.
Long Beach Fwy.
DOWNEY
Santa Ana Mts.
INGLEWOOD
LAX
Santa Ana Fwy.
TORRANCE
Harbor Fwy.
San Diego Fwy.
Artesia Fwy.
ANAHEIM
LONG BEACH
WILMINGTON
SANTA ANA
COSTA MESA
IRVINE
NEWPORT BEACH
1
2
3
4
5
6
THE URBAN REALMS OF METROPOLITAN LOS ANGELES
1-West/Pacific Foothills
2-Northwest/San Fernando
3-East/San Gabriel Valley
4-Southeast/Orange County
5-Southwest/Pacific Lowlands
6-Central Los Angeles

Example: Los Angeles Metropolitan Area

Hinterland

- Literally means *'country behind'*

- A term that applies to the service area 'behind' (often surrounding) an urban center
- An urban center is the focus of goods and services (often 'the market') produced in the hinterland, and is the latter's dominant focal point as well

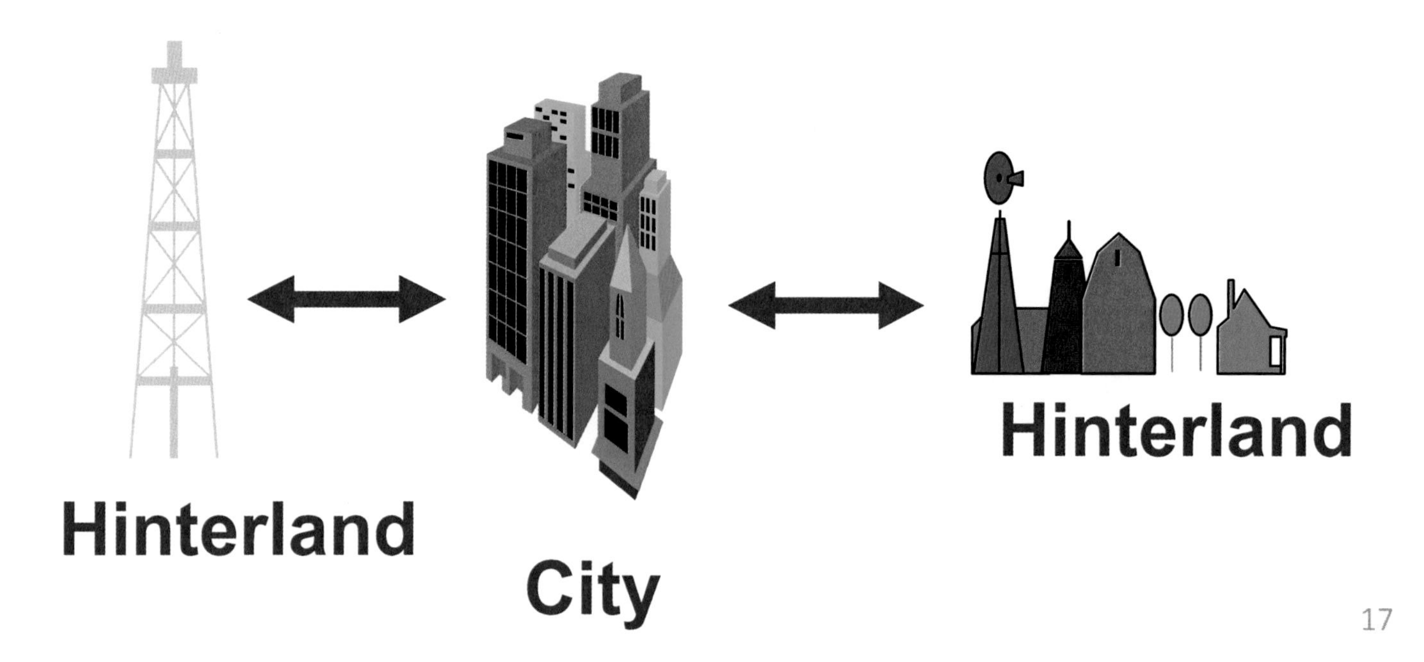

Hinterland
City
Hinterland

The Physical Setting

Climate

- Hydrologic cycle
- Precipitation patterns
- Climate regions

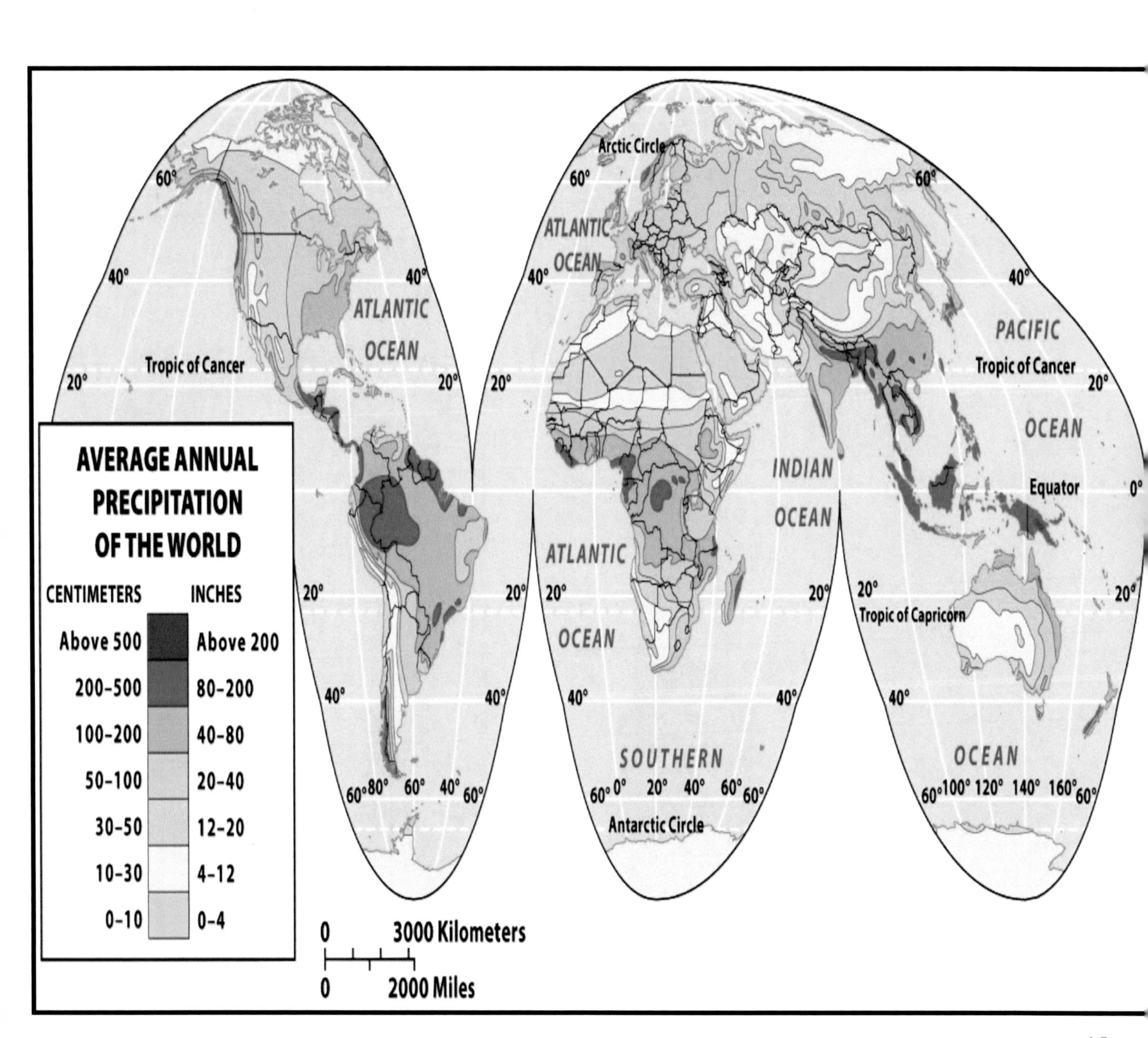

AVERAGE ANNUAL PRECIPITATION OF THE WORLD
CENTIMETERS
INCHES
Above 500
Above 200
200-500
80-200
100-200
40-80
50-100
20-40
30-50
12-20
10-30
4-12
0-10
0-4
ATLANTIC OCEAN
PACIFIC OCEAN
INDIAN OCEAN
SOUTHERN OCEAN
Arctic Circle
Tropic of Cancer
Equator
Tropic of Capricorn
Antarctic Circle
0 3000 Kilometers
0 2000 Miles

Climate Regions of the World

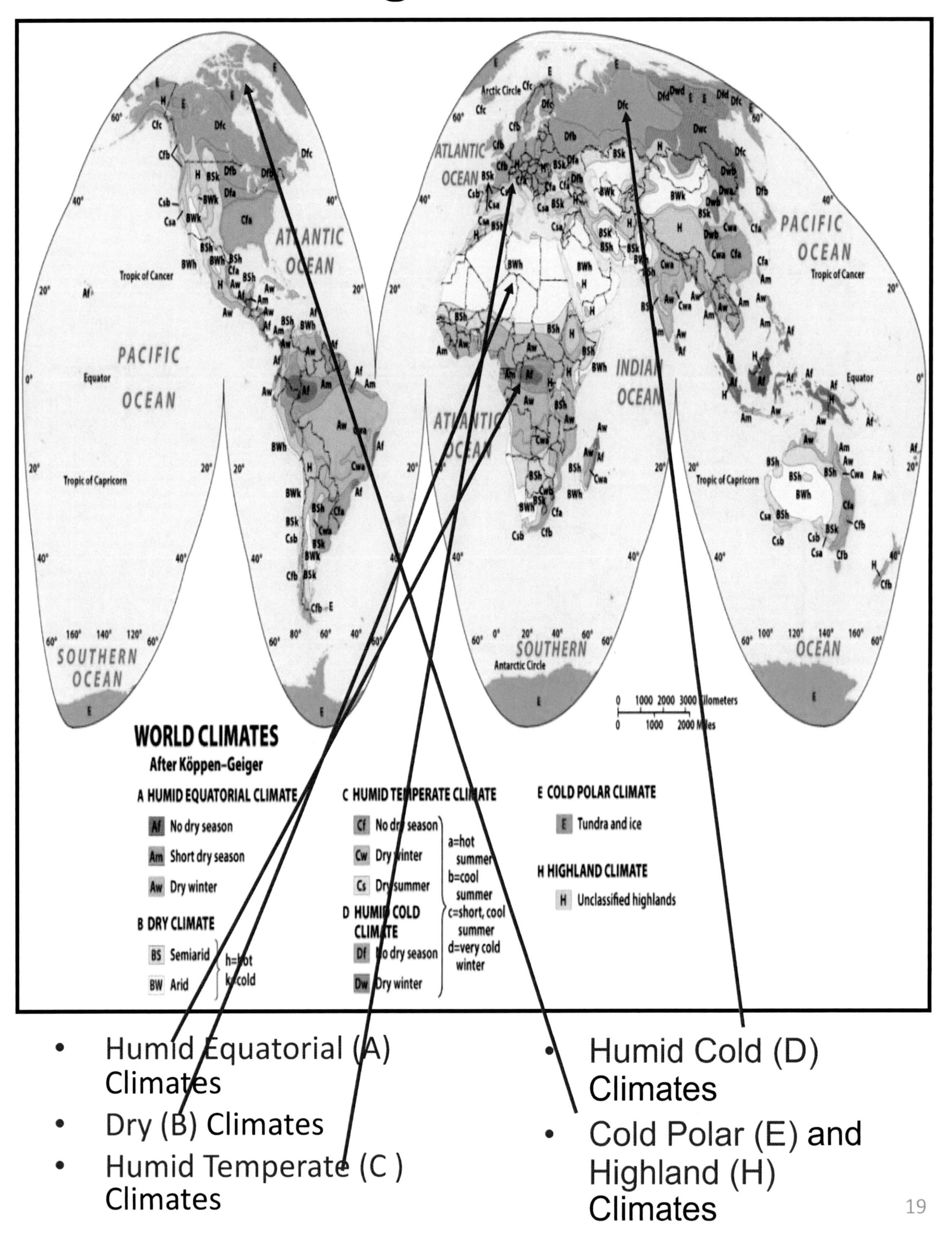
WORLD CLIMATES
After Köppen-Geiger
A HUMID EQUATORIAL CLIMATE
Af No dry season
Am Short dry season
Aw Dry winter
B DRY CLIMATE
BS Semiarid
BW Arid
h=hot
k=cold
C HUMID TEMPERATE CLIMATE
Cf No dry season
Cw Dry winter
Cs Dry summer
D HUMID COLD CLIMATE
Df No dry season
Dw Dry winter
a=hot summer
b=cool summer
c=short, cool summer
d=very cold winter
E COLD POLAR CLIMATE
E Tundra and ice
H HIGHLAND CLIMATE
H Unclassified highlands
PACIFIC OCEAN
ATLANTIC OCEAN
INDIAN OCEAN
SOUTHERN OCEAN
Tropic of Cancer
Equator
Tropic of Capricorn
Arctic Circle
Antarctic Circle
0 1000 2000 3000 Kilometers
0 1000 2000 Miles

- Humid Equatorial (A) Climates
- Dry (B) Climates
- Humid Temperate (C) Climates
- Humid Cold (D) Climates
- Cold Polar (E) and Highland (H) Climates

Climate Change

- On a geologic time-scale climate change has gone on for a long time
  - Cold periods
  - Warm periods
- Currently: human accelerated climate change

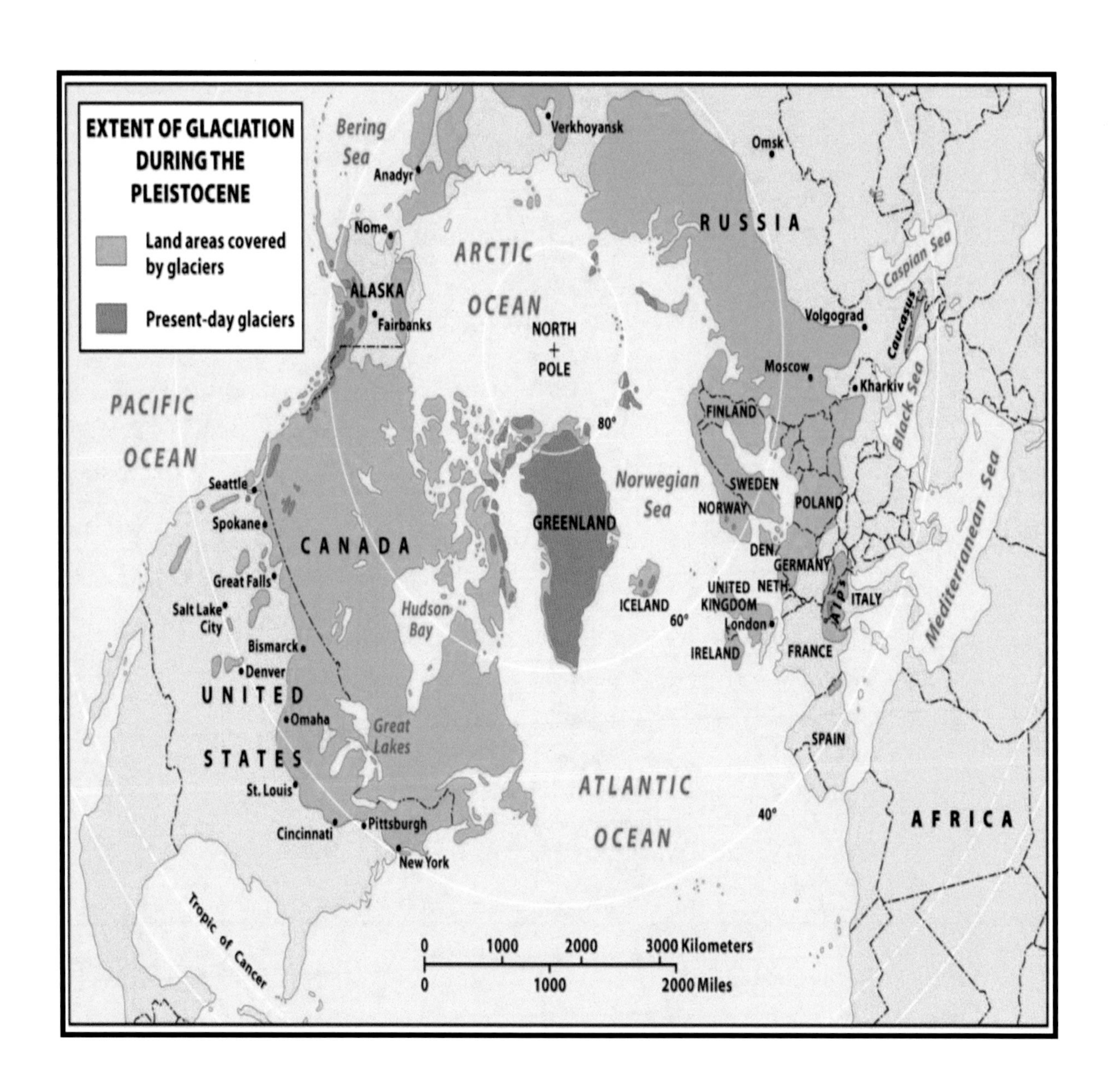

EXTENT OF GLACIATION DURING THE PLEISTOCENE
Land areas covered by glaciers
Present-day glaciers
Bering Sea
Verkhoyansk
Anadyr
Omsk
Nome
RUSSIA
ARCTIC OCEAN
ALASKA
Fairbanks
NORTH POLE
Volgograd
Caspian Sea
Caucasus
Moscow
Kharkiv
PACIFIC OCEAN
FINLAND
Black Sea
80°
Seattle
Norwegian Sea
SWEDEN
Spokane
GREENLAND
NORWAY
POLAND
CANADA
DEN.
GERMANY
Mediterranean Sea
Great Falls
ICELAND
UNITED KINGDOM
NETH.
ALPS
ITALY
Salt Lake City
Hudson Bay
60°
London
Bismarck
IRELAND
FRANCE
Denver
UNITED STATES
Omaha
Great Lakes
SPAIN
St. Louis
ATLANTIC OCEAN
40°
AFRICA
Cincinnati
Pittsburgh
New York
Tropic of Cancer
0 1000 2000 3000 Kilometers
0 1000 2000 Miles

Culture

- **Definition**: Shared patterns of learned behavior
- **Components**:
  - Beliefs
  - Institutions
  - Technology

Tyrell Heaton - Istanbul, Turkey

Cultural Geography

- A wide-ranging and comprehensive field that studies **spatial aspects** of **human cultures**
- **Major components** focus on:
  - Cultural landscapes
  - Cultural hearths
  - Cultural diffusion
  - Language and religion
  - Ethnicity

732-5554
ARBUCKS COFFEE
IBIZA
OPEN
STARBUCKS COFFEE
DVD
KINEMA

Tyrell Heaton - Seoul, South Korea

Cultural Landscape

- The composite of human imprints on the earth's surface.
- *"The cultural landscape is fashioned from a natural landscape by a culture group"*
  - Carl Sauer, 1925
- Culture is the agent
- Natural environment is the medium

北の家族
安心確実!
レイク
麻雀
プロミス
5%

Tyrell Heaton - Tokyo, Japan

Cultural Landscape

Tyrell Heaton - Athens, Greece

Tyrell Heaton - Iquitos, Peru

Tyrell Heaton - Copenhagen, Denmark

Cultural Hearth

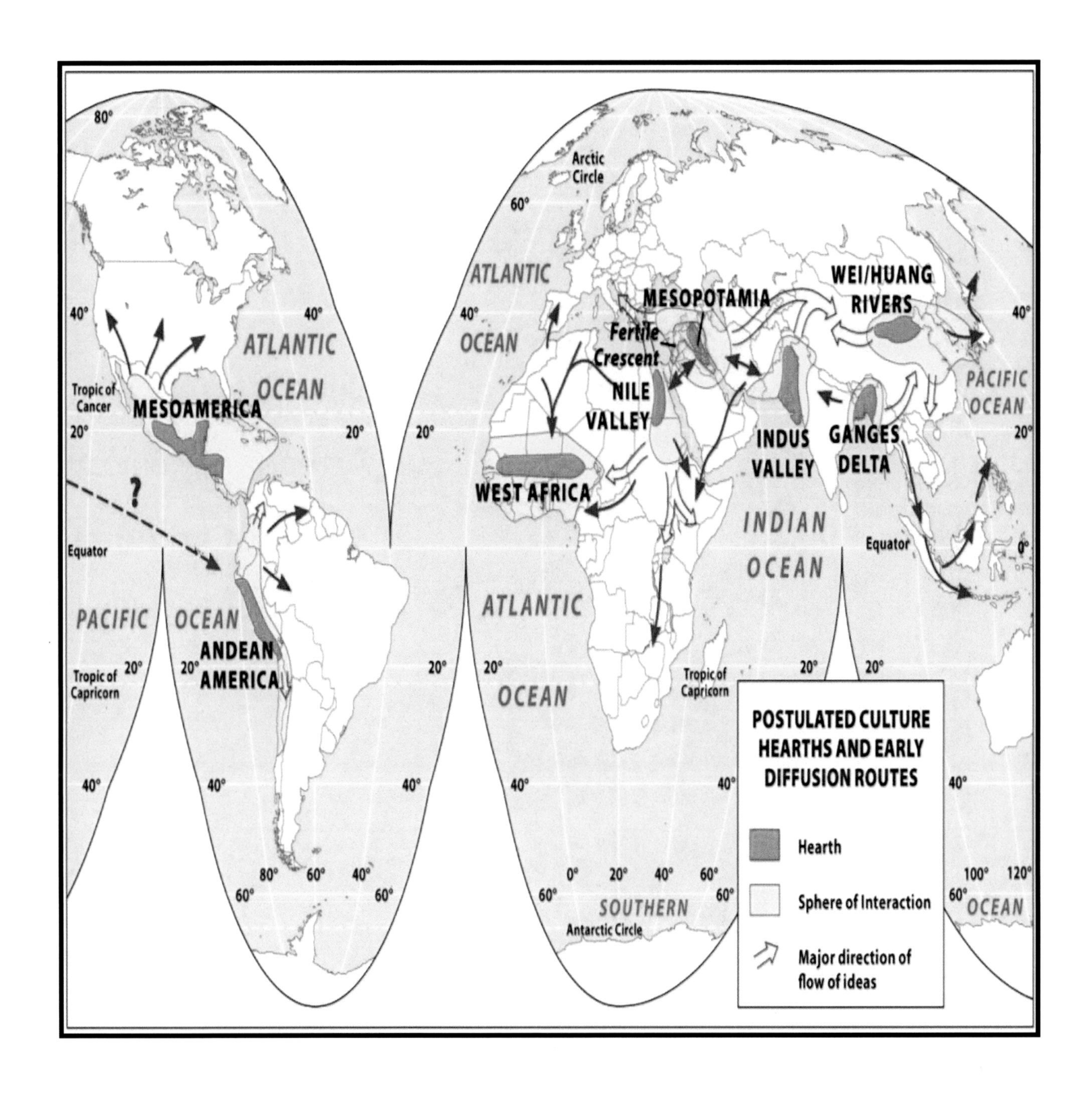

MESOAMERICA
ANDEAN AMERICA
WEST AFRICA
NILE VALLEY
Fertile Crescent
MESOPOTAMIA
INDUS VALLEY
GANGES DELTA
WEI/HUANG RIVERS
ATLANTIC OCEAN
PACIFIC OCEAN
INDIAN OCEAN
SOUTHERN OCEAN
Arctic Circle
Tropic of Cancer
Equator
Tropic of Capricorn
Antarctic Circle
POSTULATED CULTURE HEARTHS AND EARLY DIFFUSION ROUTES
Hearth
Sphere of Interaction
Major direction of flow of ideas

The **source areas** from which radiated ideas, innovations, and ideologies that change the world beyond

Sequent Occupance

Mexico City

1) Aztec Templo Mayor
2) Spanish Cathedral
3) Modern skyscraper

Popular Languages of the World

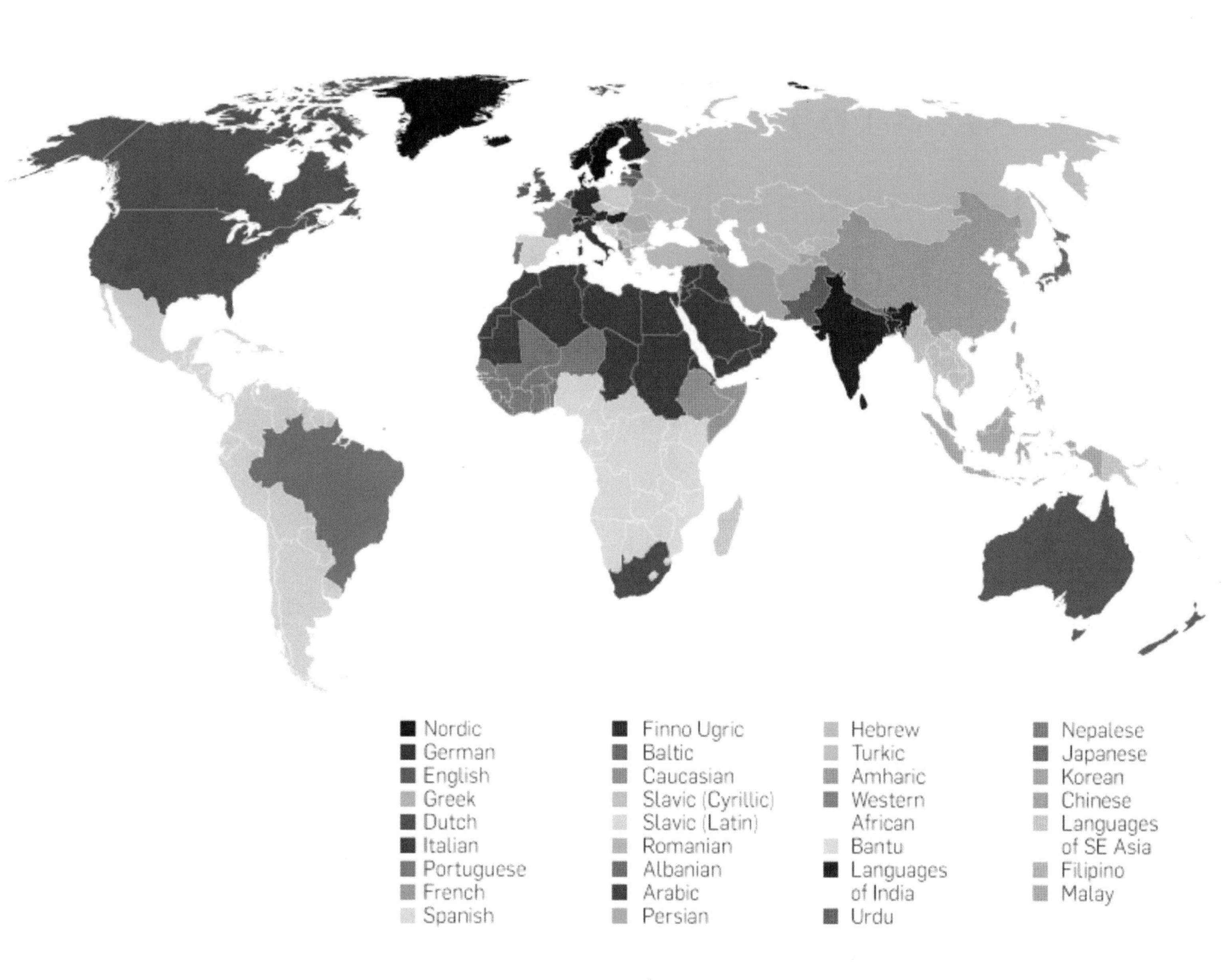
Nordic
German
English
Greek
Dutch
Italian
Portuguese
French
Spanish
Finno Ugric
Baltic
Caucasian
Slavic (Cyrillic)
Slavic (Latin)
Romanian
Albanian
Arabic
Persian
Hebrew
Turkic
Amharic
Western African
Bantu
Languages of India
Urdu
Nepalese
Japanese
Korean
Chinese
Languages of SE Asia
Filipino
Malay

Political Geography

- A subfield within the human branch of geography
- The study of the interaction of geographical area and political process
- The spatial analysis of political phenomena and processes

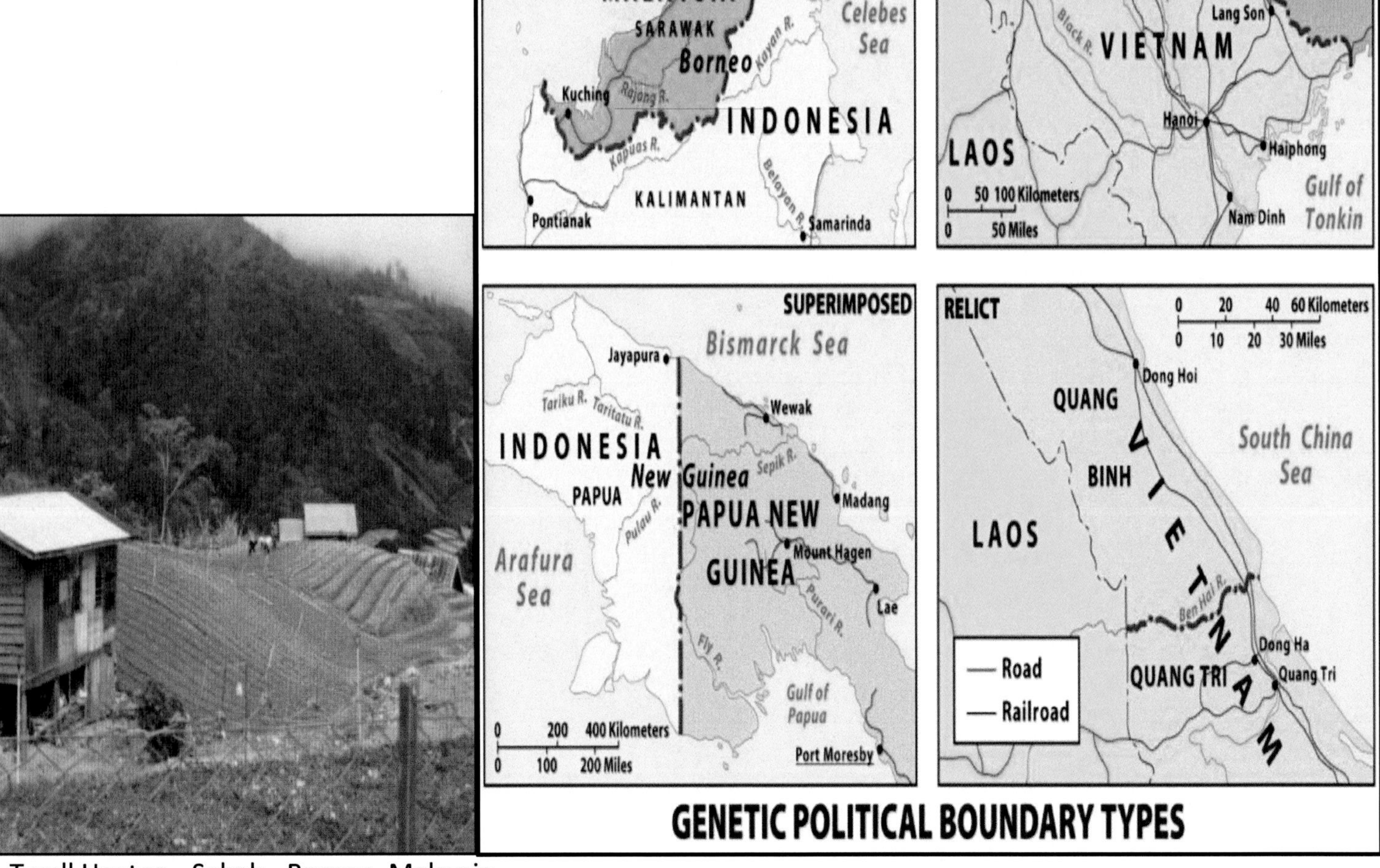
ANTECEDENT
0 200 400 Kilometers
0 100 200 Miles
Kota Kinabalu
PHILIPPINES
Bandar Seri Begawan
SABAH
South China Sea
BRUNEI
MALAYSIA
SARAWAK
Celebes Sea
Borneo
Kayan R.
Kuching
Rajang R.
INDONESIA
Kapuas R.
KALIMANTAN
Belayan R.
Pontianak
Samarinda
SUBSEQUENT
Wenshan
CHINA
You R.
Hu Giang
Nanning
Lao Cai
Red R.
Lo R.
Pingxiang
Lang Son
Black R.
VIETNAM
Hanoi
Haiphong
LAOS
0 50 100 Kilometers
0 50 Miles
Nam Dinh
Gulf of Tonkin
SUPERIMPOSED
Bismarck Sea
Jayapura
Wewak
Tariku R.
Taritatu R.
INDONESIA
Sepik R.
New Guinea
Madang
PAPUA
Pulau R.
PAPUA NEW GUINEA
Mount Hagen
Arafura Sea
Lae
Purari R.
Fly R.
Gulf of Papua
0 200 400 Kilometers
0 100 200 Miles
Port Moresby
RELICT
0 20 40 60 Kilometers
0 10 20 30 Miles
Dong Hoi
QUANG
BINH
South China Sea
LAOS
VIETNAM
Ben Hai R.
Dong Ha
— Road
— Railroad
QUANG TRI
Quang Tri
GENETIC POLITICAL BOUNDARY TYPES

Tyrell Heaton - Sabah - Borneo, Malaysia

State

México
México City

- A **politically organized** territory
- Administered by a **sovereign government**
- **Recognized** by a significant portion of the international community.
- A state must also contain:
  - a **permanent resident population**
  - an **organized economy**
  - a functioning **internal circulation** system

Nation
IRAQ
POPULATION
Under 50,000
50,000–250,000
250,000–1,000,000
1,000,000–5,000,000
Over 5,000,000
National capitals are underlined
Oilfield
Road
Railroad
Oil pipeline
Province boundary
T Turkmen Minority
Su Sunni Minority
Domains depict prevailing majorities; minorities (Turkmen, Assyrians) not shown. Borderlands between domains have mixed populations.
Longitude East of Greenwich
TURKEY
SYRIA
IRAN
JORDAN
SAUDI ARABIA
KUWAIT
Kurdish Domain
Sunni Domain
Shia Domain
"Sunni Triangle"
Zagros Mts.
Mosul
Baghdad
Kirkuk
Basra
Persian Gulf
PROVINCES OF IRAQ
Kurdish Region
Must a nation be a place?
Is a Nation a State?
© H. J. de Blij, P. O. Muller, and John Wiley & Sons, Inc.

- Some examples of stateless nations: the Cherokee Nation, the Palestinians, the Kurds

Nation - State

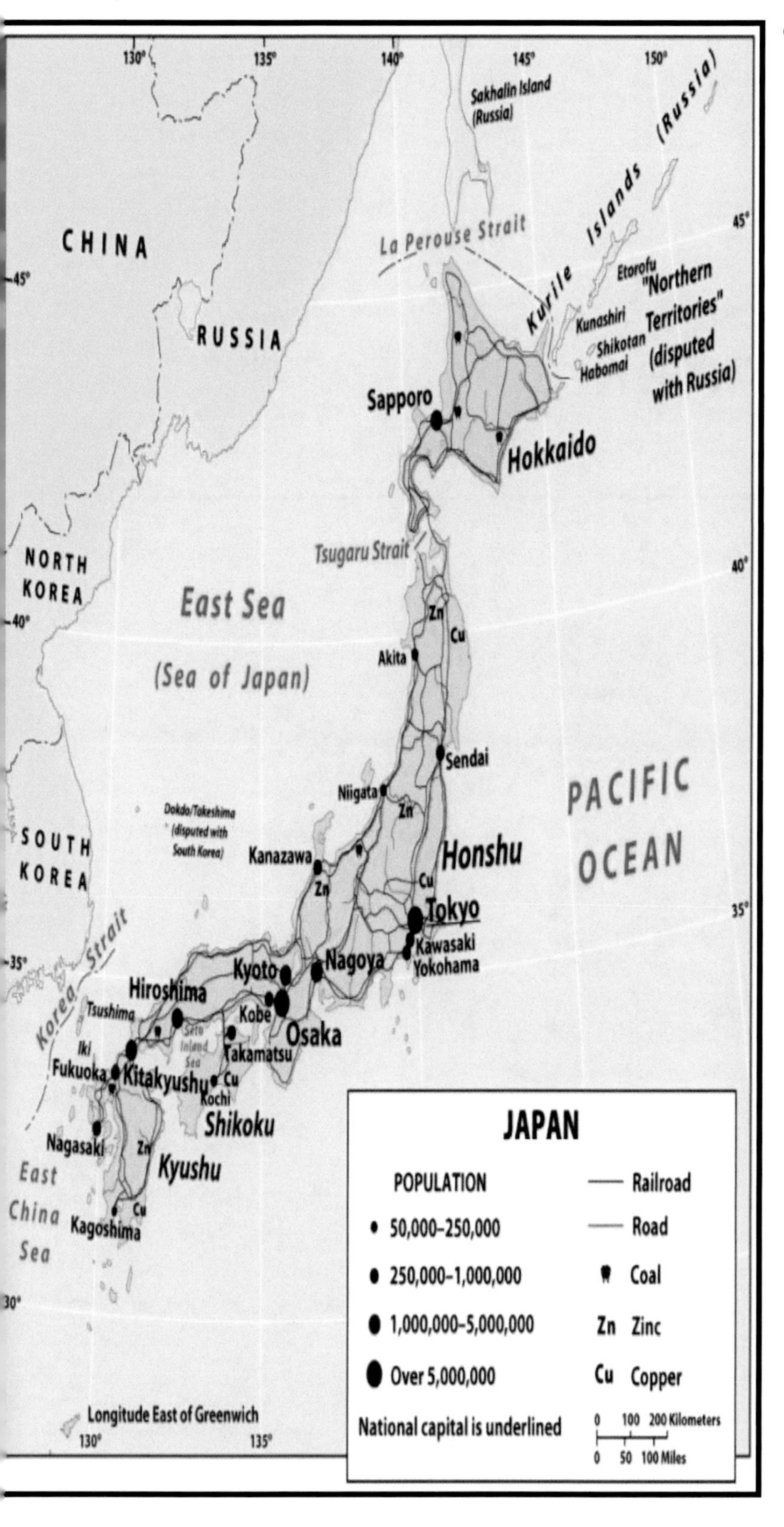

CHINA
RUSSIA
NORTH KOREA
SOUTH KOREA
East Sea
(Sea of Japan)
Sakhalin Island (Russia)
Kurile Islands (Russia)
La Perouse Strait
Etorofu
Kunashiri
Shikotan
Habomai
"Northern Territories" (disputed with Russia)
Sapporo
Hokkaido
Tsugaru Strait
Akita
Sendai
Niigata
Kanazawa
Honshu
PACIFIC OCEAN
Tokyo
Kawasaki
Yokohama
Nagoya
Kyoto
Kobe
Osaka
Hiroshima
Takamatsu
Kochi
Shikoku
Tsushima
Iki
Korea Strait
Fukuoka
Kitakyushu
Nagasaki
Kyushu
Kagoshima
East China Sea
Dokdo/Takeshima (disputed with South Korea)
JAPAN
POPULATION
50,000–250,000
250,000–1,000,000
1,000,000–5,000,000
Over 5,000,000
National capital is underlined
Railroad
Road
Coal
Zn Zinc
Cu Copper
0 100 200 Kilometers
0 50 100 Miles
Longitude East of Greenwich

- A country whose **population** possesses a substantial degree of cultural homogeneity and unity

An **example** of a nation-state: ***Japan***

Population Distribution

- Four major **clusters**
  1) East Asia
  2) South Asia
  3) Europe
  4) Eastern North America

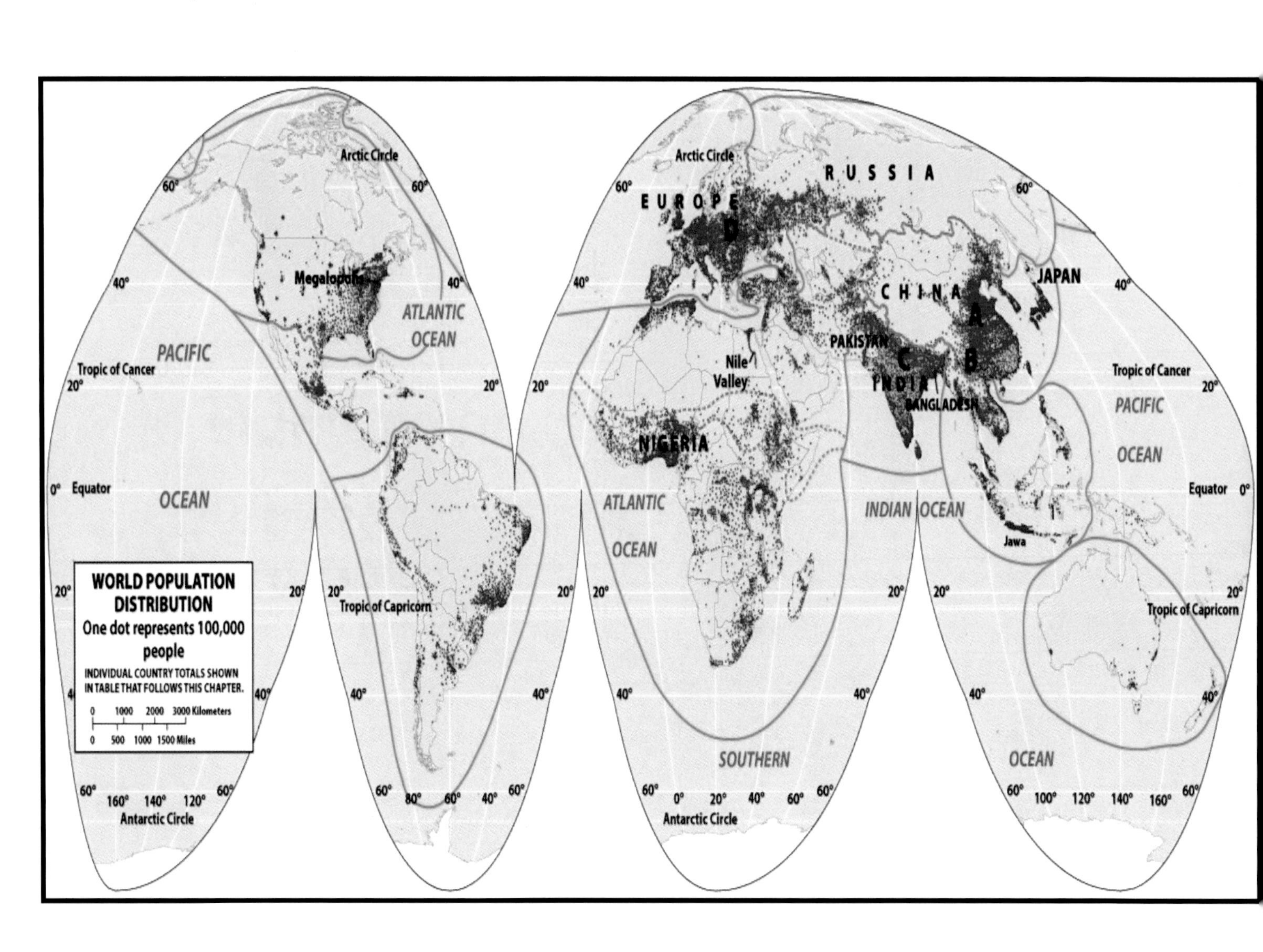

WORLD POPULATION DISTRIBUTION
One dot represents 100,000 people
INDIVIDUAL COUNTRY TOTALS SHOWN IN TABLE THAT FOLLOWS THIS CHAPTER.
Arctic Circle
Antarctic Circle
Tropic of Cancer
Tropic of Capricorn
Equator
PACIFIC
OCEAN
ATLANTIC OCEAN
INDIAN OCEAN
SOUTHERN
Megalopolis
EUROPE
RUSSIA
CHINA
JAPAN
PAKISTAN
INDIA
BANGLADESH
NIGERIA
Nile Valley
Jawa

Population Distribution

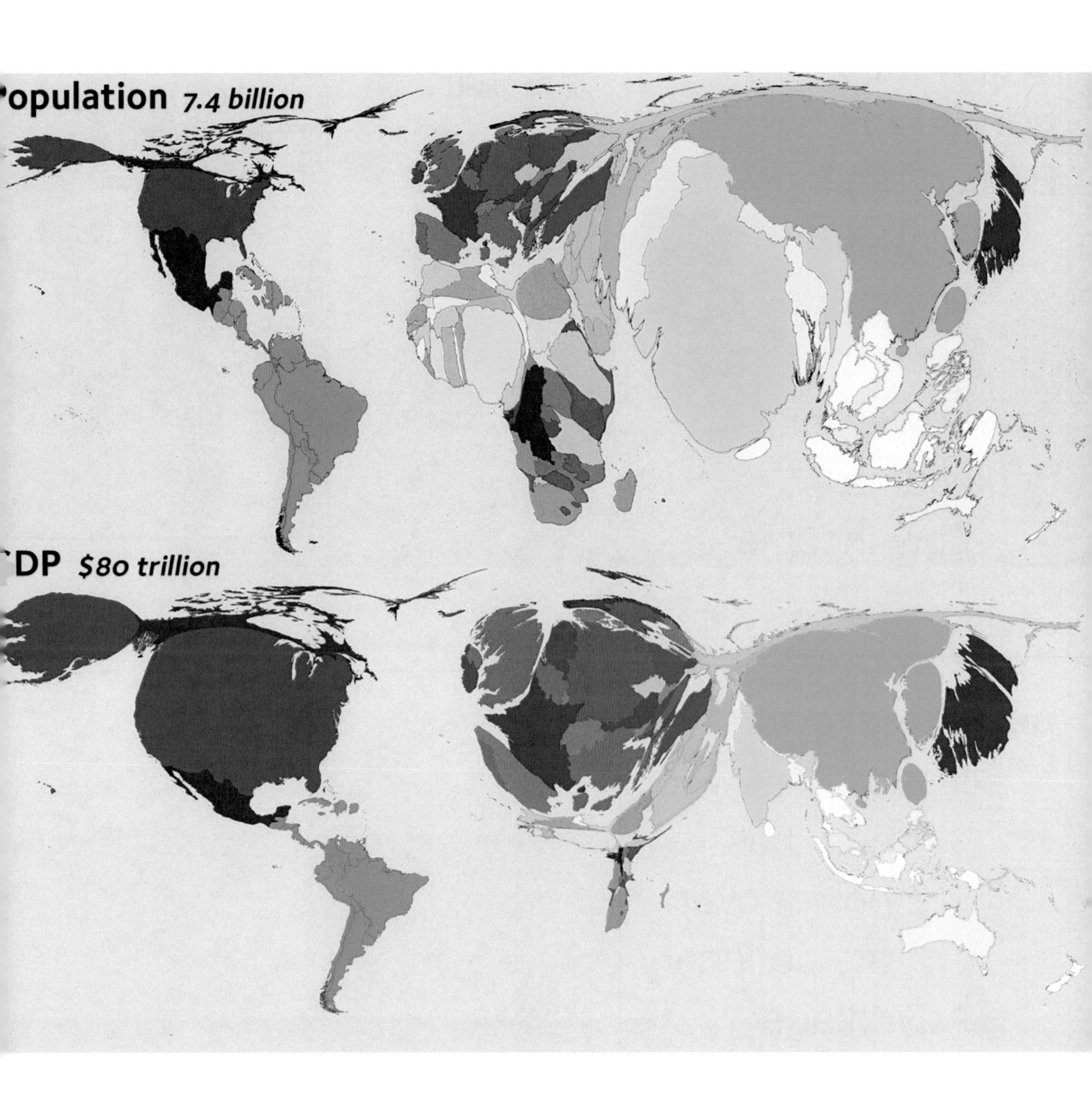
opulation 7.4 billion
DP $80 trillion

Patterns of Development

- **Economic conditions** (World Bank groupings)
  - High-income
  - Upper-middle-income
  - Lower-middle-income
  - Low-income

STATES AND ECONOMIES OF THE WORLD, 2007

- High income economies
- Upper-middle income economies
- Lower-middle income economies
- Low income economies
- Data unavailable

Data source: World Bank.

TRINIDAD & TOBAGO
VENEZUELA
PANAMA
SURINAME
COLOMBIA
GUYANA
FRENCH GUIANA
ECUADOR
BRAZIL
PERU
BOLIVIA
PARAGUAY
ARGENTINA
CHILE
URUGUAY
0°

- **Core versus peripheral areas**
  - Issues of power:
    - core has power over the periphery
  - Advantage
  - Exploitation

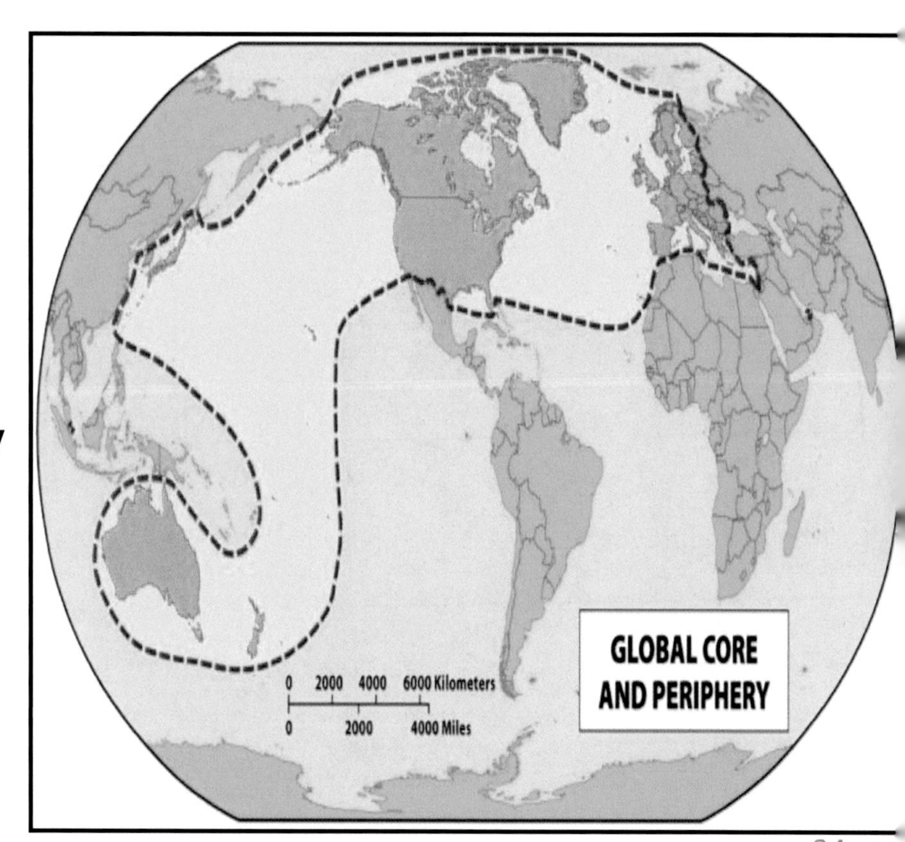

GLOBAL CORE AND PERIPHERY
0 2000 4000 6000 Kilometers
0 2000 4000 Miles

Patterns of Development

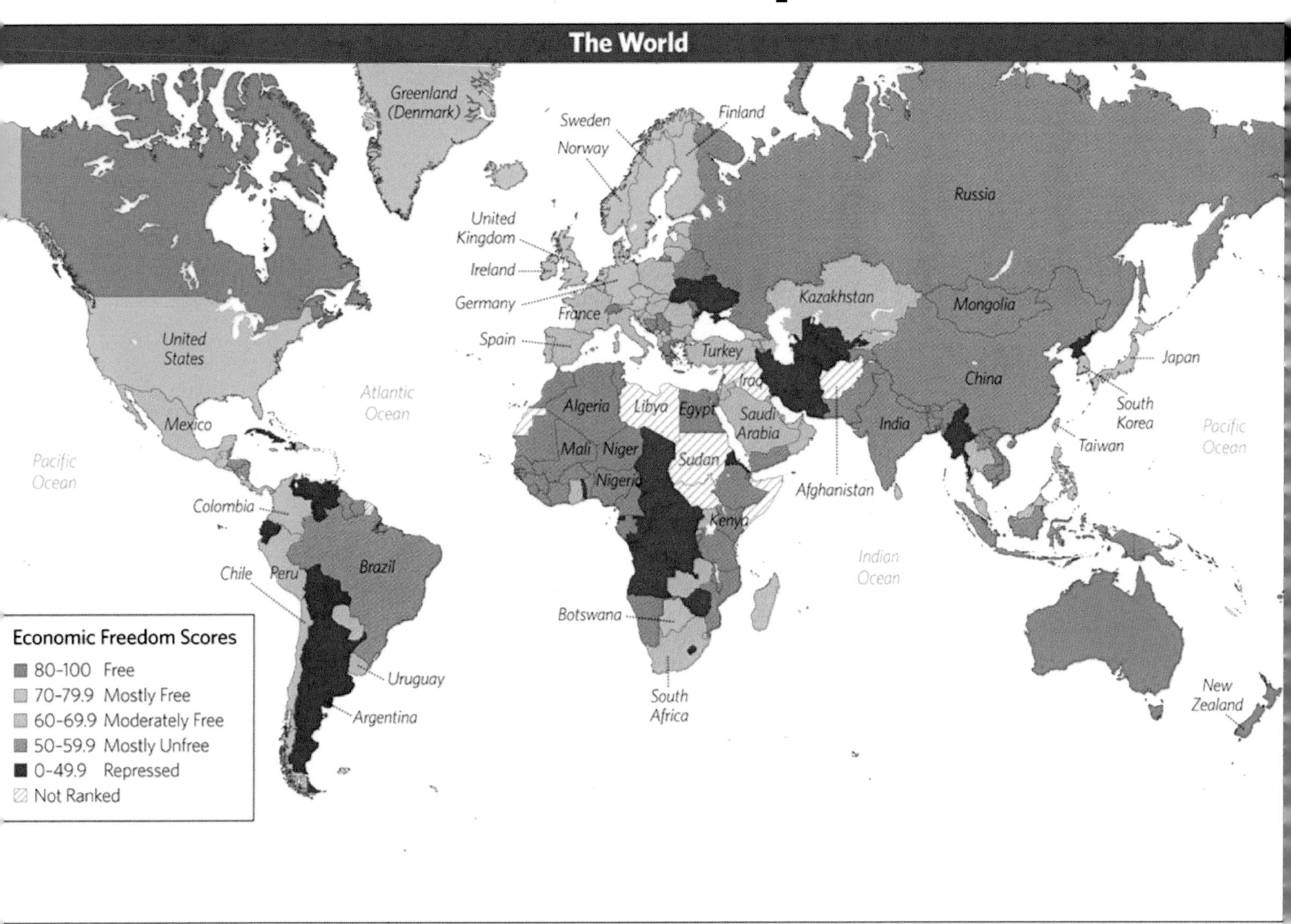

The World
Greenland (Denmark)
Sweden
Norway
Finland
Russia
United Kingdom
Ireland
Germany
France
Spain
Kazakhstan
Mongolia
Turkey
Iraq
China
Japan
South Korea
Taiwan
United States
Atlantic Ocean
Algeria
Libya
Egypt
Saudi Arabia
India
Mexico
Mali
Niger
Sudan
Nigeria
Pacific Ocean
Colombia
Afghanistan
Kenya
Brazil
Chile
Peru
Indian Ocean
Botswana
Economic Freedom Scores
80-100 Free
70-79.9 Mostly Free
60-69.9 Moderately Free
50-59.9 Mostly Unfree
0-49.9 Repressed
Not Ranked
Uruguay
Argentina
South Africa
New Zealand

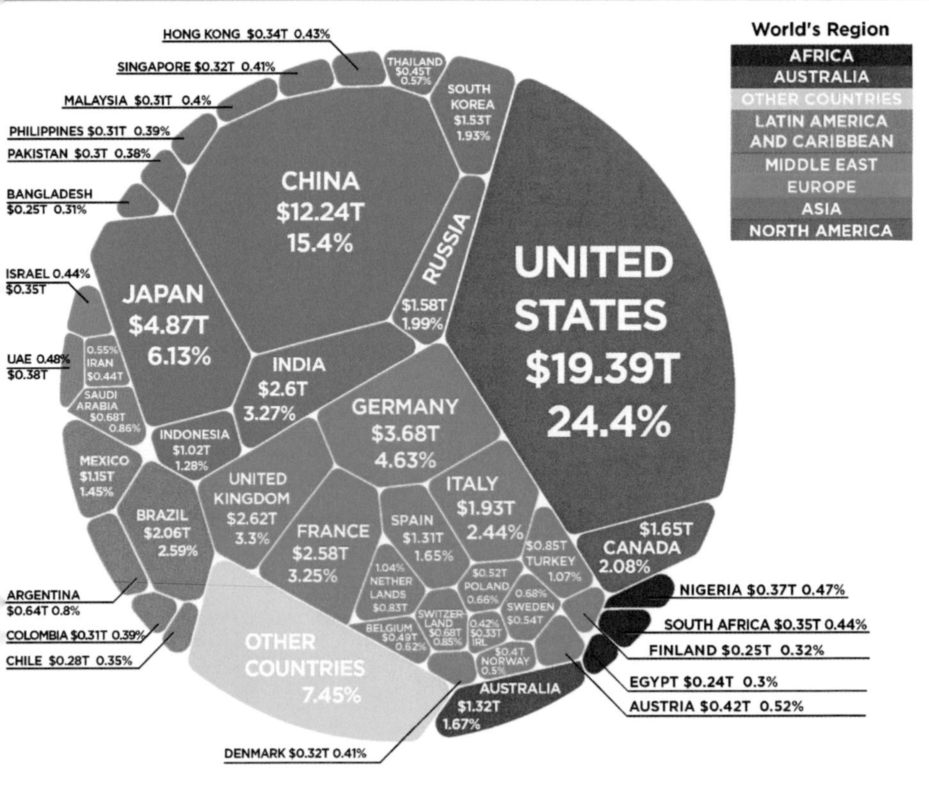

HONG KONG $0.34T 0.43%
SINGAPORE $0.32T 0.41%
MALAYSIA $0.31T 0.4%
PHILIPPINES $0.31T 0.39%
PAKISTAN $0.3T 0.38%
BANGLADESH $0.25T 0.31%
ISRAEL 0.44% $0.35T
UAE 0.48% $0.38T
THAILAND $0.45T 0.57%
SOUTH KOREA $1.53T 1.93%
CHINA $12.24T 15.4%
RUSSIA $1.58T 1.99%
UNITED STATES $19.39T 24.4%
JAPAN $4.87T 6.13%
0.55% IRAN $0.44T
SAUDI ARABIA $0.68T 0.86%
INDIA $2.6T 3.27%
GERMANY $3.68T 4.63%
INDONESIA $1.02T 1.28%
MEXICO $1.15T 1.45%
UNITED KINGDOM $2.62T 3.3%
ITALY $1.93T 2.44%
BRAZIL $2.06T 2.59%
FRANCE $2.58T 3.25%
SPAIN $1.31T 1.65%
$0.85T TURKEY 1.07%
$1.65T CANADA 2.08%
1.04% NETHER LANDS $0.83T
$0.52T POLAND 0.66%
0.68% SWEDEN $0.54T
SWITZERLAND $0.68T 0.85%
BELGIUM $0.49T 0.62%
0.42% $0.33T IRL
$0.4T NORWAY 0.5%
ARGENTINA $0.64T 0.8%
COLOMBIA $0.31T 0.39%
CHILE $0.28T 0.35%
OTHER COUNTRIES 7.45%
AUSTRALIA $1.32T 1.67%
DENMARK $0.32T 0.41%
NIGERIA $0.37T 0.47%
SOUTH AFRICA $0.35T 0.44%
FINLAND $0.25T 0.32%
EGYPT $0.24T 0.3%
AUSTRIA $0.42T 0.52%
World's Region
AFRICA
AUSTRALIA
OTHER COUNTRIES
LATIN AMERICA AND CARIBBEAN
MIDDLE EAST
EUROPE
ASIA
NORTH AMERICA

The $80 Trillion World Economy in One Chart

Globalization

- Global economic integration
- Cultural homogenization
- Winners and losers;

  The world is not flat for the poor and powerless in debt-ridden countries

麦当劳

Pudong, China

ИНДИАНА ДЖОНС
КОРОЛЕВСТВО ХРУСТАЛЬНОГО ЧЕРЕПА
С 22 МАЯ
С 15 МАЯ

Tyrell Heaton - Moscow, Russia

The Geographer's Perspective

THE RELATIONSHIP BETWEEN REGIONAL AND SYSTEMIC GEOGRAPHY

REGIONAL GEOGRAPHY

MARINE SCIENCE
MARINE GEOGRAPHY
GEOLOGY
GEOMOR-PHOLOGY
METEOROLOGY
CLIMATOLOGY
PLANNING, URBAN STUDIES
URBAN GEOGRAPHY
HISTORY
HISTORICAL GEOGRAPHY
ECONOMICS
ECONOMIC GEOGRAPHY
HEALTH SCIENCES
MEDICAL GEOGRAPHY
ANTHRO-POLOGY AND SOCIOLOGY
CULTURAL GEOGRAPHY
DEMOGRAPHY
POPULATION GEOGRAPHY
PSYCHOLOGY
BEHAVIORAL GEOGRAPHY
POLITICAL SCIENCE
POLITICAL GEOGRAPHY
BIOLOGY
BIO-GEOGRAPHY

Notice the difference between the houses, much of Guyana is like this.

Also there are Mosques, Churches, and Temples all within blocks of each other and there is no religious conflict in this area.

Tyrell Heaton - Georgetown, Guyana

Geography Themes
& Essential Elements
Arches
National
Park
Moab, Utah – Tyrell Heaton

Geography Themes and Essential Elements

The Big Idea

Geographers have created two different but related systems for organizing geographic studies.

Main Ideas

- The five themes of geography help us organize our studies of the world.
- The six essential elements of geography highlight some of the subject's most important ideas.

Main Idea 1:
The five themes of geography help us organize our studies of the world.

- Geographers use themes that can be applied to nearly everything that they study.
  - Location
  - Place
  - Human-Environment Interaction
  - Movement
  - Regions

Themes of Geography

Location

- Every point on Earth has a location.
- **Absolute location** is a specific description of where a place is, such as an address.
- **Relative location** is a general description of where a place is.

Place

- Place refers to an area's landscape, the features that define the area and make it different from other places.
- Can include land, climate, and people

Themes of Geography, continued

Human-Environment Interaction

- An area's **environment** includes its land, water, climate, plants, and animals.
- Geographers study how people interact with their environment.

Movement

- Study of why and how people move, including the roads and routes that make movement so common

Regions

- Geographers divide the world into regions.
- Make comparisons between regions to help geographers learn why each place has developed the way it has

Main Idea 2:
The six essential elements of geography highlight some of the subject's most important ideas.

- In addition to the five themes, geographers use a system of standards and essential elements.
  - Identify the most important ideas in the study of geography
- The six essential elements build on the five themes of geography, so they are closely related.

Essential Elements of Geography

The World in Spatial Terms

- How to use maps and other geographic representations, tools, and technologies to acquire, process, and report information from a spatial perspective
- How to use mental maps to organize information about people, places, and environments in a spatial context
- How to analyze the spatial organization of people, places, and environments on Earth's surface

Places and Regions

- The physical and human characteristics of places
- How people create regions to interpret Earth's complexity
- How culture and experience influence people's perceptions of places and regions

Essential Elements, continued

Physical Systems

- The physical processes that shape the patterns of Earth's surface
- The characteristics and spatial distribution of ecosystems on Earth's surface

Human Systems

- The characteristics, distributions, and migration of human populations
- The characteristics, distribution, and complexity of Earth's cultural mosaics
- The patterns and networks of economic interdependence
- The processes, patterns, and functions of human settlement
- How the forces of cooperation and conflict among people influence the division and control of Earth's surface

Essential Elements, continued

Environment and Society

- How human actions modify the physical environment
- How physical systems affect human systems
- Changes that occur in the meaning, use, distribution, and importance of resources

The Uses of Geography

- How to apply geography to interpret the past
- How to apply geography to interpret the present and plan for the future

The Branches of Geography

The Big Idea

Geography is divided into two main branches—physical and human geography.

Main Ideas

- Physical geography is the study of landforms, water bodies, and other physical features.
- Human geography focuses on people, their cultures, and the landscapes they create.
- Other branches of geography examine specific aspects of the physical or human world.

Main Idea 1:
Physical geography is the study of landforms, water bodies, and other physical features.

- **Physical geography** is the study of the world's features—its landforms, bodies of water, climates, soils, and plants.
- Physical geographers
  - Want to know all about the different features found on Earth and what causes them
  - Take detailed measurements and track changes over time to help answer questions
- Reasons to study physical geography include:
  - To learn how the world works and to better understand our world
  - To help us to learn to live with Earth's changes and dangers and be prepared for them

Main Idea 2:
Human geography focuses on people, their cultures, and the landscapes they create.

- **Human geography** is the study of the world's people, communities, and landscapes.
- Human geographers
  - Study the world's people, past and present
  - Look at where people live and why
  - Study what people do

Studying Human Geography

Specialization

- Many human geographers specialize in a specific area of study because people's lives are so different around the world.

Reasons to study human geography include:

- Helping us to better understand people in other cultures
- Helping people improve their landscapes and situations
- Making contributions to improve city planning and development and to protect the environment

Main Idea 3:
Other branches of geography examine specific aspects of the physical or human world

Cartography

- The science of making maps
- Develop accurate maps on almost any scale and keep them up to date

Hydrology

- The study of water on Earth
- Work to measure and protect world's supply of water by studying the world's river systems and rainfall patterns

Meteorology

- The study of weather and what causes it
- Use information about weather patterns to make predictions

What Is Geography?
Geography is the study of the world, its people, and the landscapes they create. To study a place's geography, we look at its physical and human features.
The physical features of Algeria include huge deserts full of tall sand dunes.
Many Algerians live in small villages like this one. The village is one of Algeria's human features.
Together, Algeria's physical and human features create the country's landscape.
Notice the landscape of this part of Algeria

Local – Regional - Global

Looking at the World

Geographers look at the world at many levels. At each level, they ask different questions and discover different types of information. By putting information gathered at different levels together, geographers can better understand a place and its role in the world.

ANALYZING VISUALS Based on these photos, what are some questions a geographer might ask about London?

Local Level – This busy neighborhood in London, England is a local area. A geographer here might study local foods, housing, or clothing.

Regional Level – As a major city, London is also a region. At this level, a geographer might study the city's population or transportation systems.

London

Global Level – London is one of the world's main financial centers. Here a geographer might study how London's economy affects the world.

Physical Geography
The study of Earth's physical features, including rivers, mountains, oceans, weather, and other features, such as Victoria Falls in southern Africa
Human Geography
The study of Earth's people, including their ways of life, homes, cities, beliefs, and customs, like those of these children in Malawi, a country in central Africa
Geography
The study of Earth's physical and cultural features

The Five Themes of Geography

Geographers use five major themes, or ideas, to organize and guide their studies.

Location The theme of location describes where something is. The mountain shown above, Mount Rainier, is in west-central Washington.

Place Place describes the features that make a site unique. For example, Washington, D.C., is our nation's capital and has many great monuments.

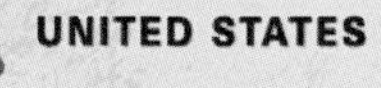
UNITED STATES

Regions Regions are areas that share common characteristics. The Mojave Desert, shown here, is defined by its distinctive climate and plant life.

Human-Environment Interaction People interact with their enviroments in many ways. Some, like this man in Florida, use the land to grow crops.

Movement This theme looks at how and why people and things move. Airports like this one in Dallas, Texas, help people move around the world.

ANALYSIS
SKILL
ANALYZING VISUALS

Which of the five themes deals with the relationships between people and their surroundings?

APPLYING THE FIVE THEMES

What is my **topic**?	(ex., **Japan**)
What is my **disciplinary approach**?	(ex., **Geography**)
What is my **organizational matrix**?	(ex., **"Five Themes"**)
What is my **purpose** and **focus**?	(ex., **"Japan: Miracle of the Orient,"** how Japan overcome adversity to become a strong, cohesive state and global economic power)

DEFINING GEOGRAPHY

WHAT is **WHERE, WHY THERE,** and **WHY CARE?**

(In regard to Earth's varied **physical** and **human** features)

GEOGRAPHY'S "FIVE THEMES"

LOCATION	(Position on Earth's surface) **Where is Japan?** (Specific, Relative?) **In what ways is Japan's location important?**
PLACE	(Physical and human characteristics) **What is Japan like?**
INTERACTION	(How humans live in and change the environment) **How have Japanese, culturally adapted to, used, and changed the land in which they live?**
MOVEMENT	(The flow of people, materials, and ideas) **What types of movement are essential to Japan? How do the Japanese handle their daily commuting? What foodstuffs, raw materials, and natural resources must be imported? What is exported?**
REGION	(Areas of homogeneity used to compare and contrast) **Within what regions is Japan included? What is Japan's role within the Pacific Rim?**

LOCATION

WHAT IS "LOCATION"?

Location is **position on Earth's surface**. It poses or answers the most fundamental geographic question: **WHERE?**

HOW ARE POSITIONS LOCATED ON EARTH'S SURFACE?

SPECIFIC LOCATION (site)

Based upon a mathematical grid system of parallels and meridians, measuring degrees of **latitude** and **longitude**.

RELATIVE LOCATION (situation)

Location expressed in relation to other locations: **distance** (how far?), **direction** (which way?), and occasionally **time** (how long?).

RELATED CONCEPTS:

(SPATIAL) DISTRIBUTION and **PATTERN** (Where things are, how they are arranged, and why they are there)

ACCESSIBILITY vs. **ISOLATION** (How easy/difficult is it to establish internal or external linkages of any kind?)

COMPARATIVE ADVANTAGE IN SPATIAL INTERACTION (What advantages/disadvantages do certain places have because of their location?)

CHANGING IMPORTANCE OF LOCATION (How and in what way/s can the importance of location change?)

ASSOCIATED SKILLS:

Maps & Globes (direction, distance scale, grid system, symbols, projections)

PLACE

WHAT IS "PLACE"?

Place is the **character of an area** as defined by its **physical and human features.** Each place on earth has certain unique **properties** (conditions) and **qualities** (human perceptions). The concept of place tells us **WHAT** is **WHERE** and **what it is like there.**

WHAT ARE THE PROPERTIES OF PLACE?

PHYSICAL/NATURAL	**HUMAN /CULTURAL**
Landforms	Population
Weather & Climate	Settlement
Natural Vegetation	Cultural Institutions
Wildlife	Skills & Technology
Water Features	Economic Activities
Soils	Transportation
Minerals	Communications

RELATED CONCEPTS:

LANDSCAPE describes the sensed elements of place, both physical and cultural.

*What is there and what does it look like?

PERCEPTIONS of place vary greatly and are conditioned by countless factors.

*How do you feel about certain places?

NATURAL (and HUMAN) RESOURCES are elements of place that are of use or value to a particular culture.

* What are people using (or not using) there? How are human resources used?

CHANGE is constant in both the natural and human environment.

* How has this place changed through time and why?

HOW ARE THE ELEMENTS OF PLACE RELATED?

Identifying and explaining **INTERRELATIONSHIPS** that exist between and among physical and human elements of place are fundamental to geographic study.

INTERACTION

What is "Interaction"?

Interaction refers to the **varied ways humans culturally adapt to, use, and change the natural environment.** Each culture (humans sharing a common "way of life") has its own actual and perceived needs, environmental understanding and perceptions, and certain technological and capital resources. The concept tells us **what is happening** where **in terms of humans and the physical places they occupy.**

Related Concepts:

NATURAL ENVIRONMENT. All elements and conditions occurring as a result of natural processes (lithosphere, atmosphere, biosphere, hydrosphere).

CULTURAL ADAPTATION. The varied ways by which humans, acting as cultural agents adapt to the natural environment. [How does **this** culture live in, use, and change **this** place?]

NATURAL RESOURCES. Naturally occurring elements that are **used** by a particular culture. [What is here? What is (is not) being used and how? What is valued and why?]

CULTURAL LANDSCAPE. Human imprint on Earth's surface. [How has human activity changed the natural environment?]

PHILOSOPHICAL PERSPECTIVES:

The Environmental Determinism/Possibilism/Cultural Determinism debate, i.e., is the environment, or is culture (learned human behavior), responsible for the way(s) humans interact with the natural environment?

Nature can not "communicate." Physical places serve only as a "stage" upon which human planned and directed activities are played out. Humans are the active agent in interaction.

Patterns of cultural adaptation and land/resource use change through space and time in similar environmental settings. One culture may occupy many natural environments; one natural environment may be "home" to many diverse cultures.

Environmental change is a cultural variable: humans **occupy space, consume resources,** and **pollute.** How these are done and with what resulting impact, is much more a function of culture than of population.

"There are no unproductive regions, only unproductive people." Mao Tse Tung

MOVEMENT

WHAT IS "MOVEMENT"?

Movement is the **flow of people, materials, ideas, and physical elements** from place to place. In essence, the concept describes and explains **what comes** and **what goes, from and to where,** and **why?**

RELATED CONCEPTS: (processes, means, spatial networks)

Migration: Movement of people (emigration, immigration)

Diffusion: Movement of culture traits (ideas and things) through space and time

Communication: Movement of Information

Transportation: Movement of material items or objects

Linkages: Spatial network of communication or transportation connections

Systems: Movement within a spatially integrated body or unit

SPATIAL VARIATION IN MOVEMENT AND DISTRIBUTION:

Concepts helping to explain local, regional, and global patterns of movement and distribution

- **Push vs. Pull**
- **Supply vs. Demand**
- **Access vs. Isolation**
- **Opportunity vs. Inability**

REGIONS

WHAT IS A "REGION"?

A region is an **area that displays unity in terms of one or more arbitrarily selected criteria.** Regions are the **basic unit of geographic study**. The region is to the geographer what an era or period is to the historian – a means of organizing and analyzing information. The concept helps us know **how certain places are associated with, or perhaps differ from, others** in terms of like or dissimilar features or characteristics.

WHAT ARE THE CHIEF CHARACTERISTICS OF REGIONS?

Geographers have developed the concept of region as a **TOOL** used in examining, defining, describing, analyzing, and explaining patterns and relationships in the natural and human environments of Earth's surface.

- All regions are **abstractions**; they exist only in the human mind.
- All regions are based on one or more **arbitrarily selected criteria**.
- Regions **change through time.**
- Regions **overlap.**
- Individual places fall within **many regions** of varied nature.

WHAT TYPES OF REGIONS EXIST?

FORMAL REGIONS: Single and multiple feature

FUNCTIONAL REGIONS: Have "nodes" and serve a function

VERNACULAR (PERCEPTUAL) REGIONS: Recognized by laymen (locals)

Techniques of Geographic Analysis

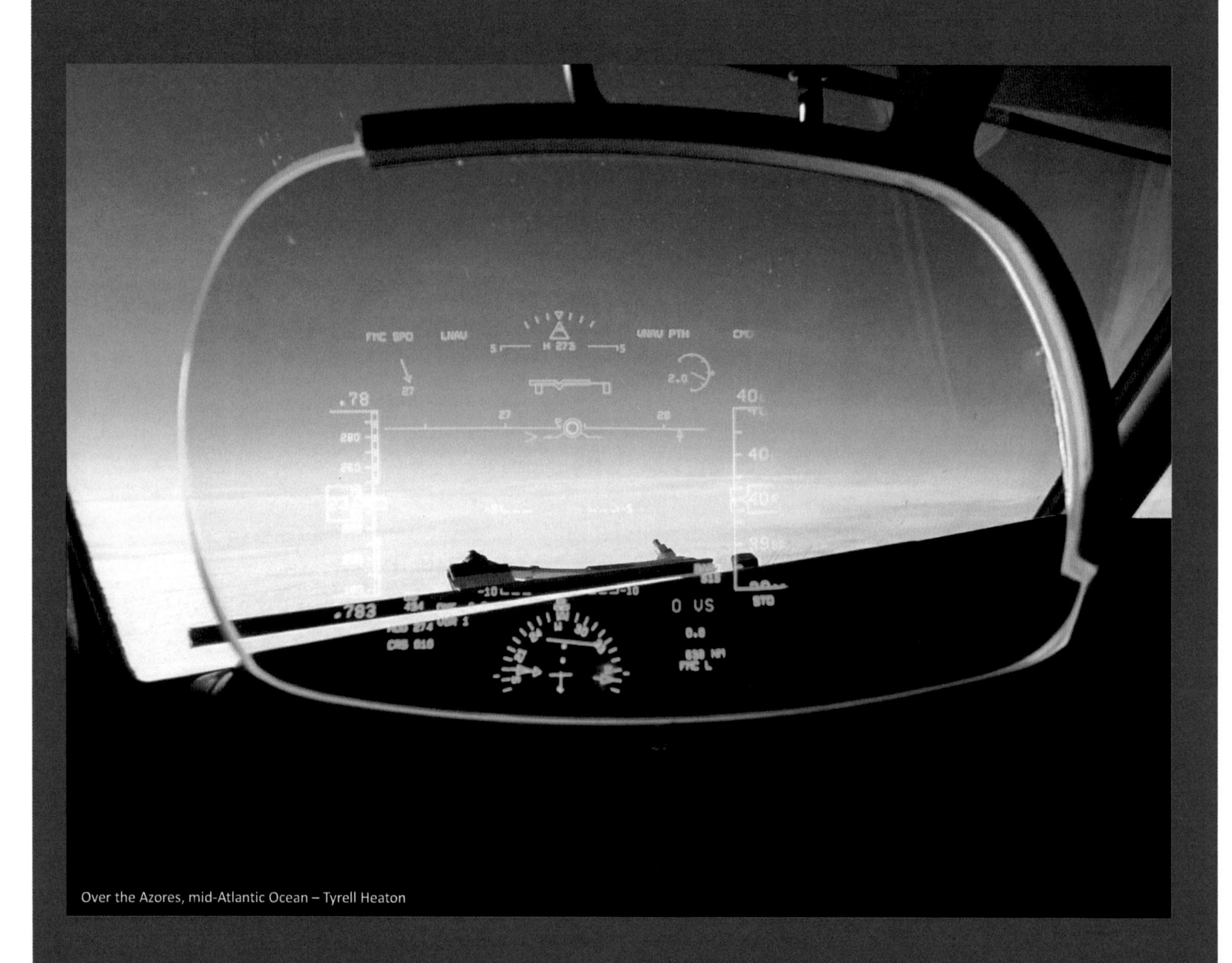
FMC SPD
LNAV
VNAV PTH
.78
0 VS
.783

Over the Azores, mid-Atlantic Ocean – Tyrell Heaton

Techniques of Geographic Analysis

When new to the concepts of Latitude and Longitude (those imaginary lines we use to identify a location's specific place on Earth) it's not unusual to have some difficulties. Here are some thoughts to help you visualize how these lines run around and across Earth to help us identify locations:

Latitude lines run across the globe and are measured in degrees. Lines of latitude begin with the Equator at 0 degrees and increase in number as one moves north or south of the Equator. The maximum point of latitude is 90 degrees (at either pole).

These lines are often described as ***BELTS*** around the globe. They go around our circumference (think, our waist) and are the widest near our middle, getting smaller as the latitude circle moves closer to the earth's poles (or to our head or feet).

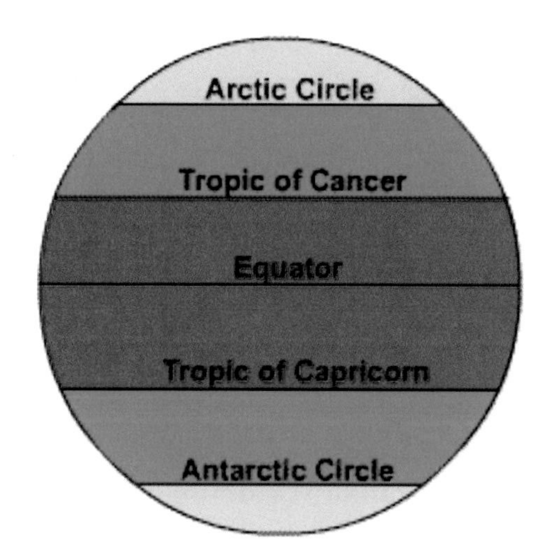
Arctic Circle
Tropic of Cancer
Equator
Tropic of Capricorn
Antarctic Circle

Longitude lines run north-to-south from pole to pole and are measured in degree East or West of the Prime Meridian. The Prime Meridian is the 0 degrees Longitude line and measured from Greenwich, England (near London). Longitude degrees go from 0 degrees up to 180 degrees, either moving East of the Prime Meridian (towards Europe/Russia/China) or moving West of the Prime Meridian (towards the Atlantic Ocean, North America and then across the Pacific Ocean towards Asia).

The Earth is measured and lined with Longitude circles going from 0 degrees to 180 degrees at the opposite side of the Earth. That location lies in the midst of the Pacific Ocean and is called the International Date Line.

Longitude lines can be thought of similar to segments of an orange that is cut from its top to bottom. The cutting line is like a Longitude arc as it goes from the orange slice's top to its bottom.

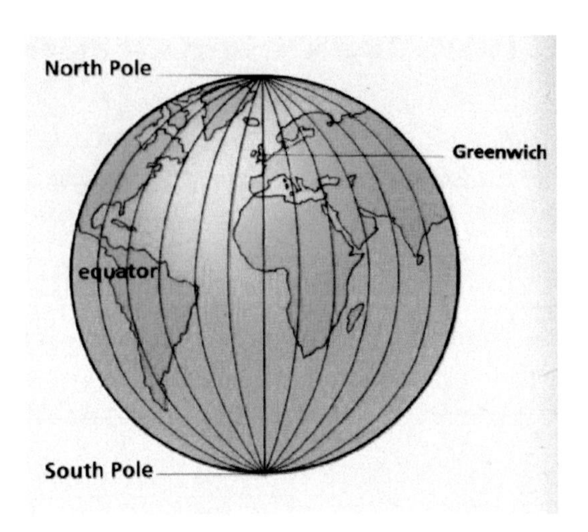
North Pole
Greenwich
equator
South Pole

General Rules of Thumb:

- Locations can only have one Latitude and one Longitude when describing its position on Earth.
- Cardinal directions (North, South, East or West) are necessary when giving coordinates for a location.
  - Latitude is either **North** or **South** depending on if it is north or south of the Equator, for example, Minnesota's approximate Latitude is 47 degrees North.
  - Longitude is **East** or **West** depending on whether it lies east or west of the Prime Meridian, for example, Minnesota's approximate Longitude is 103 degrees West.
- When providing coordinates for a location you need to include the form of measurement (usually degrees).

Getting more specific with coordinates:

One degree of latitude and longitude actually covers a very large area (many square miles) and varies depending upon the location on the Earth. So, if we wanted to figure out the exact location of your house, we'd have to use either fractions of degrees or the standard measurements in location: degrees, minutes, and seconds.

Think of the coordinates as you think of time. The degrees (in location) can be compared to the hours (in time). If we want to be more specific, we then move on to minutes and then seconds (in terms of time).

Likewise, to get more specific in location, fractions of degrees are broken down into minutes and seconds. And just like time, there are 60 seconds in a minute and 60 minutes in a degree.

In the atlas you will notice that locations are not listed in just degrees, there are secondary numbers, these represent minutes and seconds. For example, a location within Anchorage, Alaska could be listed as:

> 61 degrees 5' 30″ N, 149 degrees 53' 15″ W
>
> This is interpreted as: 61 degrees, 5 minutes and 30 seconds North, 149 degrees, 53 minutes and 15 seconds West.

Determining the coordinates of a location:

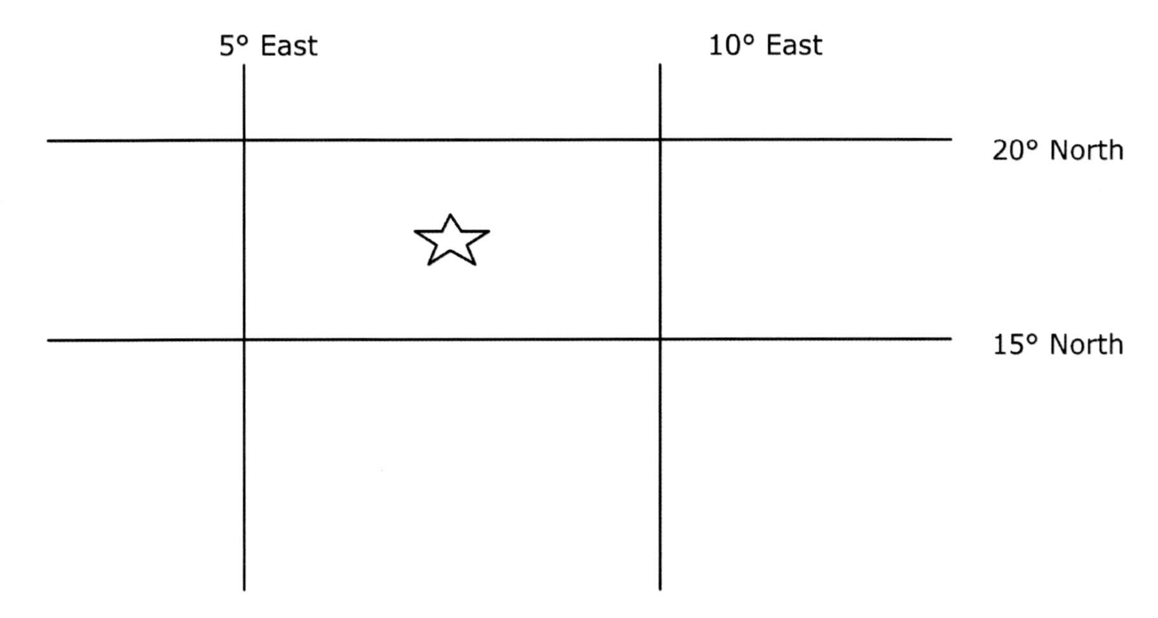
5° East
10° East
20° North
15° North

If you are searching for the coordinates of a location between the lines of latitude and longitude, you should approximate between the two closest lines. So the star above) is located at approximately 17.5° North, 7.5° East.

Another trick is to check the index in the back of the atlas for the name of the location – this will provide you with the page of the map AND the coordinates of the location.

Determining a location based on coordinates:

The best way to start is by looking at the world map and checking out the general coordinates (for example: 37 degrees North, 77 degrees West).

Think of the world as sectioned off into 4 quadrants:

- Upper left quadrant of the world is North latitude and West longitude
- Upper right quadrant of the world is North latitude and East longitude
- Lower right quadrant of the world is South latitude and East longitude
- Lower left quadrant of the world is South latitude and West longitude

From this, determine the nearest continent and locate the map of the specific continent. Looking at the continent and the same coordinates, you can then determine the country and if there is a specific map for the country, turn to it.

Looking at the country and the same coordinates, you should then able to determine the state (or similar if not in the US) and city.

While this sounds really repetitive, it's a process of narrowing down AND the best way to determine a location based on the coordinates. It will get quicker as you become more familiar with the maps.

Map Projections

A globe is the best true representation of the Earth

A Mercator projection is similar to an equal-area projection. However notice that the latitudes do not appear equal-distant to each other. The closer the poles are approach, the farther apart the latitudes are displayed. What this accomplishes is to maintain the correct scale in all directions from any particular point. This projections preserves the shape or appearance of land areas but it does not preserve area. Notice how small South America looks and how large Antarctica looks.

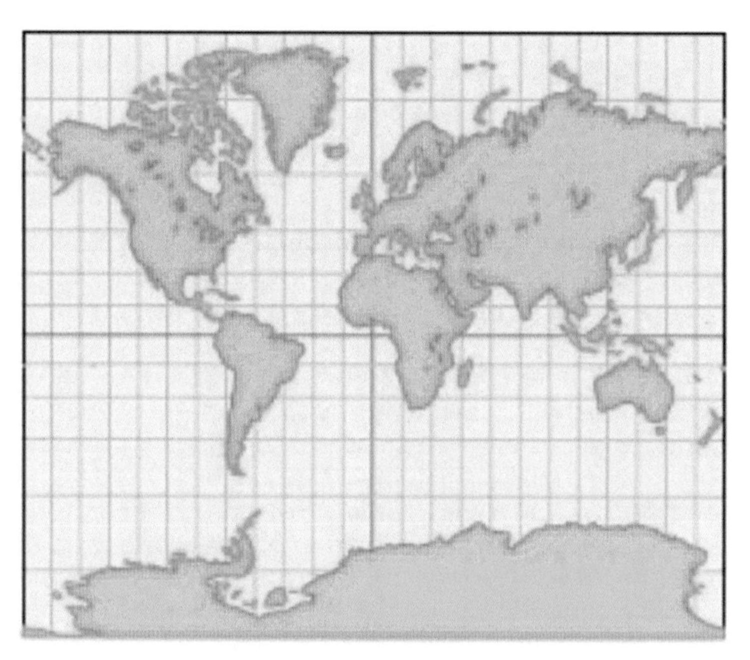

Mercator projection

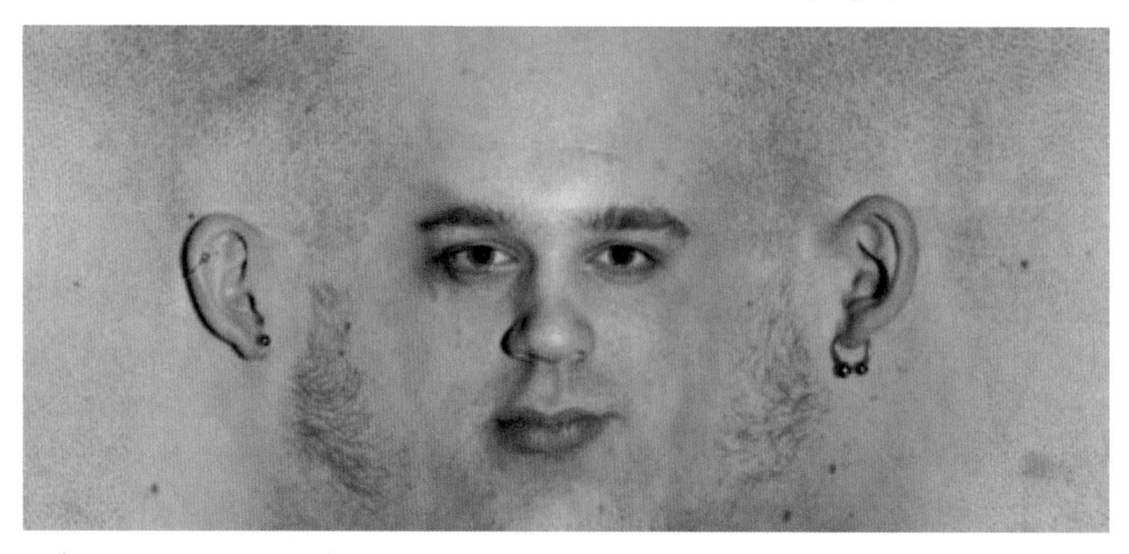

The Human Head as a Mercator Projection

An azimuth projection maintains an equal distant direction from a central point. In this case, the central point is the north pole. Any location could be selected as the central point. Area/ shape however is distorted.

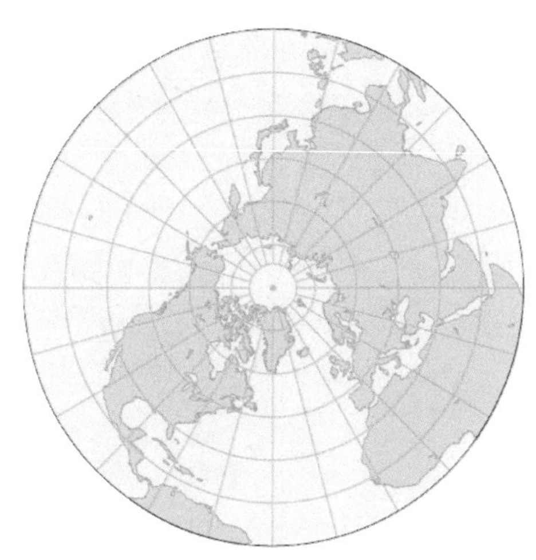

Azimuthal equidistant projection, polar case

An cylindrical equal-area projection maintains maintains a constant area regardless of what area of the map is being examined. It too distorts shape. Notice that at the poles which are in-fact a single point, that it appears that the distance east/west is equal to the distance around the equator. Notice too, that longitude (meridians) are parallel to each other.

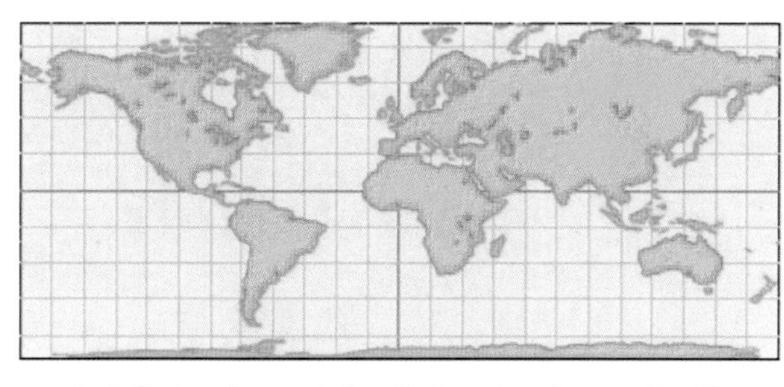

A cylindrical equal-area projection with standard parallels at 30°N and S

A Mollweide projection is another version of an equal-area map. However, notice that unlike the cylindrical equal-area map, longitude (meridians) all meet at one point at the poles. It to distorts shapes.

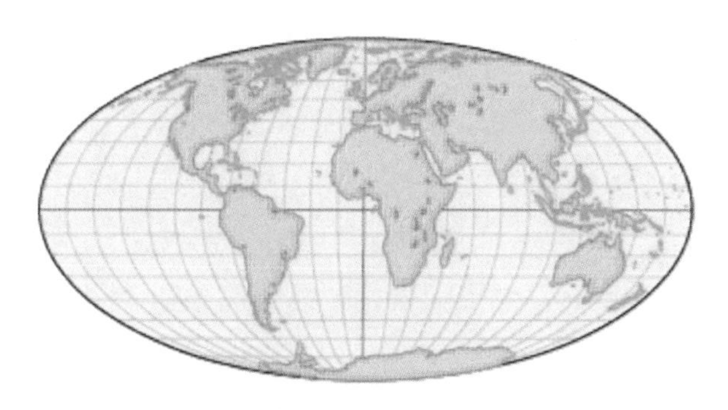

Mollweide projection

A Robinson projection represents a compromise map, as it tends to both distort shape and distance. As a compromise, it relatively preserves shape and direction. Notice that the Robinson projection's longitudes are neither parallel nor do they all meet at the poles. Latitudes are laid out as on the cylindrical equal-area projection rather than as on the Mercator projection.

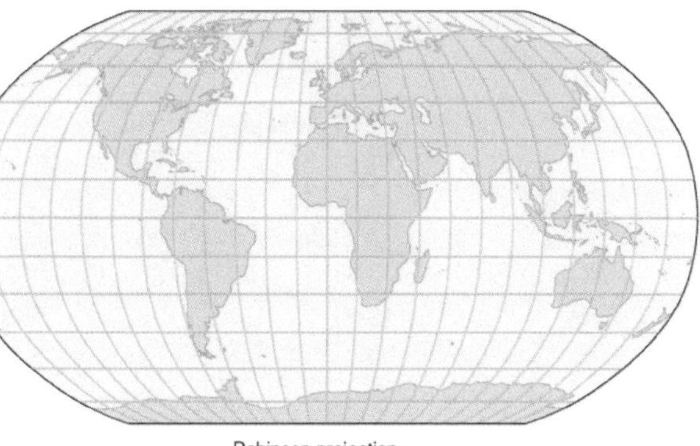

Robinson projection

Techniques of Geographic Analysis
(Spheres of Geography)

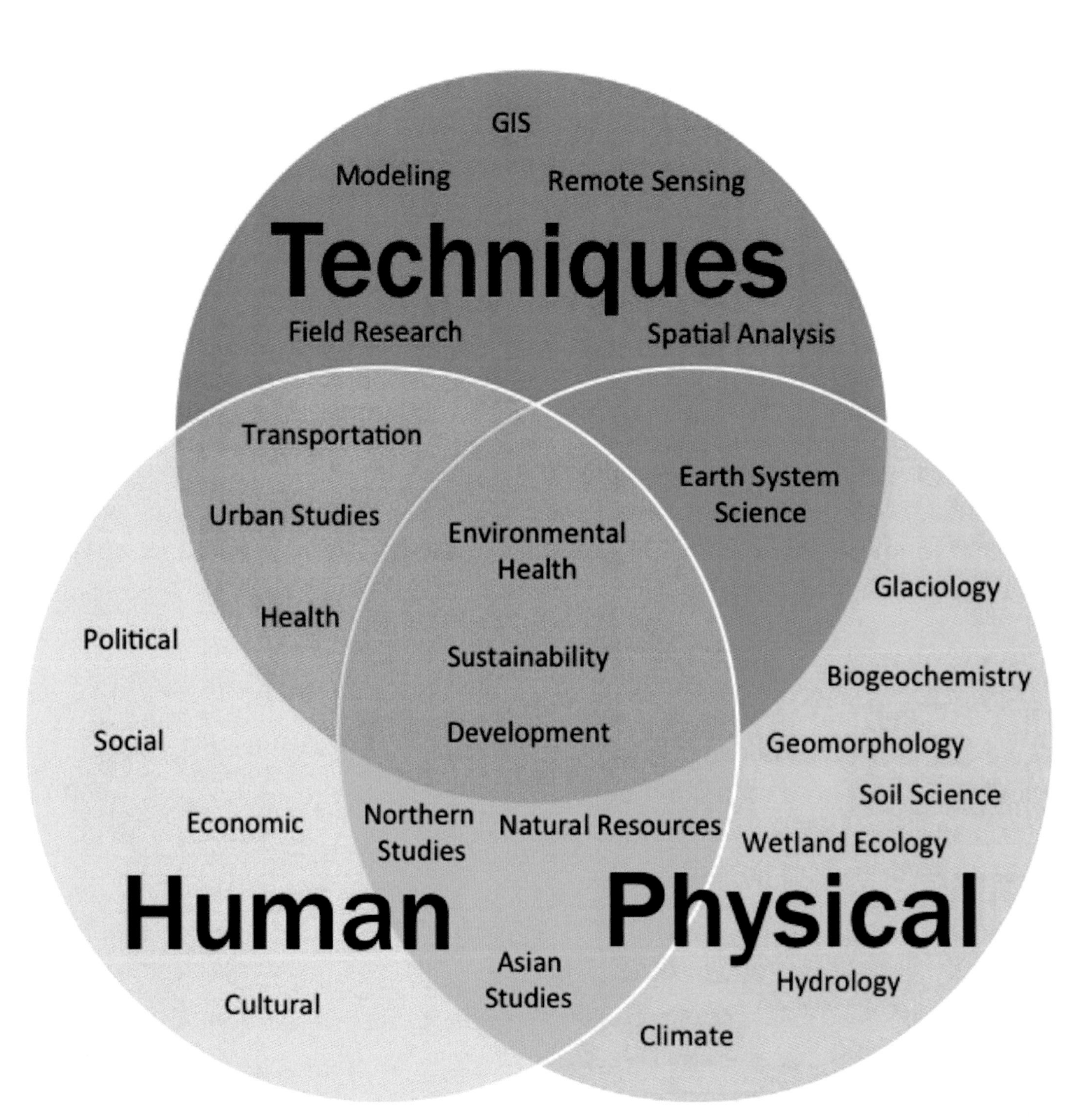
GIS
Modeling
Remote Sensing
Techniques
Field Research
Spatial Analysis
Transportation
Earth System Science
Urban Studies
Environmental Health
Glaciology
Health
Political
Sustainability
Biogeochemistry
Social
Development
Geomorphology
Soil Science
Economic
Northern Studies
Natural Resources
Wetland Ecology
Human
Physical
Asian Studies
Hydrology
Cultural
Climate

Spatial Analysis and its Purpose

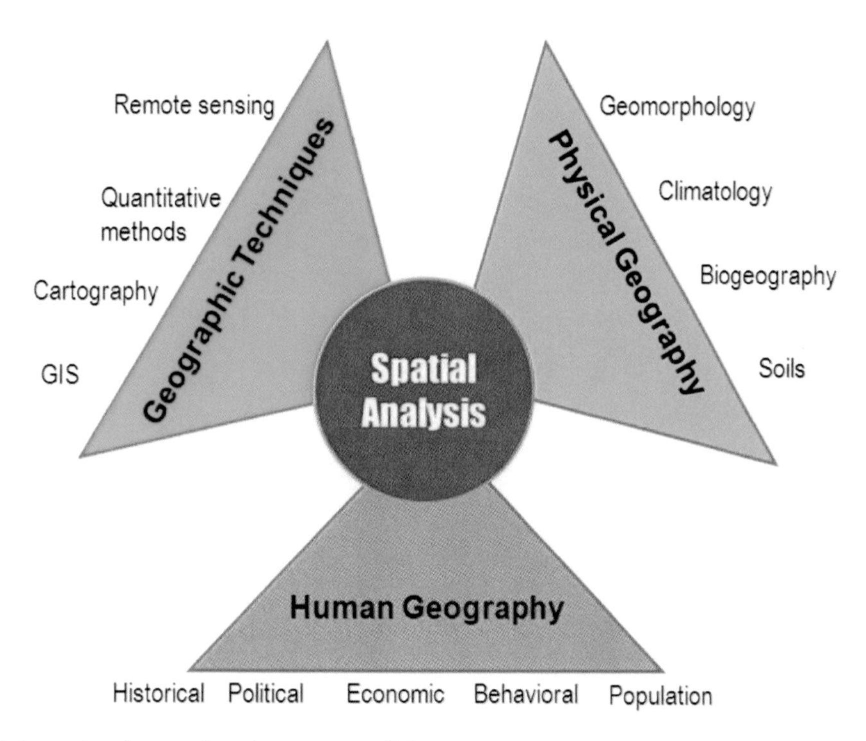
Remote sensing
Quantitative methods
Cartography
GIS
Geographic Techniques
Geomorphology
Climatology
Biogeography
Soils
Physical Geography
Spatial Analysis
Human Geography
Historical
Political
Economic
Behavioral
Population

Most people think GIS is only about "making maps" but governments, businesses and people harness the power of GIS because of the insights of spatial analysis.

Before GIS, cartographers mapped out the land using paper maps. Over the years, we've seen a gradual shift away from paper maps. Instead, users build digital maps with computer-based spatial data.

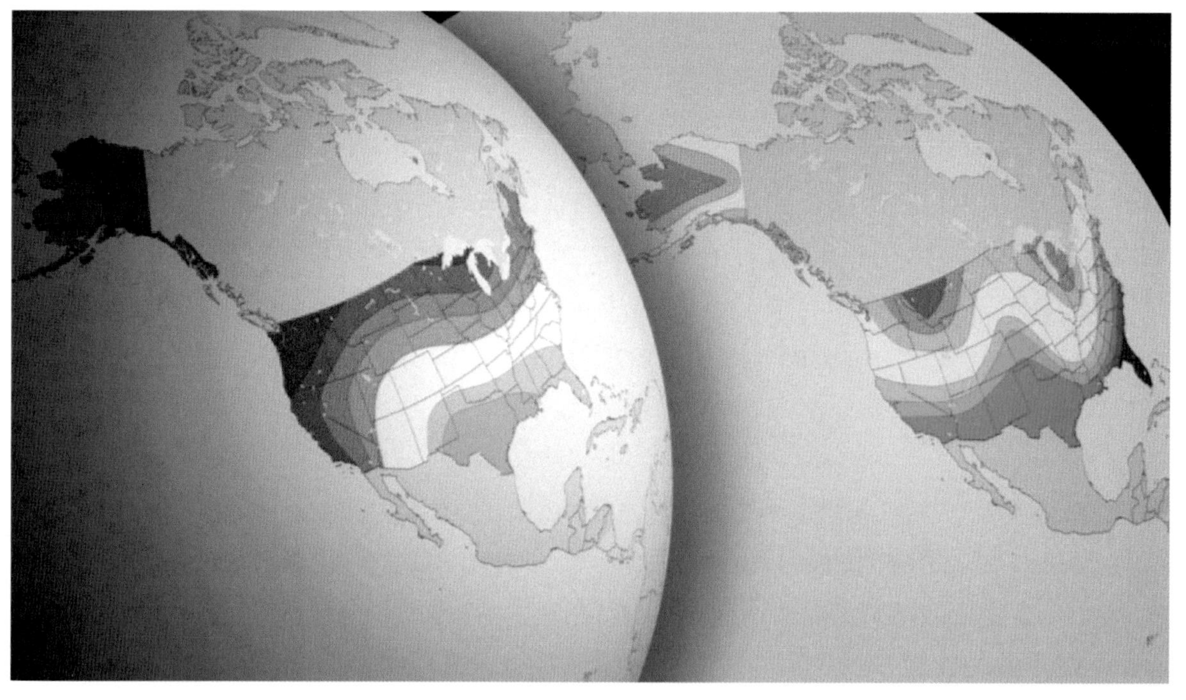

Geo-visualization (or geographic visualization) refers to a set of tools and techniques supporting the analysis of geospatial data using interactive functionality

Practical uses of maps

John Snow's Cholera Map

GIS Started by Mapping Cholera

How often does a map change the world? In 1854, one produced by Doctor John Snow, changed it forever. In the world of the 1850s, cholera was believed to be spread by miasma in the air. Germs were still not yet understood and the sudden and serious outbreak of cholera in London's Soho was a mystery.

Dr. John Snow was trying to solve the mystery and help the people, so he mapped the cases of infection. The map represents each death as a bar. It became apparent that the cases were clustered around the pump in Broad (now Broadwick) street.

Our World Has Many Problems to Solve

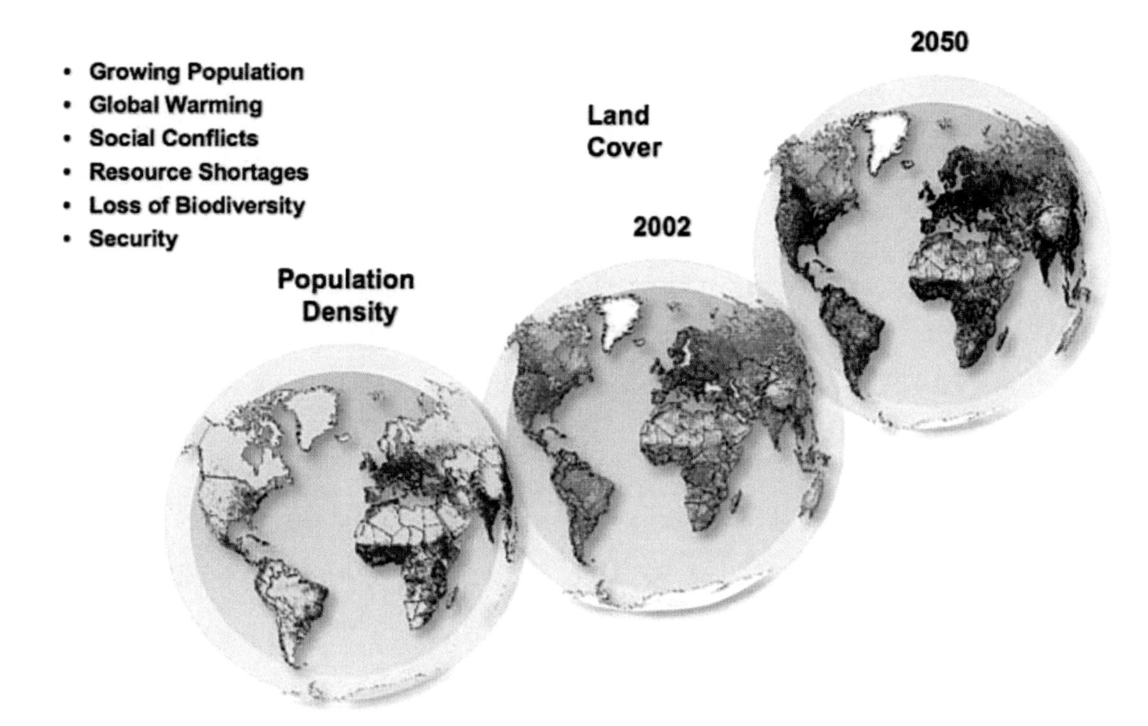

- Growing Population
- Global Warming
- Social Conflicts
- Resource Shortages
- Loss of Biodiversity
- Security

Population Density
Land Cover
2002
2050

Cartographers create maps. Actually, the origin of the job title comes from charta which means "tablet or leaf of paper" and graph "to draw"

Database managers store and extract information from structured sets of geographic data.

Programmers write code and to automate redundant GIS processes. For example, GIS programming languages includes Python, SQL, C++, Visual Basic and JavaScript.

Remote sensing analysts use satellite or aerial imagery to map the Earth.

Spatial analysts manipulate, extract, locate and analyze geographic data.

Land surveyors measure the 3-dimensional coordinates on the land.

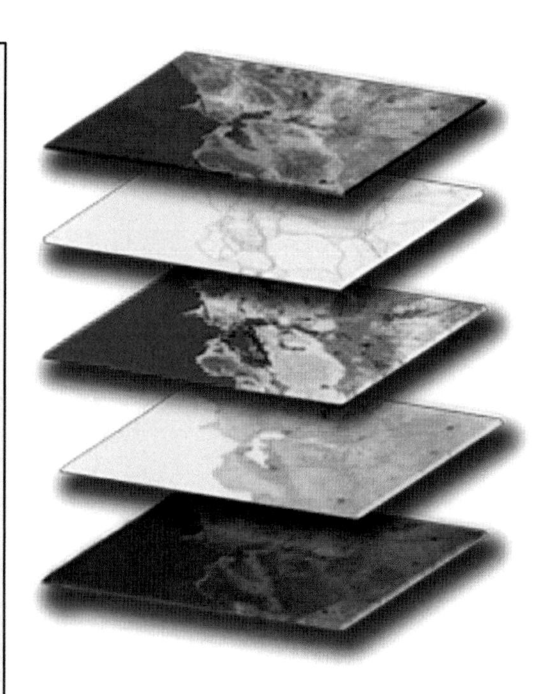

It has been estimated that 80% of the informational needs of local government policy makers are related to geographic location.

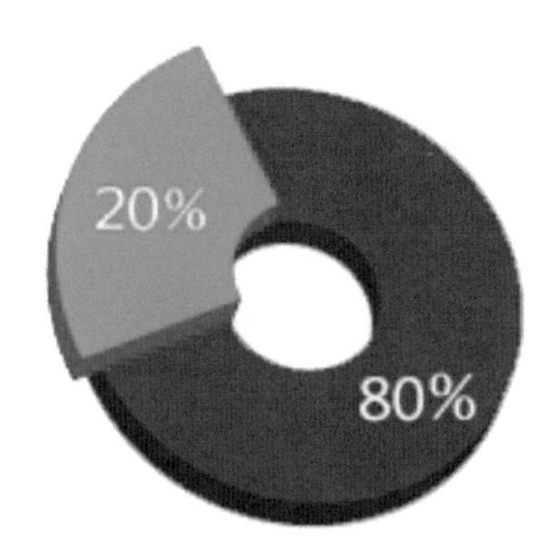
20%
80%

GIS (Geographic Information Systems) answer important questions about location, patterns and trends.

For example:

Where are land features found? includes points, lines, polygons and grids. If you need to find the closest gas station, GIS can show you the way. Or if you want to find an optimal location, you may need traffic volumes, zoning information and demographics.

What geographical patterns exist? Ecologists who want to know suitable habitat for elk can gain a better understanding by using GPS collars and land cover.

What changes have occurred over a given period of time?
Never have we've been able to understand climate change before thanks to GIS and remote sensing technology. Also, safety concerns can be better evaluated using GIS such as understanding terrain slope and the probability an avalanche can occur.

What are the spatial implications?
If an electricity company wants to build a transmission line, how will this affect nearby homes, the environment and safety. Most environmental assessments use GIS to understand the landscape.

GIS and Remote Sensing in Wildfire Response

Step 1. Ask a question:

In this step, you ask a high-level question. This high-level question will guide you to obtaining the correct data, performing the analysis and examining the results.

As a land manager in Yosemite during a wildfire, how can we track the severity and effects of the wildfire? How can we monitor the recovery of the land?

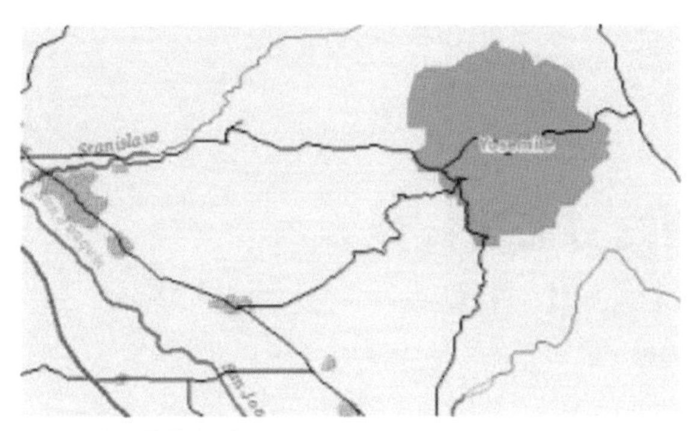

Yosemite, California

Step 2. Capture data:

You can acquire satellite imagery and inspect the extent of the wildfire. Also, what other data could be useful such as roads, infrastructure and trails?

Yosemite National Park Pre-Wildfire (Landsat imagery courtesy of USGS/NASA Landsat)

Step 3. Analyze the situation:

Satellite data can display where vegetation is, which of course is fuel for the fire. If you can model fire behavior, you can map potential risks to communities and determine post-fire effects.

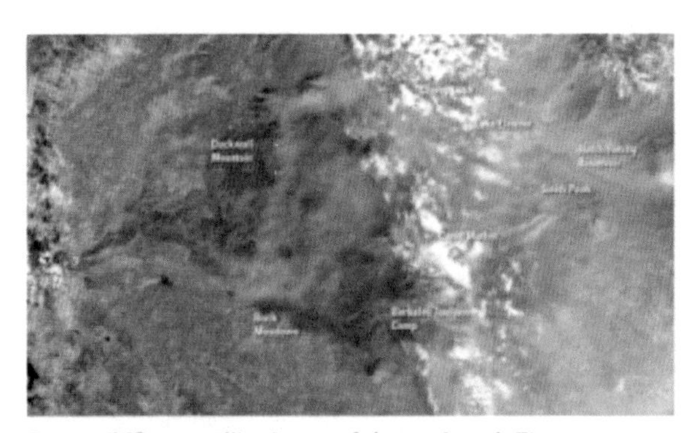

Post-wildfire satellite image false-colored. Fire appears bright red, vegetation is green, smoke is blue, clouds are white, and bare ground is tan-colored. (Landsat imagery courtesy of USGS/NASA Landsat)

Step 4. Respond to the problem:

In order to respond to the wildfire, communicate the best plan of attack to wildfire responders. After this wildfire, it's beneficial to plan for future emergency by providing timely, accurate and relevant geospatial information as a data portal. Also, you can serve webmaps to fire managers with **real-time fire perimeter data**.

GIS Fire Perimeters

The importance of maps with the geography of crime

Crime analysts use crime mapping and analysis to help law enforcement management to make better decisions, target resources, and formulate strategies, as well as for tactical analysis (e.g. crime forecasting, geographic profiling).
The boom of internet technologies, particularly web-based geographic information system (GIS) technologies, is opening new opportunities for use of crime mapping to support crime prevention. Using GIS, crime analysts can overlay other datasets such as census demographics, locations of pawn shops, schools, etc., to better understand the underlying causes of crime and help law enforcement administrators to devise strategies to deal with the problem. GIS is also useful for law enforcement operations, such as allocating police officers and dispatching to emergencies

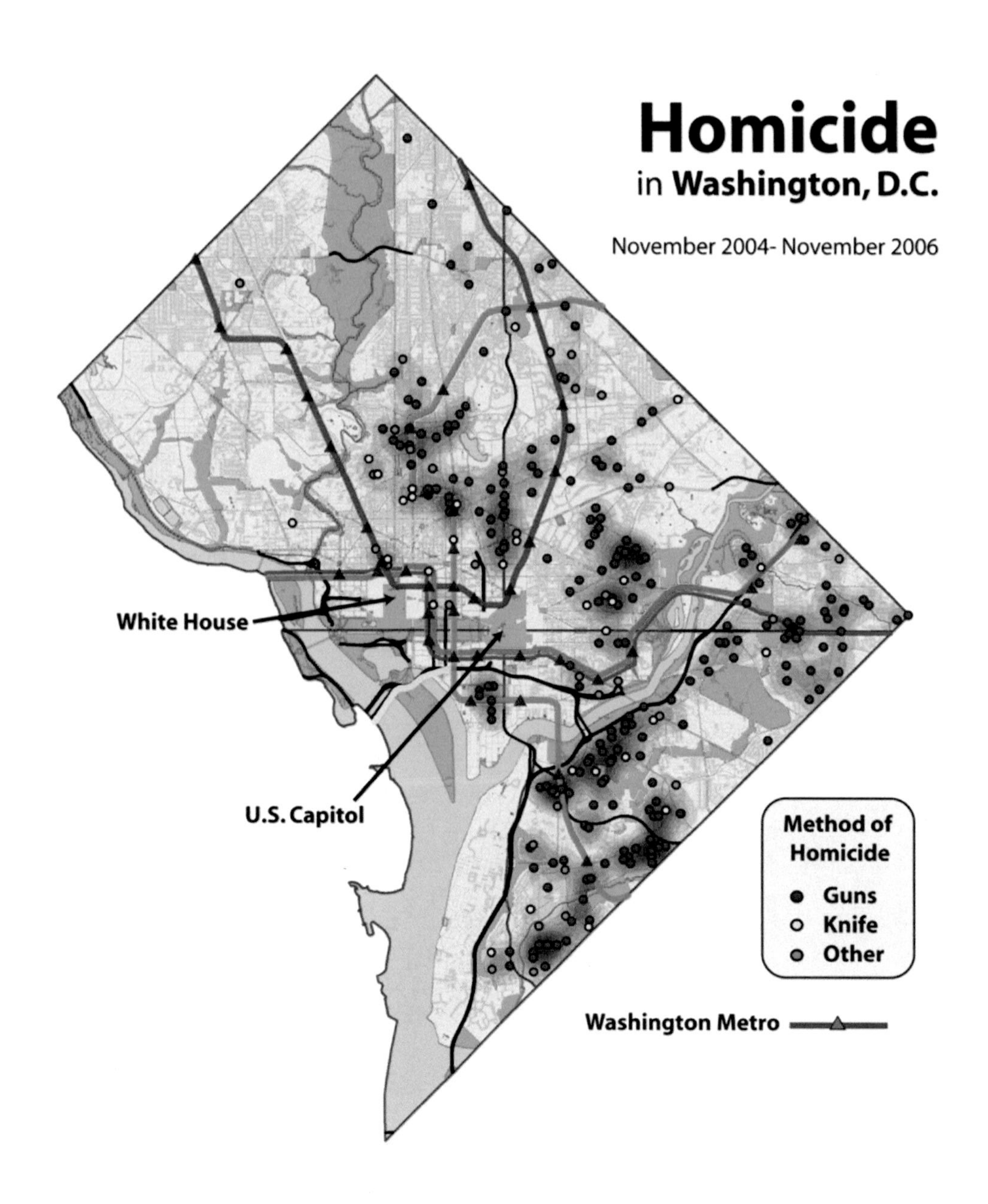
Homicide
in Washington, D.C.
November 2004- November 2006
White House
U.S. Capitol
Method of Homicide
Guns
Knife
Other
Washington Metro

There is so much meta-data available and using geographic analysis can ease a complex problem by showing it on an easily readable map.

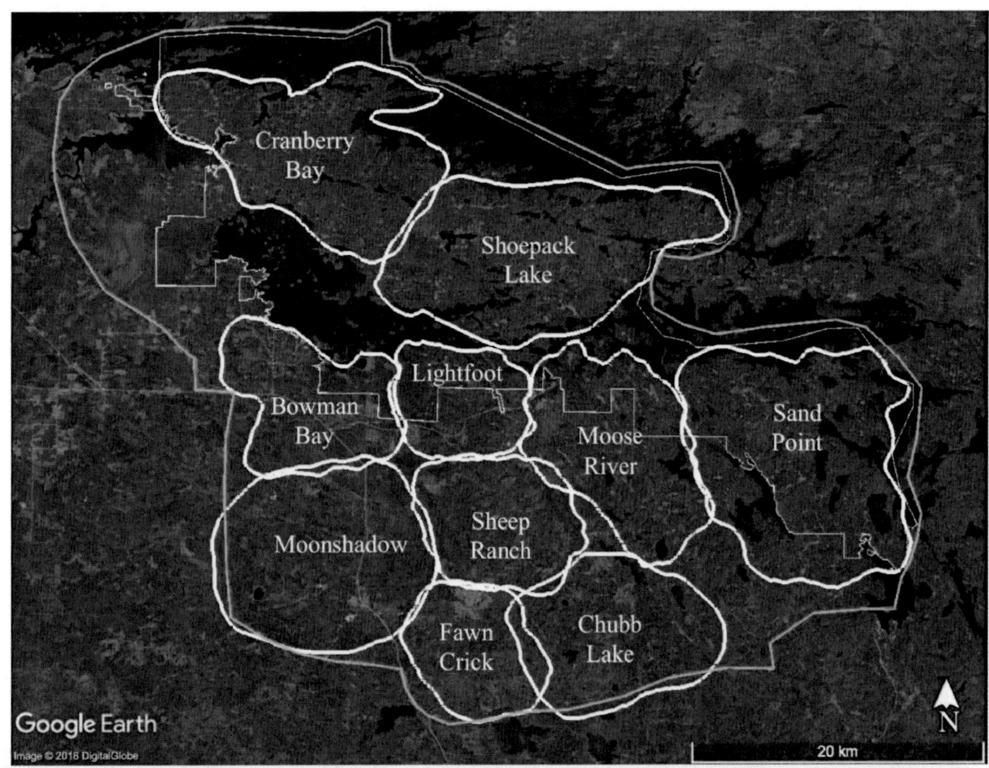
Cranberry Bay
Shoepack Lake
Lightfoot
Bowman Bay
Moose River
Sand Point
Moonshadow
Sheep Ranch
Fawn Crick
Chubb Lake
Google Earth
Image © 2018 DigitalGlobe
20 km
N

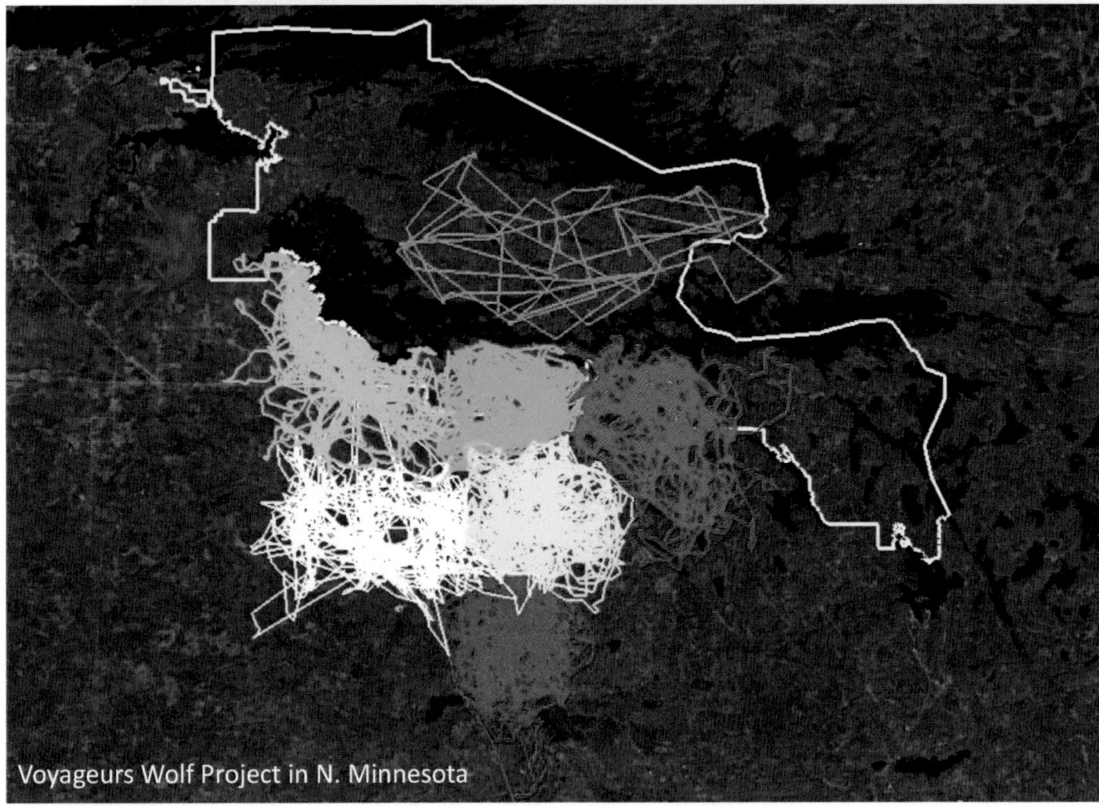
Voyageurs Wolf Project in N. Minnesota

Six wolves from different adjacent packs move around their territories at the same time based on GPS-collar location. This amazing perspective of wolf territoriality results from having GPS-collars that take locations every 20 minutes (72 locations/day), which provides detailed travel paths from each wolf.

Physical Geography

Volcán de Fuego. Guatemala – Tyrell Heaton

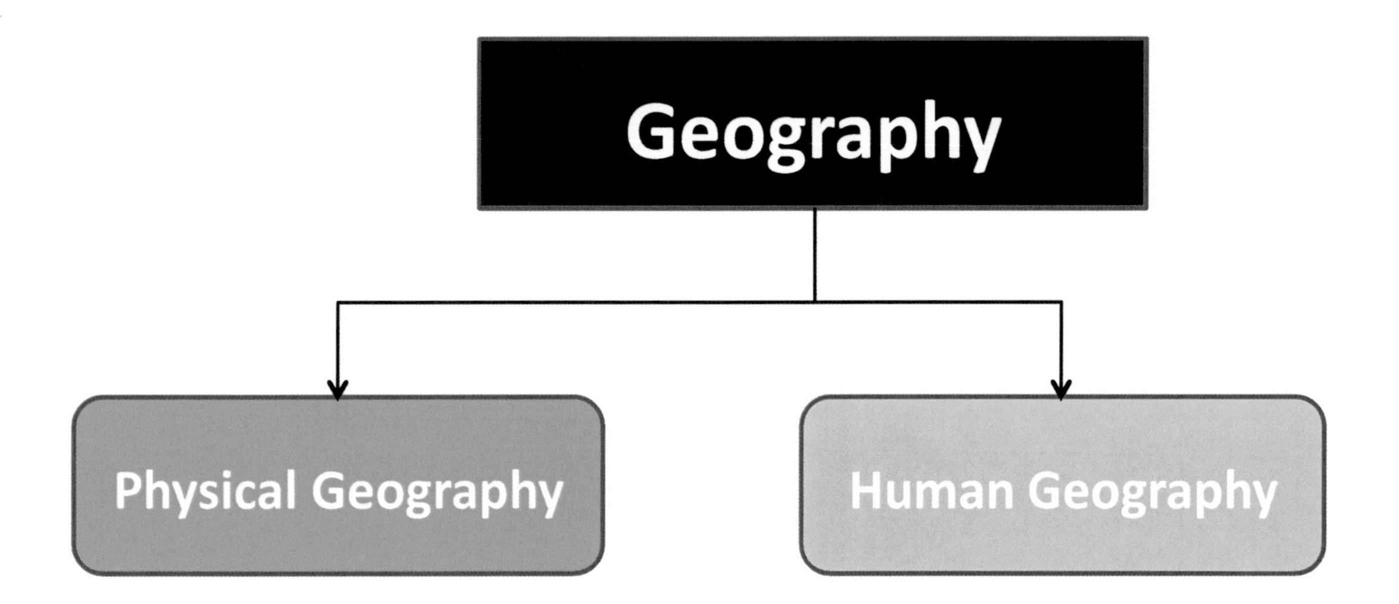
Geography
Physical Geography
Human Geography

Geomorphology
Climatology
Oceanography
Environmental Geography
Glaciology
Biogeography

Cultural Geography
Population Geography
Economic Geography
Political Geography
Urban Geography
Medical Geography

Physical Geography is one of the two subfields of geography; it is the study of the physical world.

Physical geography studies physical patterns and processes of the Earth. It aims to understand the forces that produce and change the physical features of our world.

Subfields of Physical Geography

Geomorphology: the study of the configuration of the earth's solid surface – the world's landscapes and their constituent landforms

Climatology: the study of climates; includes not only the classification of climates and the analysis of their regional distribution but also broader environmental questions that concern climate change, interrelationships with soil and vegetation and human climate interaction

Oceanography: the study of the oceans and ocean floor

Environmental Geography: the branch of geography dealing with the dynamics of Earth's surface features and their evolution through the actions of weathering and erosion.

Glaciology: the study of glaciers and their effects on the landscape

Biogeography: the study of flora (plant life) and fauna (animal life) in spatial perspective

Supercontinent or Pangaea

This sequence of maps shows how a large **supercontinent**, known as **Pangaea** was fragmented into several pieces, each being part of a mobile plate of the lithosphere.

These pieces were to become Earth's current continents. The time sequence shown through the maps traces the paths of the continents to their current positions.

This understanding of Earth's land formation comes from the study of the lithosphere (the outer portion of the earth consisting of the crust and part of the upper mantle) and the theory of **Plate Tectonics**. The lithosphere is divided into about a dozen large plates which move and interact with one another to create earthquakes, mountain ranges, volcanic activity, ocean trenches and many other features.

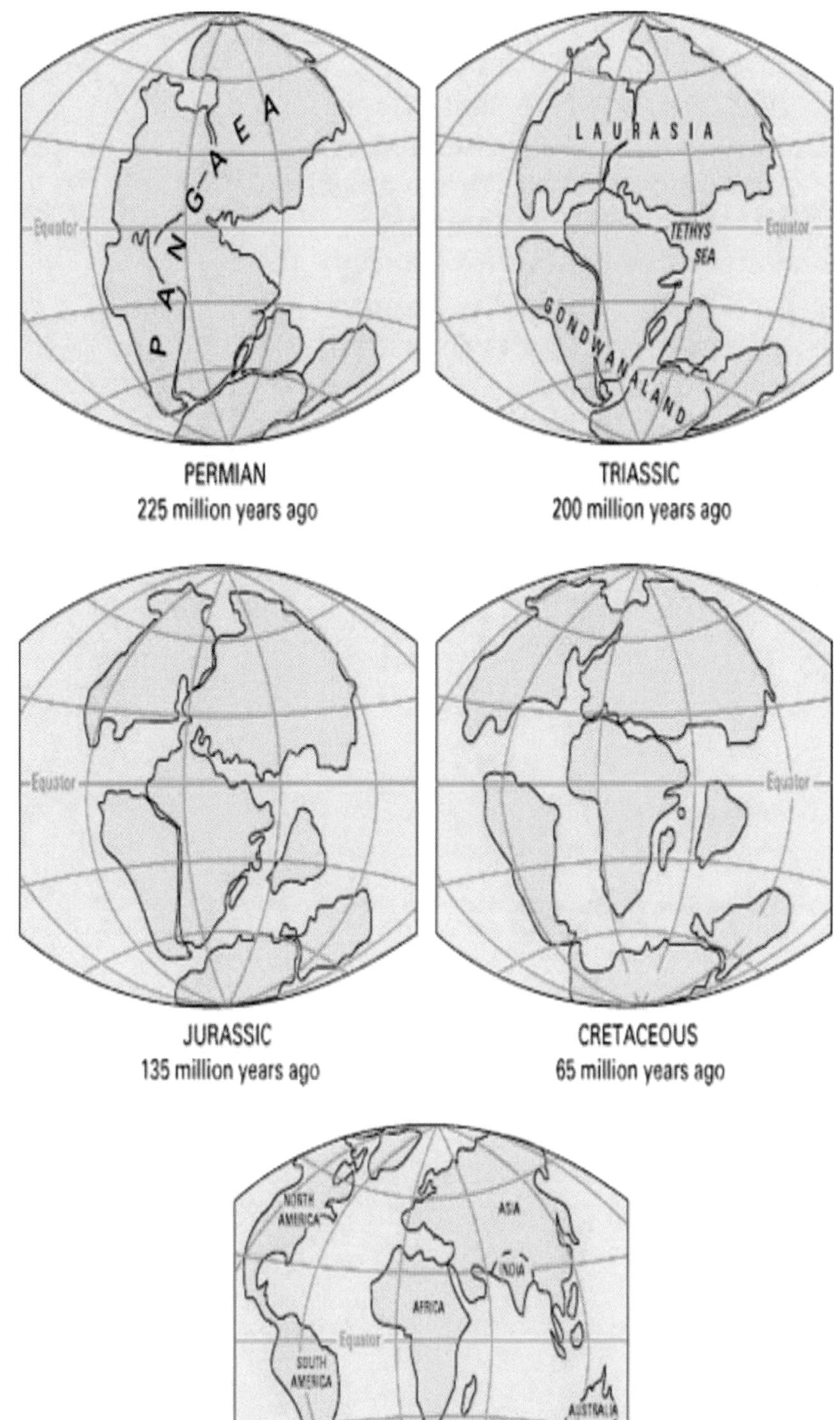
PANGAEA
Equator
PERMIAN
225 million years ago
LAURASIA
TETHYS SEA
GONDWANALAND
Equator
TRIASSIC
200 million years ago
Equator
JURASSIC
135 million years ago
Equator
CRETACEOUS
65 million years ago
NORTH AMERICA
ASIA
INDIA
AFRICA
Equator
SOUTH AMERICA
AUSTRALIA
ANTARCTICA
PRESENT DAY

Plate Tectonics

These plates are mobile, moving slowly a few centimeters (an inch or so) a year, propelled by heat-driven convection cells in the molten rock below. Where these giant plates collide the plate that consists of lighter (less heavy) rock rides up over the heavier plate, which is push downward – called subduction. Such gigantic collisions create mountain chains causing earthquakes and volcanic eruptions in the process.

The Impact: Volcanic Activity and Earthquakes

Notice how the plate edges correspond to volcano and earthquake activity.

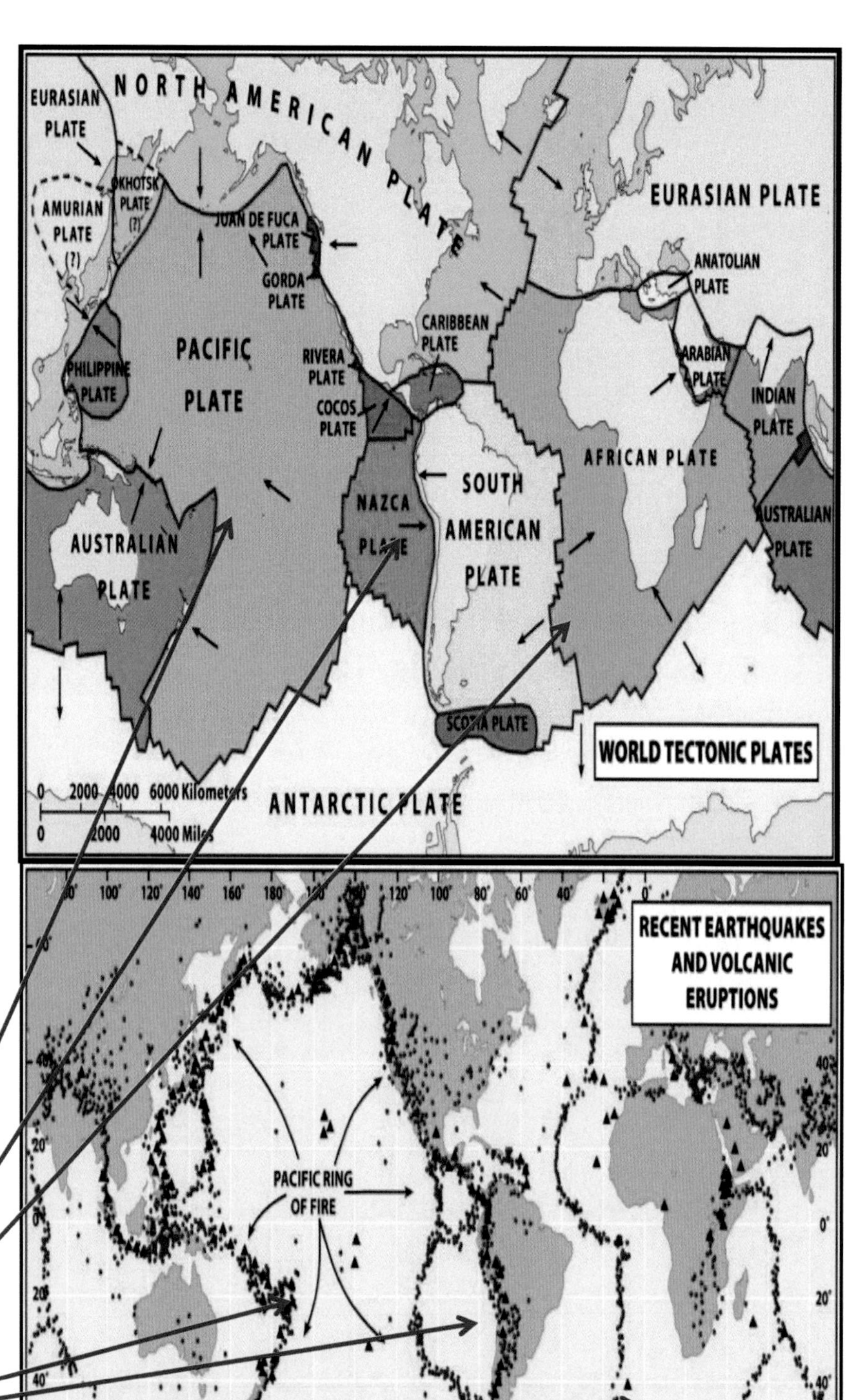

EURASIAN PLATE
NORTH AMERICAN PLATE
AMURIAN PLATE (?)
OKHOTSK PLATE (?)
JUAN DE FUCA PLATE
GORDA PLATE
PACIFIC PLATE
PHILIPPINE PLATE
RIVERA PLATE
COCOS PLATE
CARIBBEAN PLATE
EURASIAN PLATE
ANATOLIAN PLATE
ARABIAN PLATE
INDIAN PLATE
AFRICAN PLATE
NAZCA PLATE
SOUTH AMERICAN PLATE
AUSTRALIAN PLATE
AUSTRALIAN PLATE
SCOTIA PLATE
WORLD TECTONIC PLATES
ANTARCTIC PLATE
0 2000 4000 6000 Kilometers
0 2000 4000 Miles
RECENT EARTHQUAKES AND VOLCANIC ERUPTIONS
PACIFIC RING OF FIRE
0 2500 5000 Kilometers
0 2000 4000 Miles
▲ Active volcano
• Earthquake origin

Plate tectonics alter the physical geography of the landscape more dramatically than any other natural process. For instance, they may create the steep slopes associated with mountain chains and volcanoes, whose continual uplift or outpouring of lava contributes more to topography than climate. Continual fault movements in earthquake-prone areas will also tend to dominate the landscape more than the modifying effects of erosion.

Earthquake Local Landscape Effects

Santa Cruz Mountains, California

Earthquake land rift

Santa Cruz Mountains, California

Earthquake offset road

Iceland

The Mid-Atlantic Ridge passes through Iceland

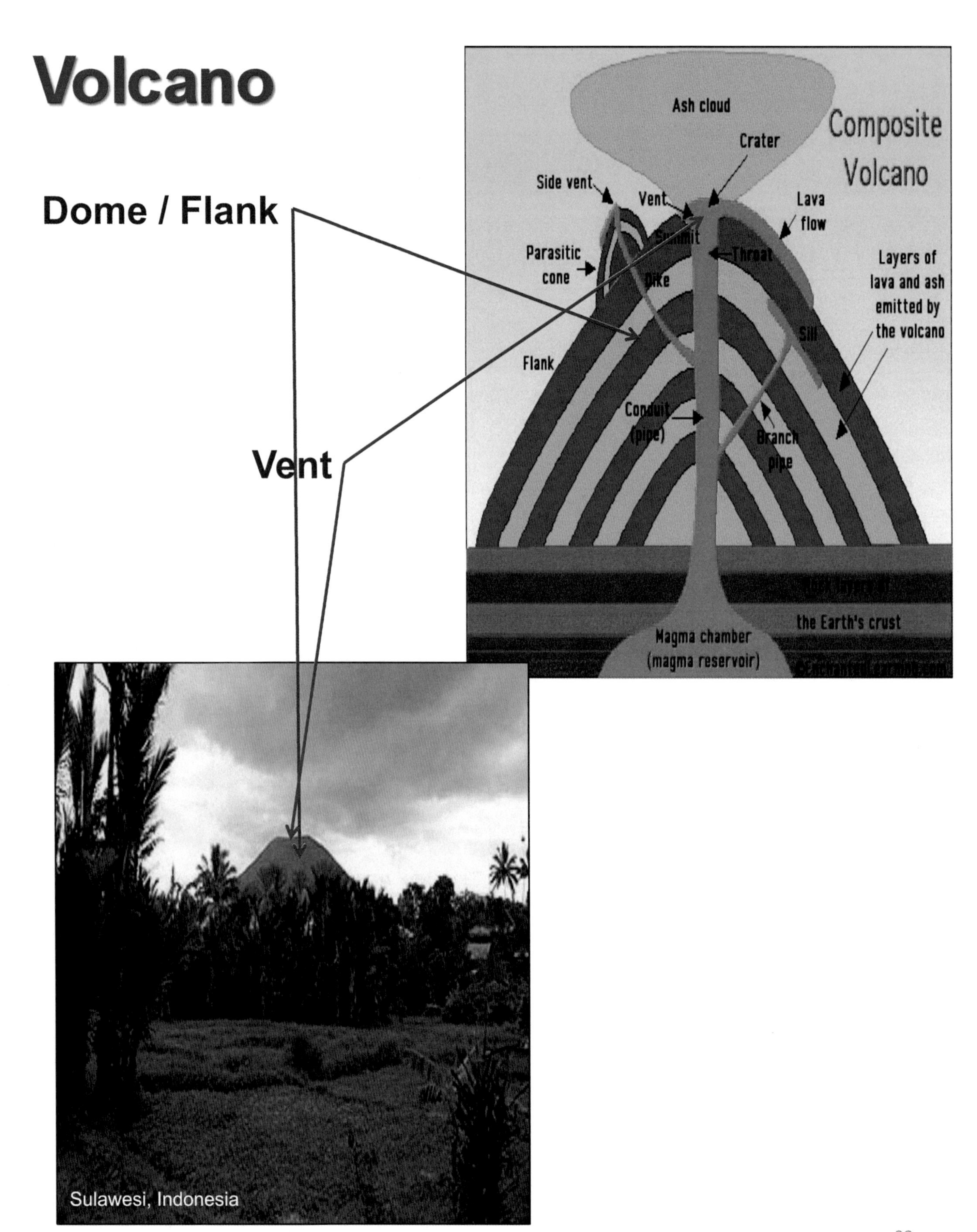

Volcano
Dome / Flank
Vent
Ash cloud
Composite
Volcano
Crater
Side vent
Vent
Lava
flow
Parasitic
cone
Summit
Throat
Layers of
lava and ash
emitted by
the volcano
Dike
Sill
Flank
Conduit
(pipe)
Branch
pipe
the Earth's crust
Magma chamber
(magma reservoir)
Sulawesi, Indonesia

Volcano

Local Landscape Effects

Mono Valley, California

Mono Craters (obsidian domes)

Kona, Hawaii

Edge of lava lake

Mt. St. Helens, Washington

Flanks of Mount Saint
Helens, Washington

The Rock Cycle

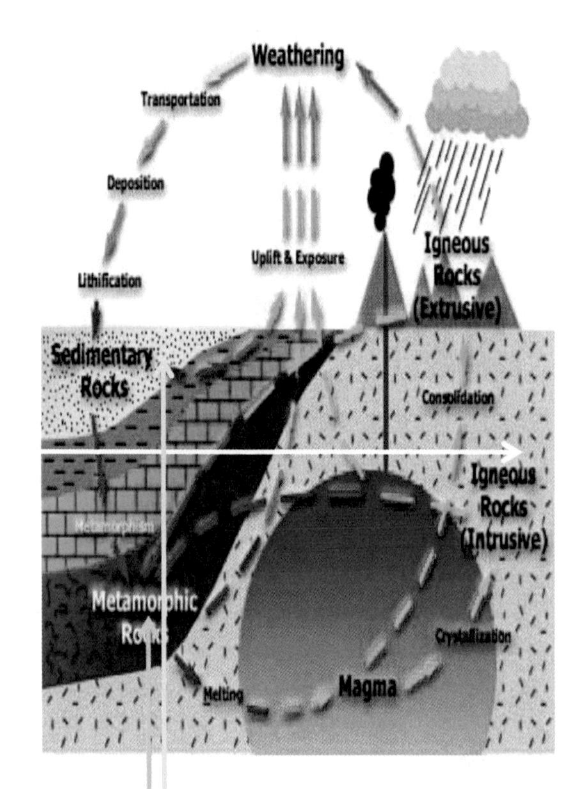
Weathering
Transportation
Deposition
Lithification
Uplift & Exposure
Igneous Rocks (Extrusive)
Sedimentary Rocks
Consolidation
Igneous Rocks (Intrusive)
Metamorphism
Metamorphic Rocks
Crystallization
Melting
Magma

Igneous rock forms when magma cools and makes crystals. Magma is a hot liquid made of melted minerals. The minerals can form crystals when they cool. Igneous rock can form underground, where the magma cools slowly. Or, igneous rock can form above ground, where the magma cools quickly.

On Earth's surface, wind and water can break rock into pieces. They can also carry rock pieces to another place. Usually, the rock pieces, called sediments, drop from the wind or water to make a layer. The layer can be buried under other layers of sediments. After a long time the sediments can be cemented together to make sedimentary rock. In this way, igneous rock can become **sedimentary rock**.

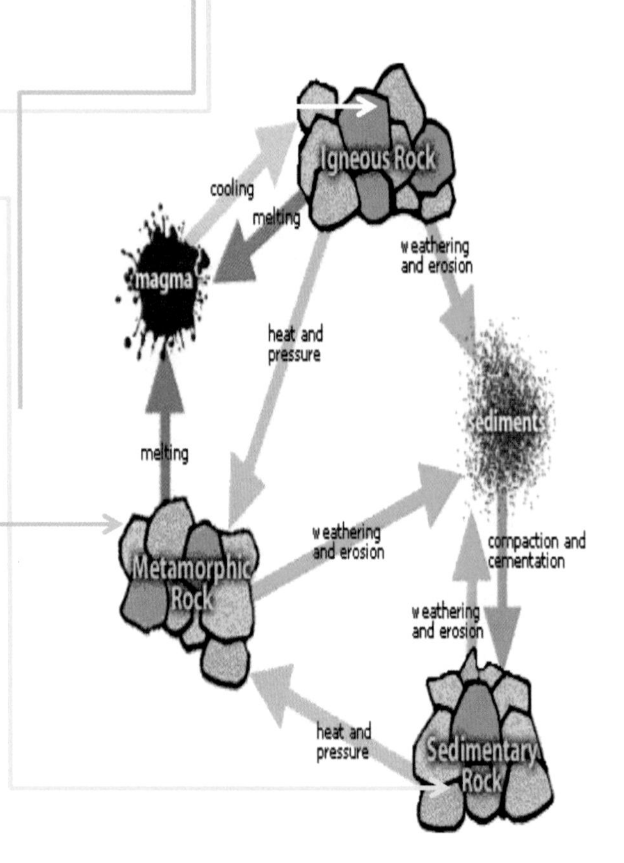
Igneous Rock
cooling
melting
magma
weathering and erosion
heat and pressure
sediments
melting
Metamorphic Rock
weathering and erosion
compaction and cementation
weathering and erosion
heat and pressure
Sedimentary Rock

All rock can be heated. Baked rock does not melt, but it does change. It forms crystals. If it has crystals already, it forms larger crystals. Because this rock changes, it is called **metamorphic rock**. When Earth's tectonic plates move around, they produce heat. When they collide, they build mountains and shape the rock.

Mountains made of metamorphic rocks can be broken up and washed away by streams. New sediments from these mountains can make new sedimentary rock.

The rock cycle never stops.

Weathering Agents

Landscapes experiencing different types of climate are subject to different types of weathering.

- In cold, mountain areas, glaciation is the dominant shaping force at work
- Water is the main weathering agent in warm, humid coastal and river regions
- Wind erosion is responsible for shaping many of the landforms in dry deserts.

Examples of sedimentary rock from flooding and weathering

Quebrada Rio Seco de Casma, Peru

Flood deposits and dune sands.

Small Scale – notice the pen

Rio Sechin, Peru

Ancient overbank flood sediments and channel gravel.

Large Scale

Weathering Effects

Cross section: soil on top of rock

Tyrell Heaton – Wellington, New Zealand

Weathering Effects of Cold Climates

At present, glacial conditions control the shape of the land in places such as Antarctica and Greenland, because the power of erosion is greater than the effects of wind or rain. Many glaciers also transport huge quantities of sediment, called till, which is deposited in ridges and piles known as moraines.

Melting glaciers produce large quantities of melt water, causing springtime floods downstream. This water also carries silt, sand, and clay that is deposited across the front of the glaciated area as an outwash fan.

Evidence of past glaciation can be seen in the U-shaped valleys of the Sierra Nevada in California, and on Norway's west coast, where these wide, flat-bottomed features have subsequently been flooded by the sea to form fjords.

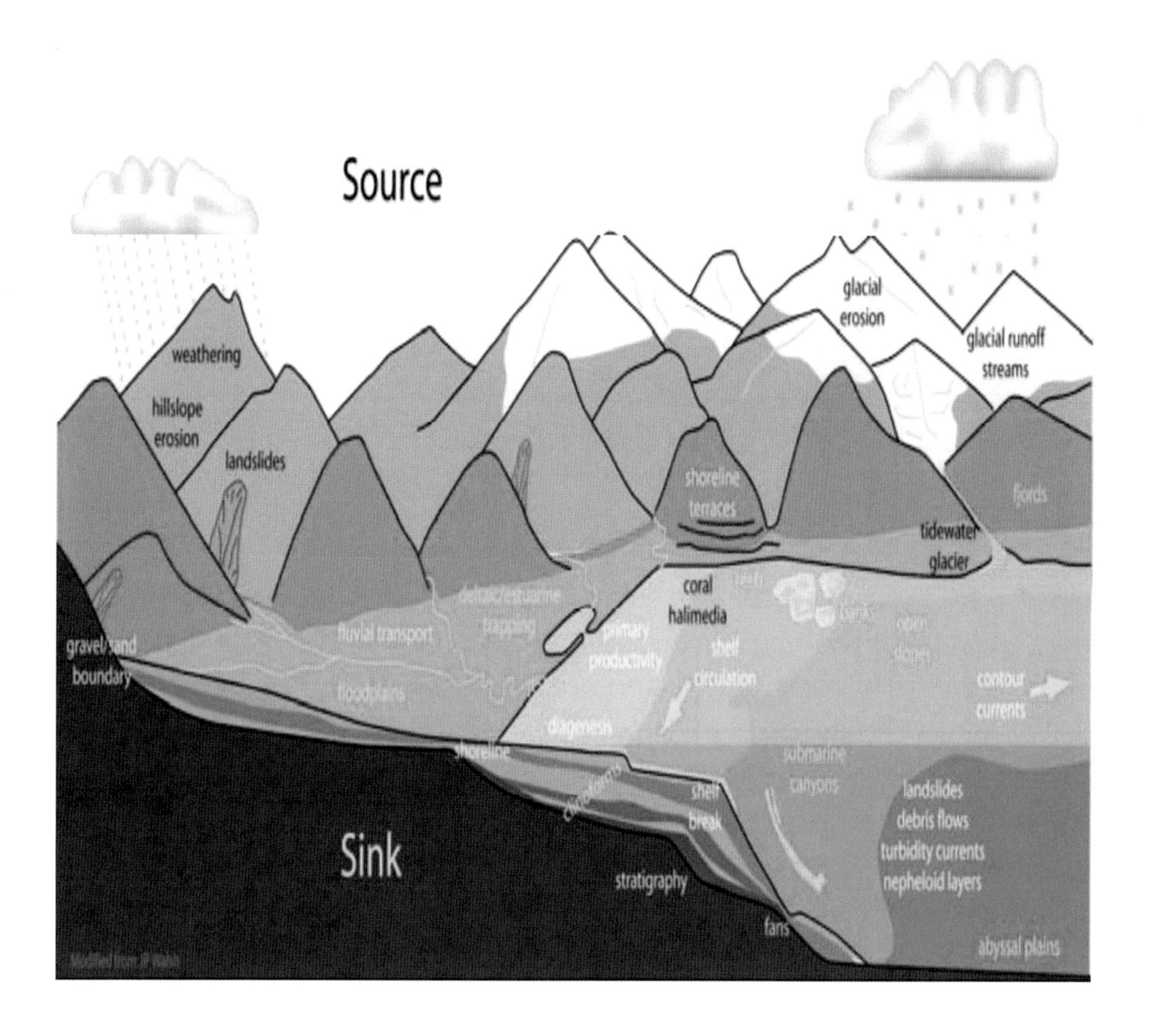

Source
weathering
hillslope erosion
landslides
glacial erosion
glacial runoff streams
shoreline terraces
fjords
tidewater glacier
coral halimedia
fluvial transport
primary productivity
shelf circulation
contour currents
floodplains
diagenesis
gravel/sand boundary
shoreline
submarine canyons
shelf break
landslides
debris flows
turbidity currents
nepheloid layers
Sink
stratigraphy
fans
abyssal plains

Evidence of Past Glaciation

Montana, USA
Cordillera Blanca, Peru

U-shaped glacial valley

The highland valley of the Callejon de Huaylas

Ice sheets can spread over mountain ranges, lowlands, and oceans. They may contain significant rock debris, and are heavy enough to depress the Earth's crust beneath them. Upon melting, the crust rebounds, causing uplift and the formation of features such as raised beaches. Today, the Malaspina Glacier ice sheet in North America is 50 miles long and more than 1,000 feet thick. Even more impressive is the great Antarctica ice sheet, which covers an area of 4,784,964 square miles.

Weathering Effects of Humid Climates

In areas where there are slopes, humid climates will create rain that feeds the streams and rivers responsible for erosion of the land. If the land is continually uplifted by Earth movements, the rivers will cut deeply into the underlying rock, for example in the Samaria Gorge in Crete.

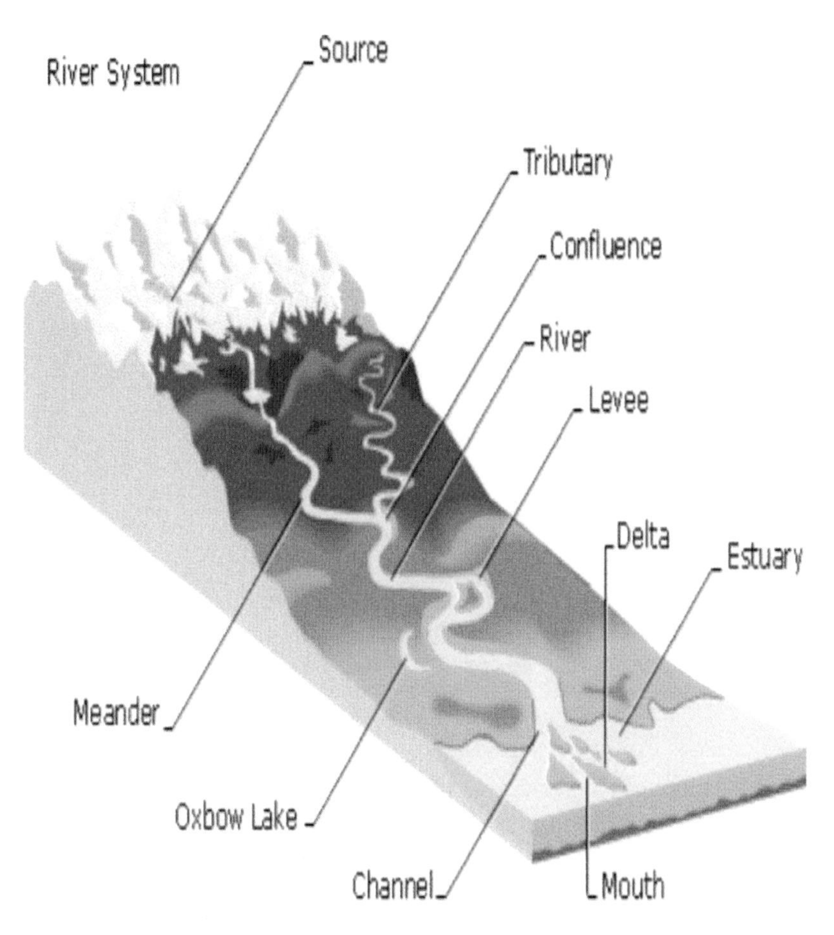
River System
Source
Tributary
Confluence
River
Levee
Delta
Estuary
Meander
Oxbow Lake
Channel
Mouth

Rivers create landforms through erosion and deposition. Most erosion takes place upstream, while deposition generally occurs downstream. River erosion is caused by water dissolving rocks, and by the abrasion caused when cobbles, pebbles, and sand grains rub along the base of the river valley and against each other. These moving, eroding fragments are known as the river's load. The amount of load depends on the strength of the river currents.

Samaria Gorge, Crete

Flooding

Downstream from hills and mountains, river sedimentation creates a flat area of land called a floodplain. As the name suggests, this landform originates from the periodic flooding of the adjacent river, a process that results in widespread deposition of sediment. Flooding may occur each year, during springtime or monsoonal floods, and plays an important role in renewing the sediment and water that help soil formation. Floodplains are continually being shaped by the settling of new sediment, the growth of vegetation, and the erosion and deposition of sediment by rivers as they meander across the floodplain. When a meander in a river is abandoned by the river taking a shortcut across the river loop, an oxbow lake may be formed. This area of still water will also gradually fill with silt and clay.

Lena Delta, Siberia (Image from Space)

Amazon River – example of meandering river

Floods are both destructive and constructive. They wash away roads, buildings, and soil from some areas, and deposit large volumes of sediment elsewhere on the floodplain or in the ocean. Floods are usually caused by rainstorms, especially cloudbursts, in upland areas, but snowmelt, earthquakes, dam bursts, and volcanic eruptions can also cause floods. Their unpredictable nature can cause huge damage to human life, as in Bangladesh, where floods occur every year. Coastal floods can also occur when high tides and onshore winds in storms or hurricanes cause lowland coasts to flood with seawater.

Coasts

There are four types of coast: rocky cliffs, where erosion is important; sandy beaches and dunes, where sediment is transported; coastal plains, such as estuaries, lagoons, and salt marshes, where clay and silt may be trapped; and deltas, where rivers enter the sea and deposit great volumes of sediment. All of these areas are related. Fragments of rock washed down from the cliffs are stored on beaches before being swept offshore during storms, or onto marshes and into lagoons.

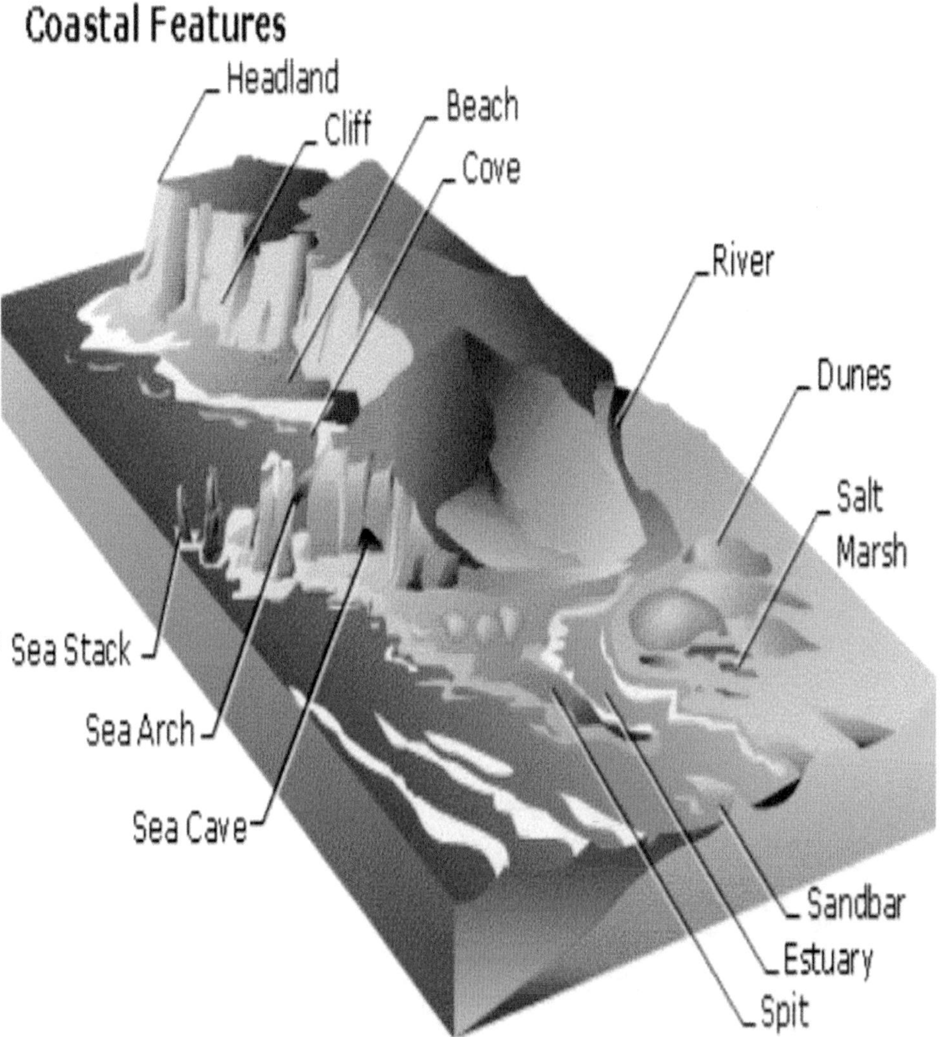
Coastal Features
Headland
Cliff
Beach
Cove
River
Dunes
Salt Marsh
Sea Stack
Sea Arch
Sea Cave
Sandbar
Estuary
Spit

Beaches are not permanent features, since the sand is often simply being stored before moving on. They also change in response to storms, when large banks of sand accumulate near to the land. Marine currents move beach sand on a more regular basis than storms.

Coasts are constantly changing due to erosion, sediment transport, and deposition, and are consequently very unstable places to live. They are also prone to storm damage when ocean waves and winds hit the land. Coastal erosion may cause the destruction of buildings, port facilities, waterways, and amenities. Sea walls and breakwaters are built to combat this destruction.

Weathering / Erosion Example Along Coast

Nauru – Island in the South Pacific

Second notch at extreme high water mark located about 15 feet above the lower notch.

Small erosion notch at high water mark on limestone bedrock.

Orographic Lifting and Rain Shadows

Mountain ranges acts as barriers to the flow of air across the surface of the earth. They act to squeeze moisture out of the air. When a parcel of warm air reaches a mountain range, it is lifted up the mountain slope, cooling as it rises. This process is known as **orographic lifting** and the cooling of the air often results in large clouds, precipitation, and even thunderstorms; orographic lifting keeps the windward sides of mountain ranges moist and filled with vegetation but the leeward sides dry and barren.

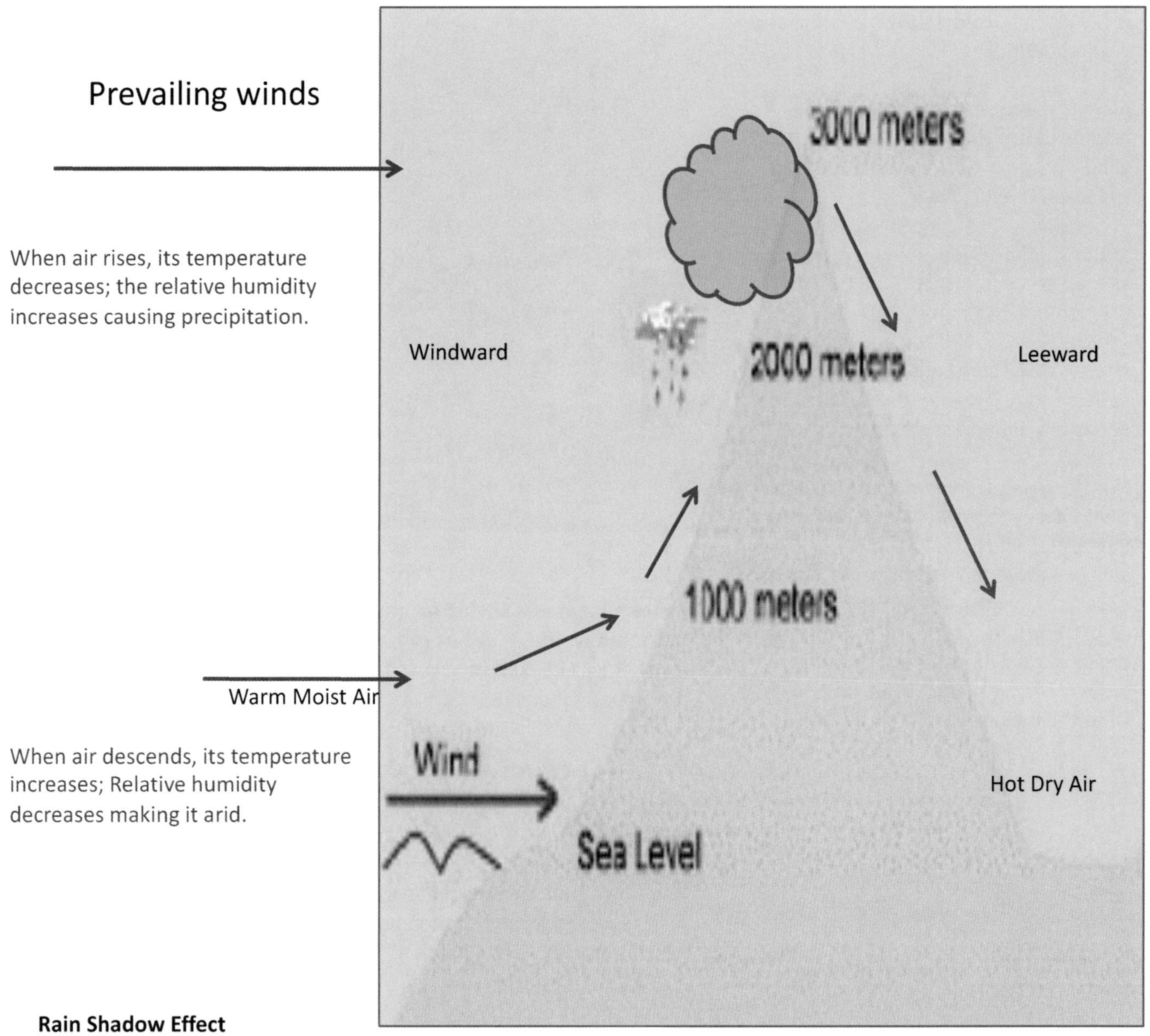

Prevailing winds
When air rises, its temperature decreases; the relative humidity increases causing precipitation.
Warm Moist Air
When air descends, its temperature increases; Relative humidity decreases making it arid.
3000 meters
Windward
2000 meters
Leeward
1000 meters
Wind
Hot Dry Air
Sea Level

Rain Shadow Effect

As a parcel of air rises up the windward side of a mountain range, it has its moisture squeezed out. Thus, when the air begins to descend the leeward side of the mountain, it is dry. As the cool air descends, it warms and expands, reducing its possibility of precipitation. This is known as the rain shadow effect and is the primary cause of leeward deserts of mountain ranges, such as California's Death Valley.

Weathering Effects of Arid Climates

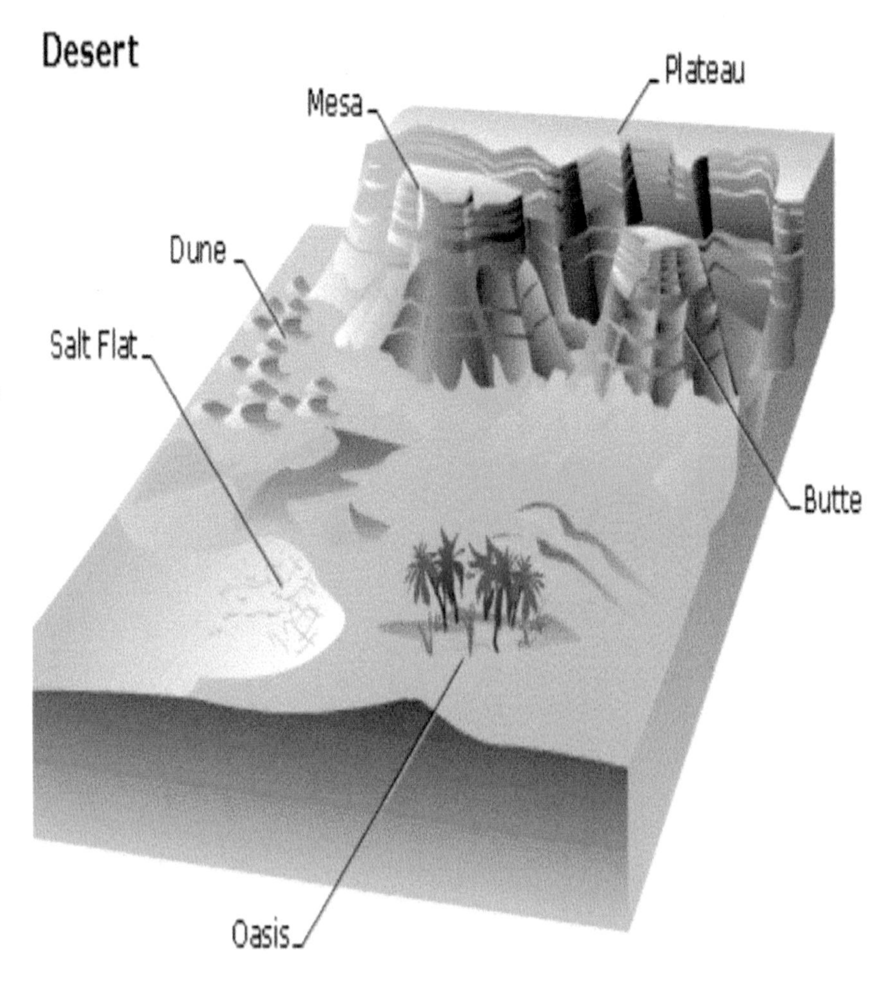
Desert
Plateau
Mesa
Dune
Salt Flat
Butte
Oasis

Deserts are arid areas of land where more water is lost through evaporation than is gained from precipitation. As well as hot, sandy deserts such as the Sahara, there are rocky deserts, cold deserts, and sparsely vegetated deserts.

All of these deserts are dry, and their landforms are shaped by wind erosion, wind transport, episodic flooding, and evaporation.

In the Southern Hemisphere, deserts such as the Atacama Desert in South America, the Namib and Kalahari Deserts in southern Africa, and the entire continental interior of Western Australia are arid because they lie under the eastern side of persistent high-pressure areas.

Northern Hemisphere deserts, such as Death Valley in Nevada and eastern California, which lies inland beyond the wall of the Sierra Nevada, are rain shadow deserts. In central China, the high, cold Gobi Desert lies north of the Himalayas, the world's highest mountains, which block moist air masses sweeping north from the Indian Ocean.

Extreme temperature variations of up to 30C between day and night are typical of desert climates. Hot daytime temperatures cause rocks to expand, and as the air cools dramatically at night, they contract again.

Global climate change and inefficient control of soil erosion in agriculture can cause desertification, which is of major concern as it affects some of the poorest countries of the world. Combating the spread of deserts depends on developing good irrigation and better methods of agriculture, both of which require energy and education.

Human Uses of the Environment

Human Interaction with the Landscape

These photos show human interaction with the landscape - unlike mechanized agriculture here in the USA these cultures still work the land by hand; please share your thoughts, especially when it comes to having to know your local soil...

Tyrell Heaton - Siberia, near Irkutsk - people farming by hand. Hard to imagine that they still do this.

Tyrell Heaton (2015 & 2016) Guatemala: two brothers on horseback checking the family coffee crops; I hiked this same trail 7 months later and saw them working hard in the field.

Tyrell Heaton - Annapurna Range of the Himalayas, Nepal. This man collected water buffalo dung to fertilize his terraced fields; those piles are manure.

Tyrell Heaton – Malaysia, agriculture in Sabah, Borneo in a lot of areas in the world they still work the land by hand.

Human Uses of the Environment

Human Interaction with Natural Processes

Do you think forms of naturally generated energy can sustain us as a human population in the future = solar, wind, water, geothermal, etc.?

Tyrell Heaton – Wind Turbines off the coast of The Netherlands in the North Sea.

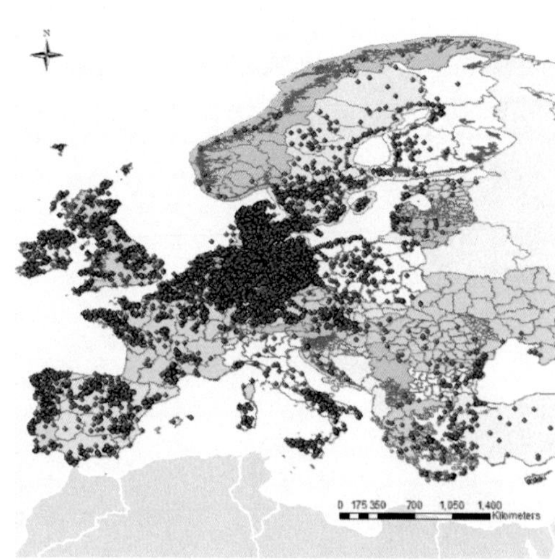
0 175 350 700 1,050 1,400
Kilometers

Map of European Wind Farms

Tyrell Heaton – Geothermal Plant in Iceland - one of the byproducts of geothermal energy production is mineral deposits in the water, hence giving it an unworldly blue appearance, it is recycled every two days and the water has supposed healing powers and helps skin remain youthful. The Blue Lagoon, is a spa created adjacent to a geothermal facility and it is very popular and expensive to visit. Despite the cold temps outside the water temperature hovers anywhere from 99-102 degrees.

Population Geography

Kathmandu, Nepal – Tyrell Heaton

Population Geography

- **Population geography**: the spatial dimension of **demography**
  - Study of population distribution, composition, rates of growth, and patterns of flow
- **Population Density**
  - **Arithmetic** density, also known as real density, is very simply the total number of people divided by the total land area.
  - **Physiologic** density is the number of people per unit area of arable land.
- **Key measure**
  - Rate of natural increase The rate of natural increase (RNI) is classified as the crude birth rate minus the crude death rate.

The **crude birth rate** is the number of live births occurring among the population of a given geographical area during a given year, per 1,000 mid-year total population of the given geographical area during the same year.

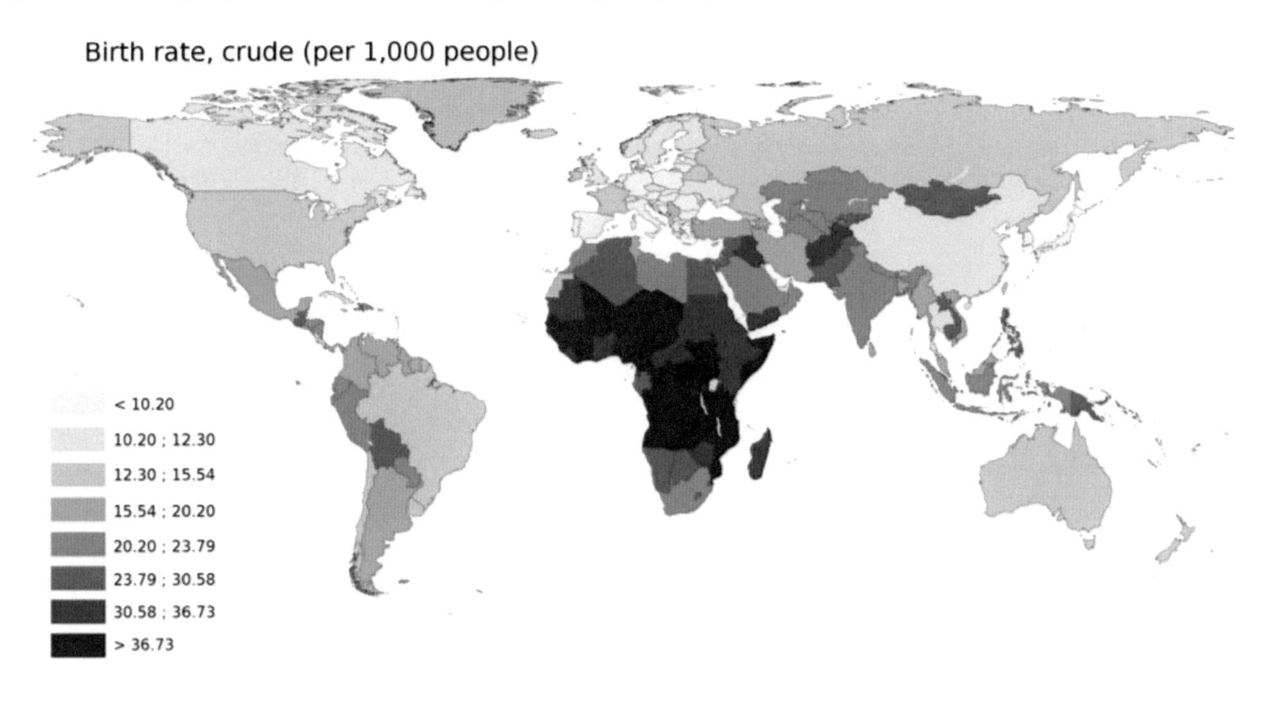

Birth rate, crude (per 1,000 people)
< 10.20
10.20 ; 12.30
12.30 ; 15.54
15.54 ; 20.20
20.20 ; 23.79
23.79 ; 30.58
30.58 ; 36.73
> 36.73

The **crude death r**ate is the number of deaths occurring among the population of a given geographical area during a given year, per 1,000 mid-year total population of the given geographical area

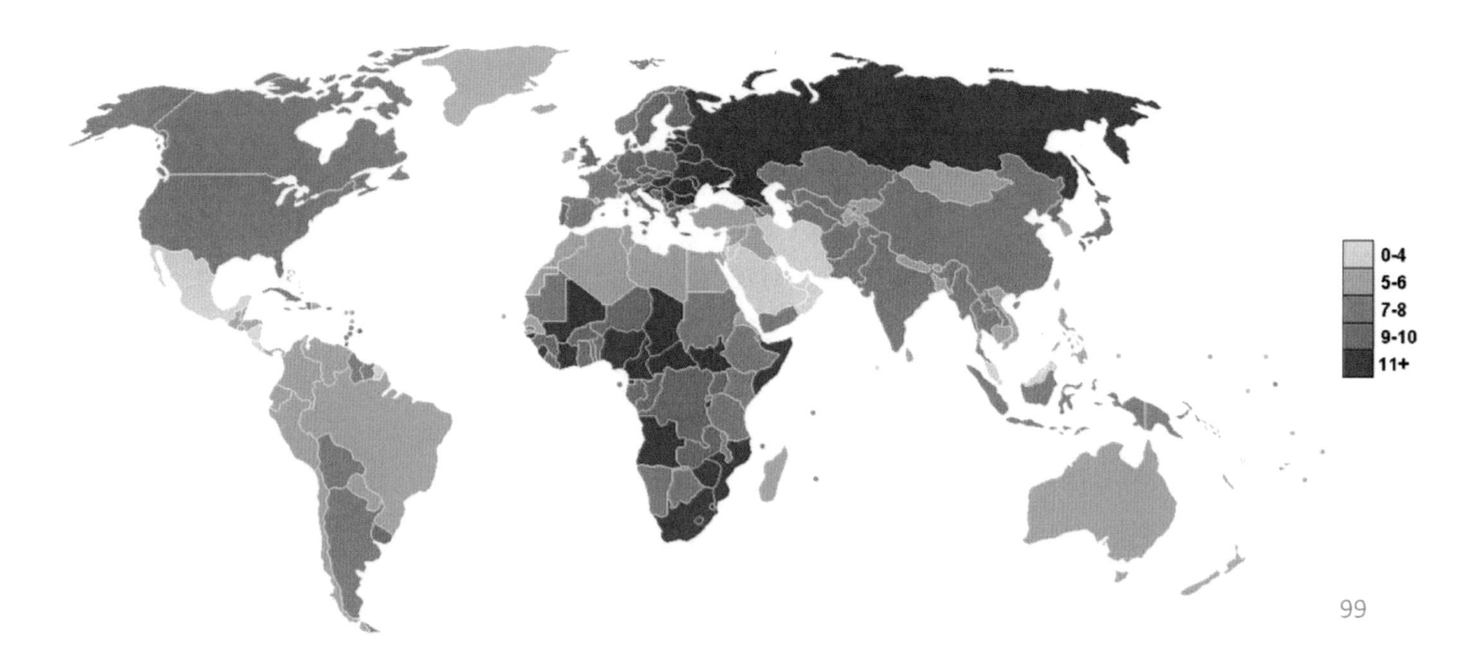

0-4
5-6
7-8
9-10
11+

Population Pyramids

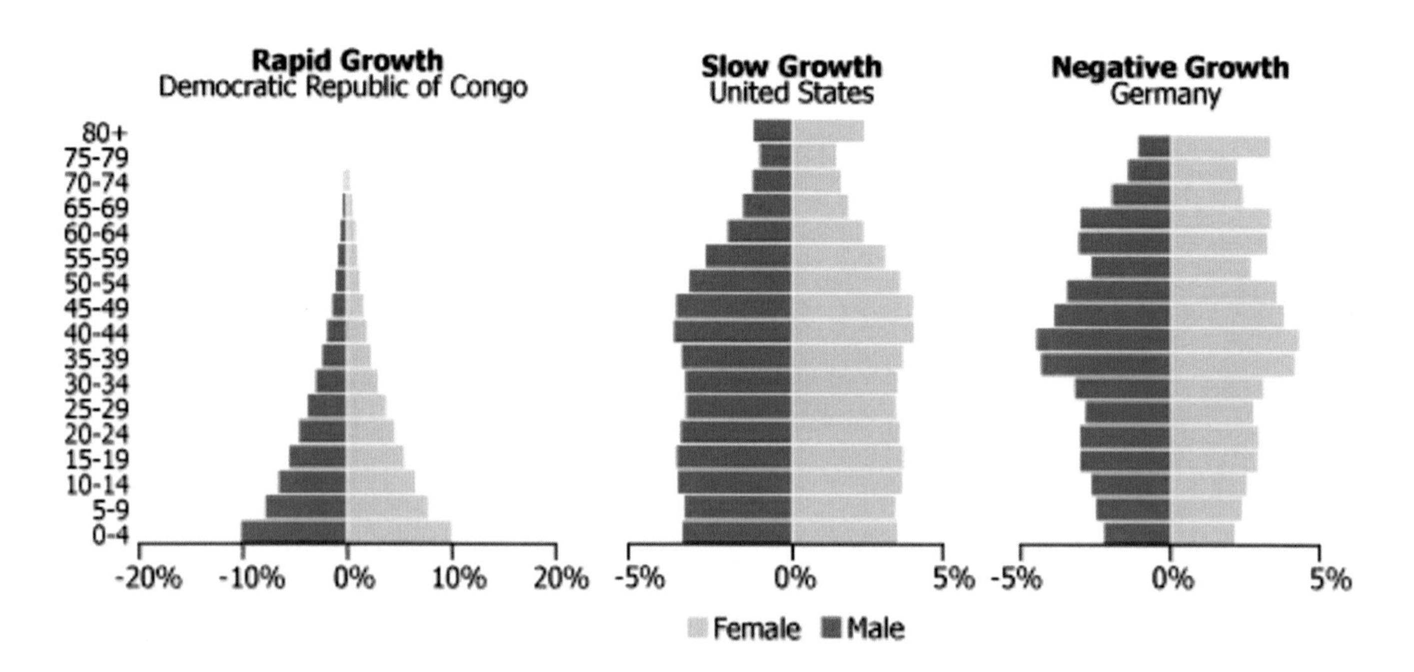
Rapid Growth
Democratic Republic of Congo
Slow Growth
United States
Negative Growth
Germany
80+
75-79
70-74
65-69
60-64
55-59
50-54
45-49
40-44
35-39
30-34
25-29
20-24
15-19
10-14
5-9
0-4
-20%
-10%
0%
10%
20%
-5%
0%
5%
-5%
0%
5%
Female
Male

Analyzing these factors can give us an idea of the direction a country is trending, and whether it will continue to grow in terms of population.

Rapid growth:
According to the above graphs countries such as, India, Indonesia, Nigeria, Mexico, Brazil, Bangladesh, and Pakistan will continue to grow their populations at a rapid pace. Nigeria is growing at a particularly fast rate, and by 2060 it will displace the U.S. as the third-largest country in the world by population.

Slow growth:
The United States stands out here as the only country in the top 10 experiencing tempered growth. That said, the U.N. sees the country hitting 400 million people around the year 2060 if trends continue.

Negative growth:
Mostly developed countries have ZPG (Zero Population Growth) or Negative Growth.

Understanding Demographics using Population Pyramids

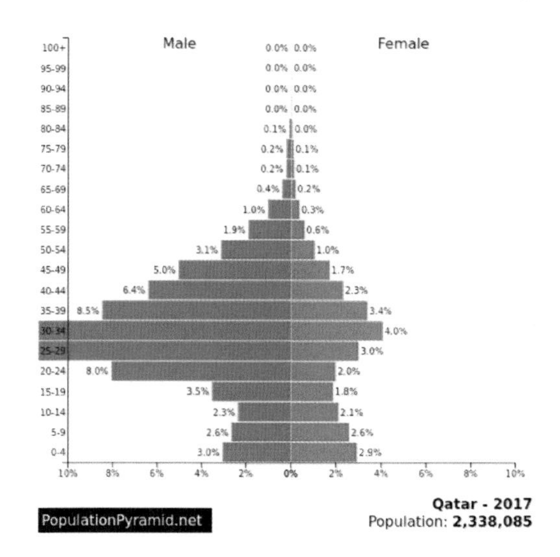

Male
Female
Qatar - 2017
Population: 2,338,085
PopulationPyramid.net

Density (Concentration)
Distribution (Location)
Dynamics (Over Time)
Demographics (Characteristics)

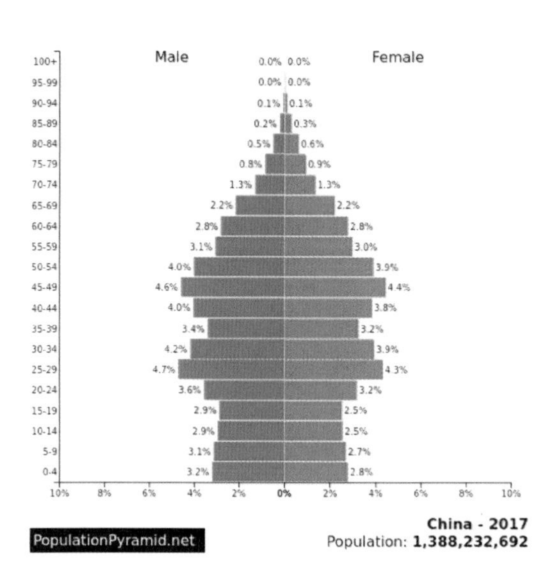

Male
Female
China - 2017
Population: 1,388,232,692
PopulationPyramid.net

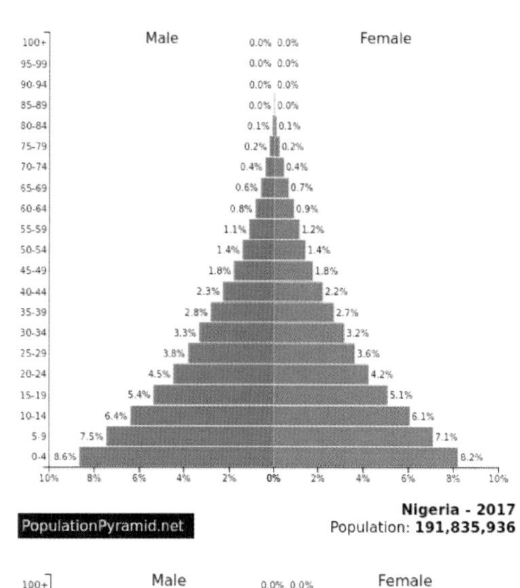

Male
Female
Nigeria - 2017
Population: 191,835,936
PopulationPyramid.net

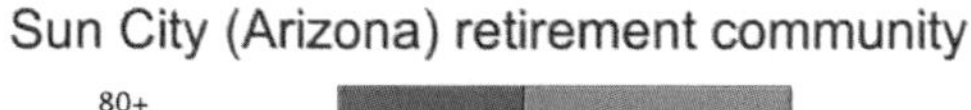

Sun City (Arizona) retirement community

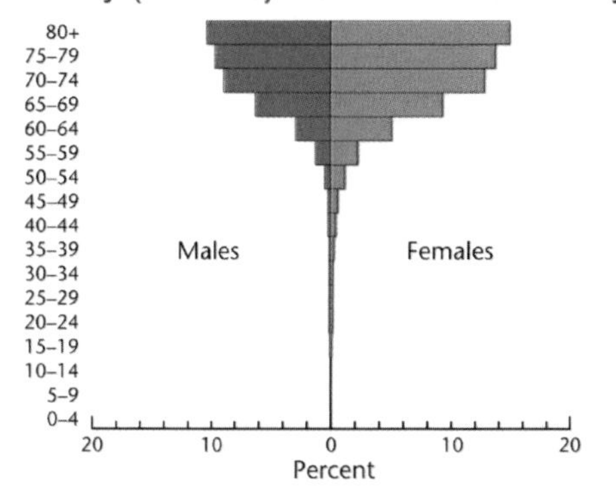

80+
75–79
70–74
65–69
60–64
55–59
50–54
45–49
40–44
35–39
30–34
25–29
20–24
15–19
10–14
5–9
0–4
Males
Females
20
10
0
10
20
Percent

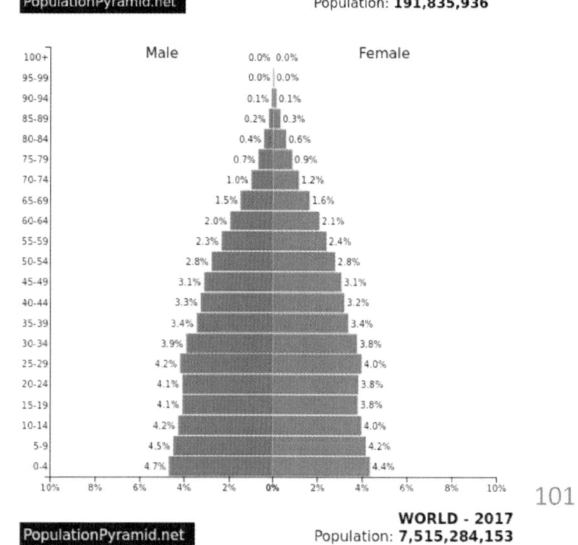

Male
Female
WORLD - 2017
Population: 7,515,284,153
PopulationPyramid.net

Demographic Transition Model

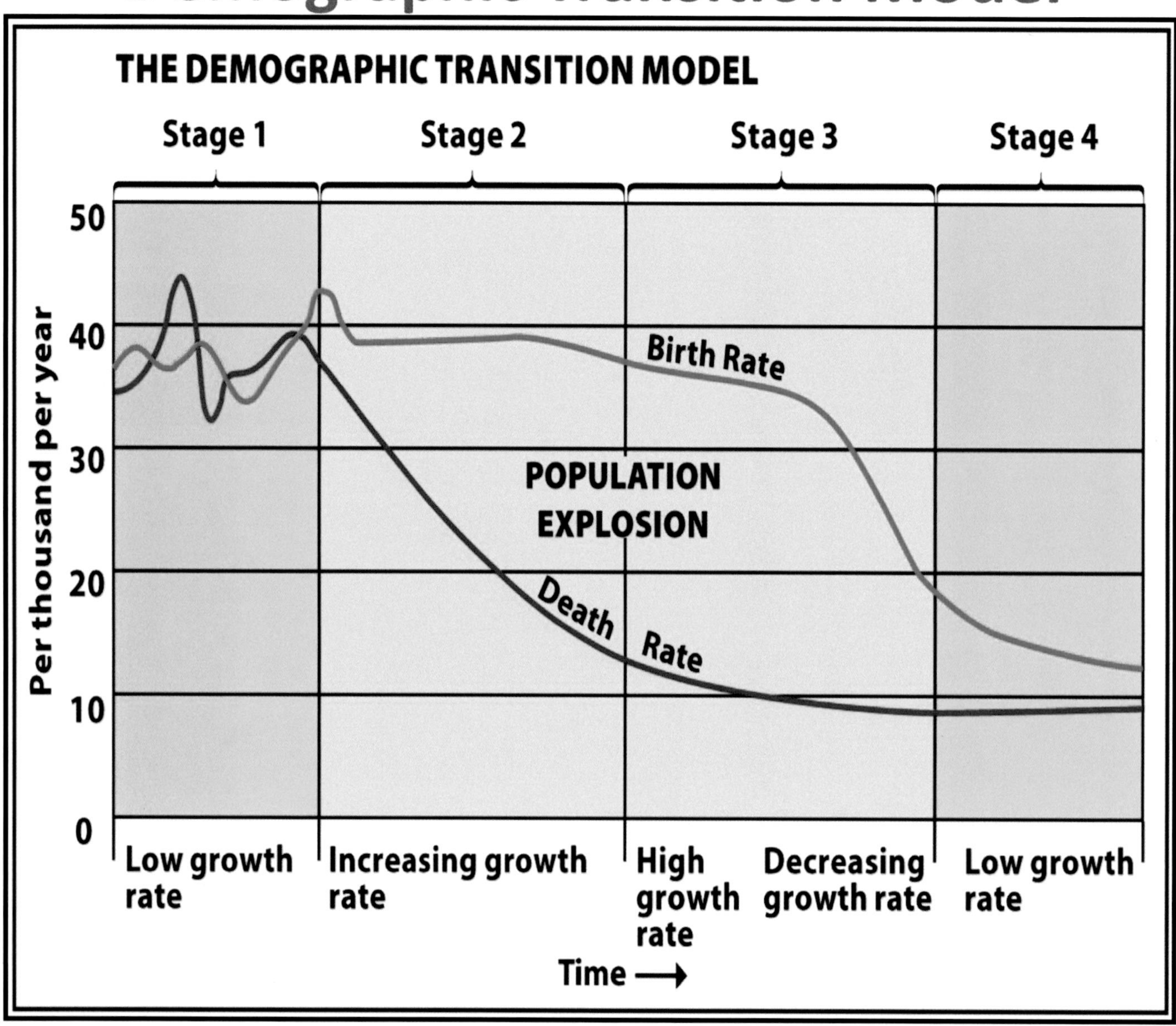

THE DEMOGRAPHIC TRANSITION MODEL
Stage 1
Stage 2
Stage 3
Stage 4
50
40
30
20
10
0
Per thousand per year
Birth Rate
POPULATION EXPLOSION
Death Rate
Low growth rate
Increasing growth rate
High growth rate
Decreasing growth rate
Low growth rate
Time

The numbers on the horizontal axis represent the following:

Hunting and Gathering Society – activities whereby people feed themselves through killing wild animals & fish and gathering fruits, roots, nuts, and other edible plants to sustain themselves.

Subsistence Agriculture – farming for direct consumption by the producers, NOT FOR SALE.
Pastoralism – subsistence activity that involves the breeding & herding of animals to satisfy the human needs of food, shelter, and clothing.

Agriculture – farming activity that involves producing goods for sale.

Mechanized Agriculture – farming that involves mechanically driven machines and use of fertilizers, pesticides, herbicides etc… to produce crops for sale. (high yield)

Basically from left to right (1, 2, 3, 4, ___) it represents advancement or time (years)

As you can see, from phase 1 through 4 societies go from being pre-industrial to industrial. Agriculture is a main driving force in the transition of a society.

In the early stages of a pre-industrial society people use primitive means to feed themselves (hunting and gathering) therefore, their technological progression is "low". As advancement in agriculture continues and people subside in more efficient and effective means the technological progression increases to "high" at the same time Birth Rates and Death Rates Drop.

Birth Rate = total number of live births in a year for every one thousand people.
Death Rate = total number of deaths in one year for every one thousand people.

Death rates and birth rates both decline during time as "technological progression" increases. Some of the main reasons for the decrease in "death rates" are better pre-natal care, lower incidence of infant mortality, more knowledge of health issues and an overall better health care system. Some reasons for the decrease in "birth rates" are availability of contraceptives, better family planning programs and the age at which people are having children in an industrial society is older. There are many other reasons for the decline of both rates, but know that technology is a catalyst behind the drop.

Notice the population explosion in the 3rd stage by the gap in birth and death rates. Also look beyond the 4th stage which would be our future. The United States as well as several other industrialized countries is post-industrial. How high will our technological progression go, how low will our death rates drop. The countries in Europe are experiencing a -0.1% growth rate thus, they are losing population. These countries are post-industrial and are moving beyond stage four. The countries in Sub-Saharan Africa have a +2.2% growth rate. Their population mathematically should double in roughly 32 years. Some of the societies in Africa as still in stage one (hunting and gathering) others in stage two and three. There is no evidence of widespread mechanized agriculture in any given Sub-Saharan African society.

Every industrialized civilization goes through the demographic transition model. Some societies take longer than others to get through the four stages; others never get out of stage one or two. There are currently societies that practice "hunting and gathering" as their main source of subsistence.

World Population Distribution

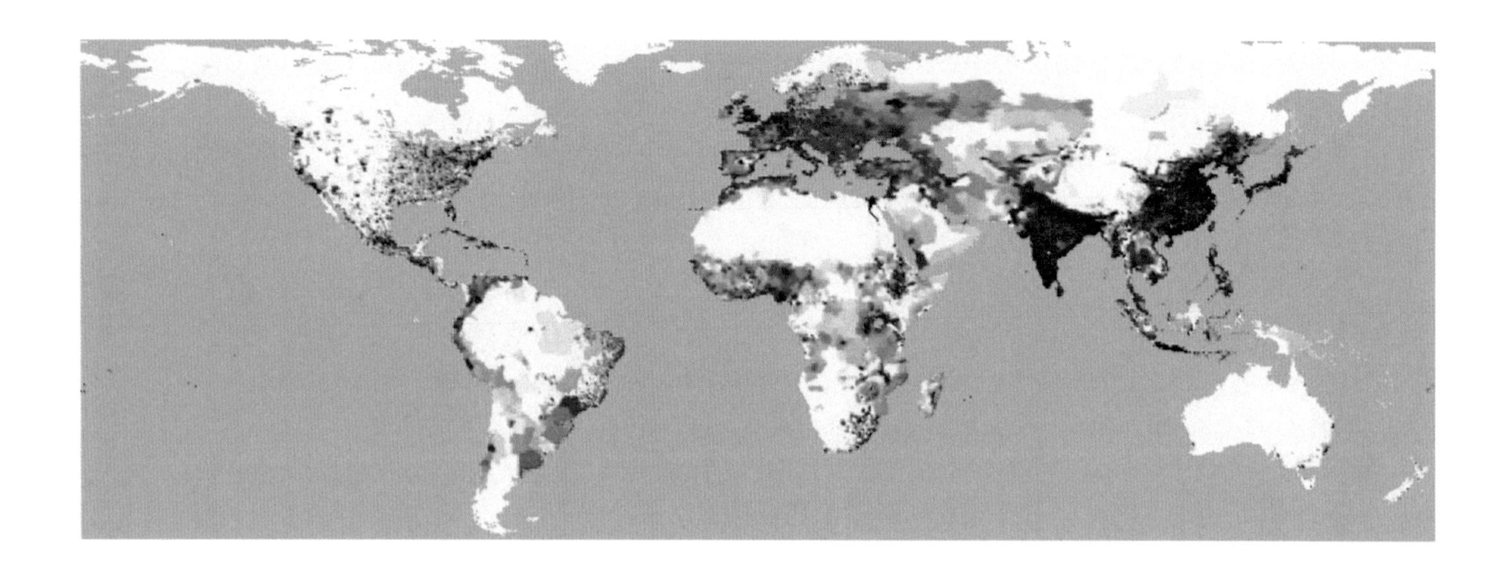

More than half of the world's population lives within this circle (51.4%)

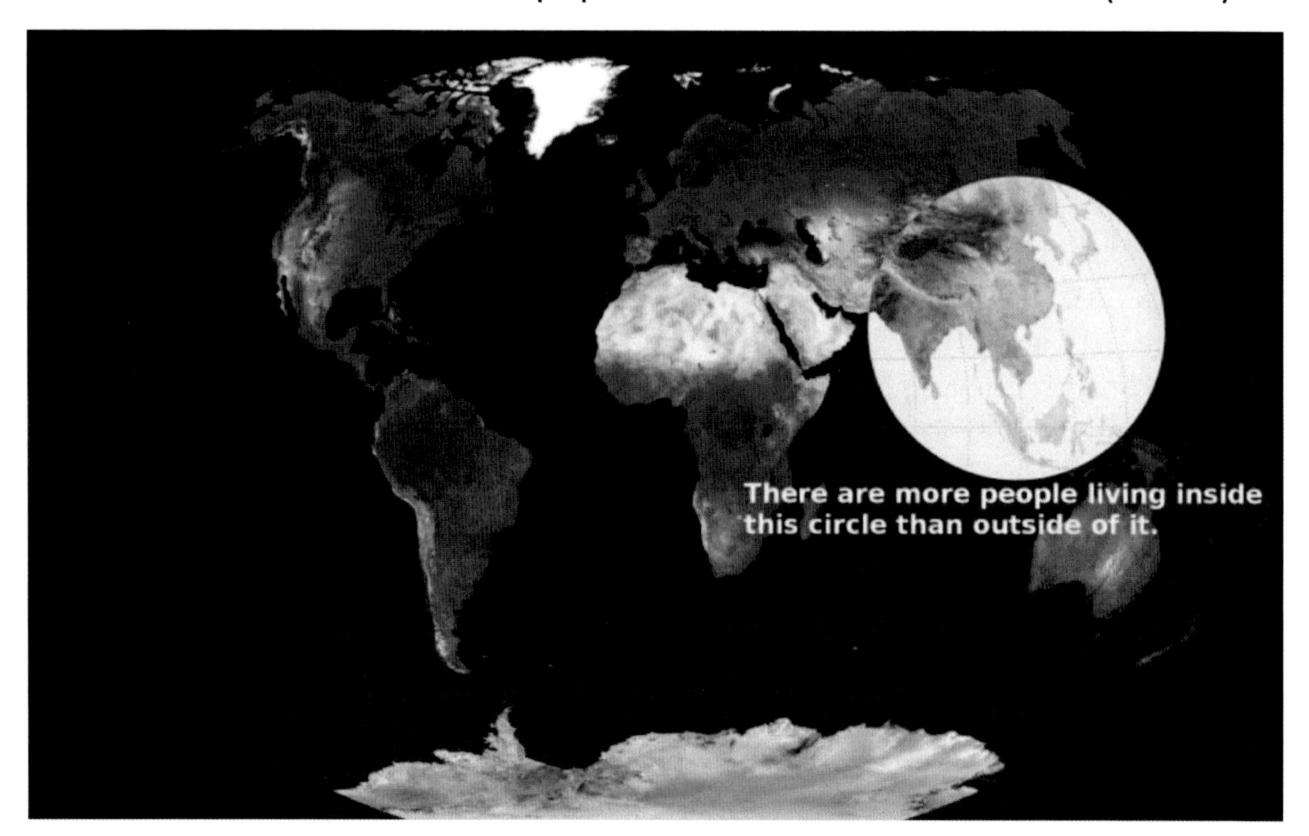
There are more people living inside
this circle than outside of it.

SPHERE OF INFLUENCE

More than half of the people on Earth live within this circle

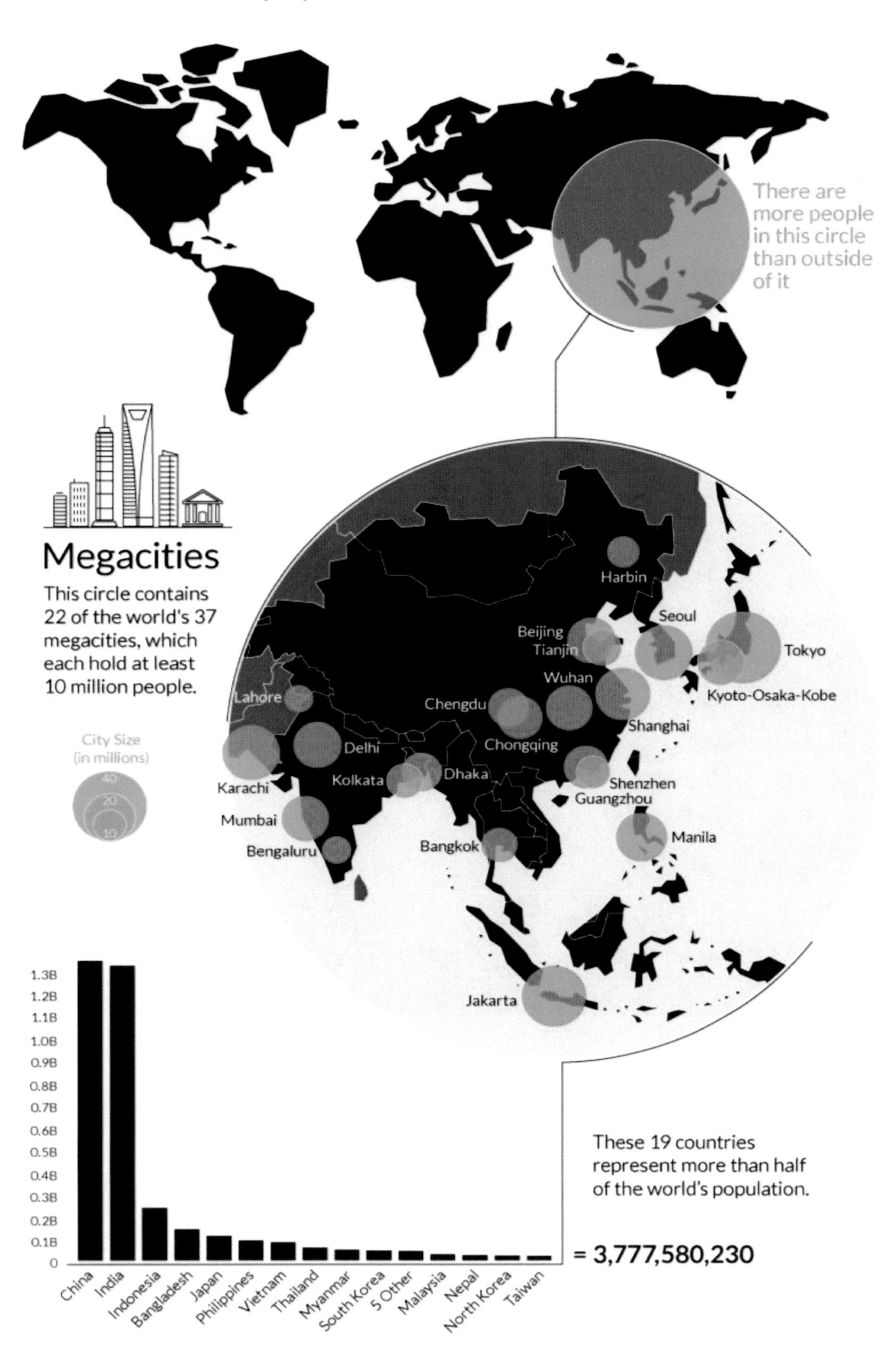

There are more people in this circle than outside of it
Megacities
This circle contains 22 of the world's 37 megacities, which each hold at least 10 million people.
City Size (in millions)
40
20
10
Harbin
Beijing
Tianjin
Seoul
Tokyo
Wuhan
Kyoto-Osaka-Kobe
Lahore
Chengdu
Shanghai
Karachi
Delhi
Chongqing
Kolkata
Dhaka
Shenzhen
Guangzhou
Mumbai
Manila
Bengaluru
Bangkok
Jakarta
1.3B
1.2B
1.1B
1.0B
0.9B
0.8B
0.7B
0.6B
0.5B
0.4B
0.3B
0.2B
0.1B
0
China
India
Indonesia
Bangladesh
Japan
Philippines
Vietnam
Thailand
Myanmar
South Korea
5 Other
Malaysia
Nepal
North Korea
Taiwan
These 19 countries represent more than half of the world's population.
= 3,777,580,230

Source: Wikipedia

Using satellite imagery to understand population from space

The United States at night

Credit: NASA Earth Observatory/NOAA NGDC

This image of the continental United States at night is a composite assembled from data acquired by the Suomi NPP satellite in April and October 2012. The image was made possible by the satellite's "day-night band" of the Visible Infrared Imaging Radiometer Suite (VIIRS), which detects light in a range of wavelengths from green to near-infrared and uses filtering techniques to observe dim signals such as city lights, gas flares, auroras, wildfires and reflected moonlight.

The Korean Peninsula

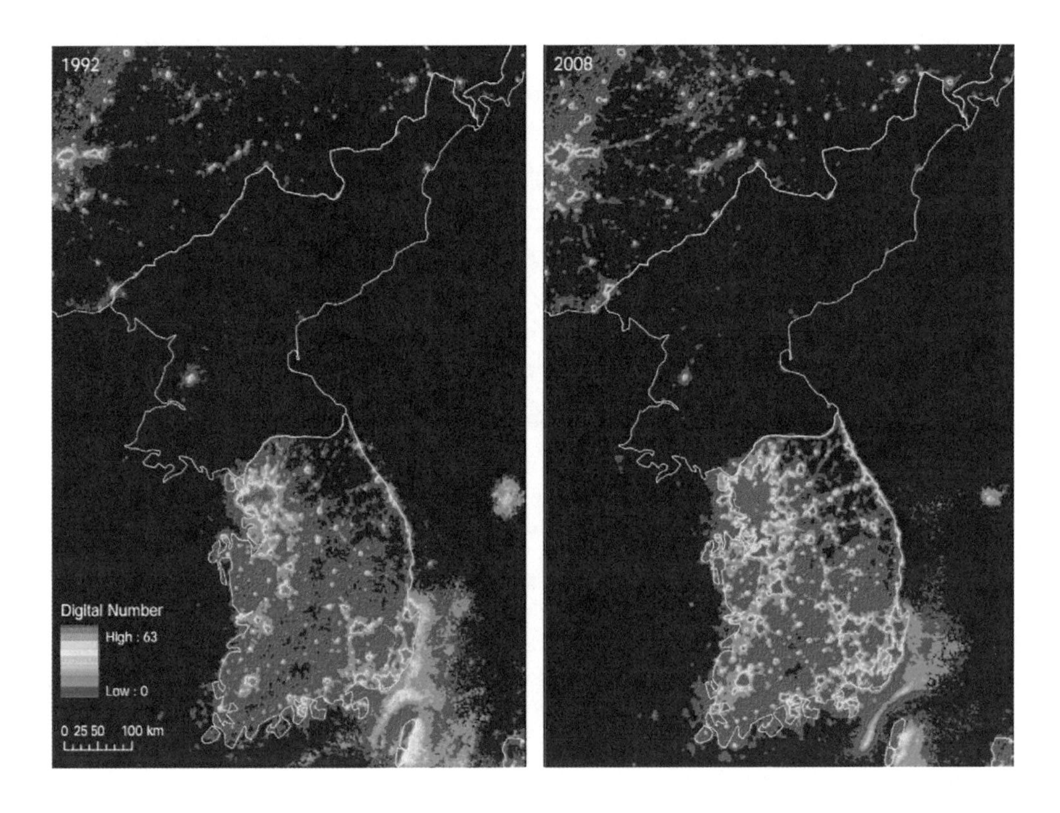
1992
2008
Digital Number
High : 63
Low : 0
0 25 50 100 km

North Korea has almost no light activity at night, especially compared to the prosperous South (that big red spot is Seoul, the South Korean capital). And while South Korea got way richer — and brighter — from 1992 to 2008, North Korea hardly budged. If anything, the one tiny bright spot, the North Korean capital of Pyongyang, appears to have gotten somewhat smaller.
Looking at nighttime lights from satellites sometimes gives us a surprisingly granular look at the North Korean situation.

According to a recent study by Stanford economist Yong Suk Lee, North Korean electricity use increases in cities after new economic sanctions are imposed, but dims in the countryside. That, Yong argues, reflects the Kim regime concentrating scarce wealth in elite urban areas at the expense of the rural poor.

Population Density

Gunkanjima “Battleship Island” Japan

On average, the population density of our planet is about 124 people living on each square mile of land. In Mongolia, there are only about 4.5 people per square mile. Currently the United States is 86 people per square mile.

At Japan's westernmost tip, 505 uninhabited islands dot the Sea of Japan. One of them, Hashima Island, was purchased by Mitsubishi Motors in 1890 when coal was discovered there. The company built a giant rectangular seawall around the island, to protect it from typhoons, and as a result, the island is still called Gunkanjima in Japanese—"Battleship Island."

Huge apartment towers, Japan's first big concrete buildings, were built to house the army of workers that Hashima's mine required. By 1959, there were 5,259 people living there, on a footprint smaller than many sports stadiums. That gave the island a population density of more than 216,000 residents per square mile, more crowded than any other island in the world.

China Population Density

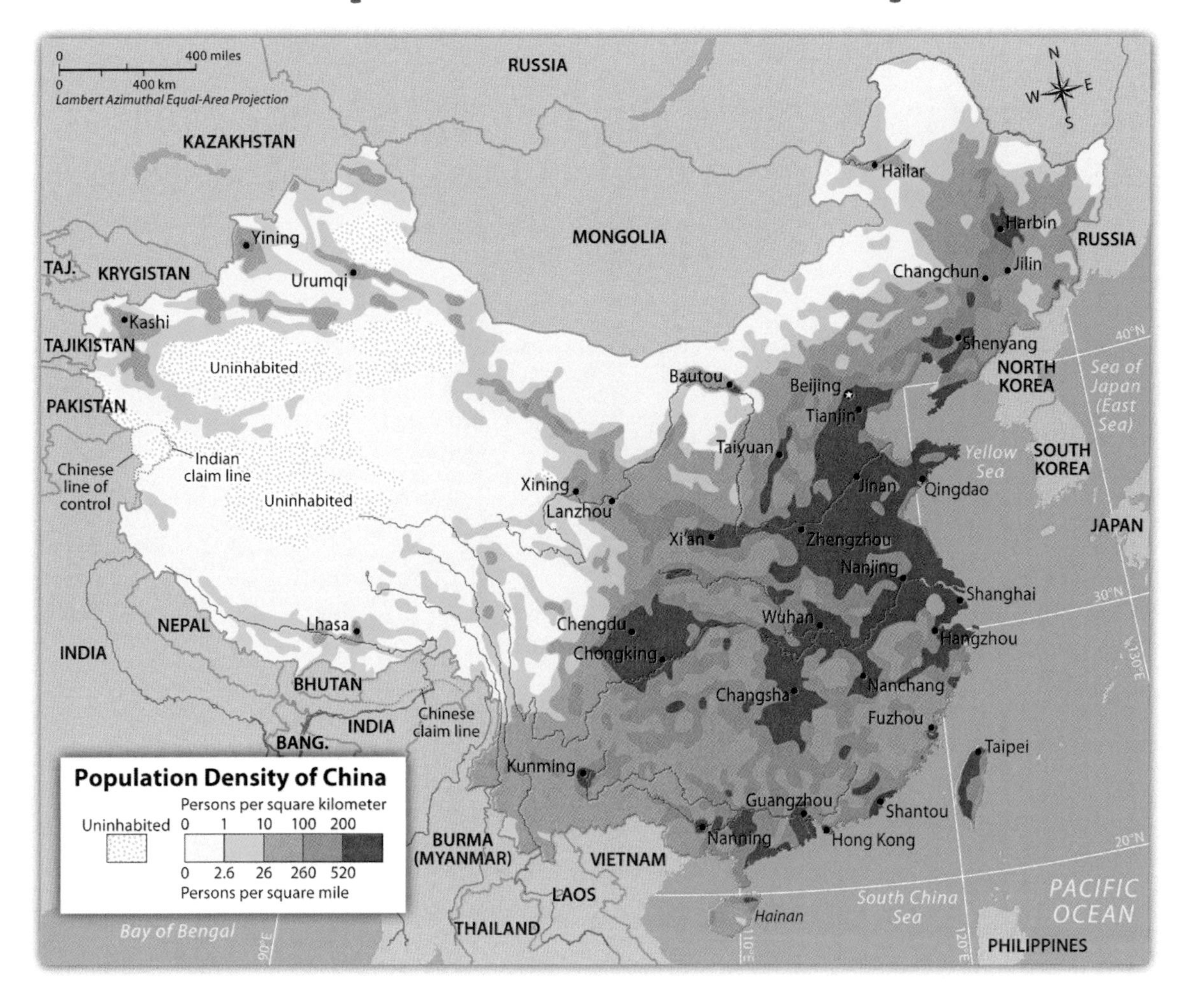
0 400 miles
0 400 km
Lambert Azimuthal Equal-Area Projection
RUSSIA
KAZAKHSTAN
MONGOLIA
TAJ.
KRYGISTAN
TAJIKISTAN
PAKISTAN
Chinese line of control
Indian claim line
Uninhabited
Uninhabited
NEPAL
INDIA
BHUTAN
INDIA
BANG.
Chinese claim line
BURMA (MYANMAR)
VIETNAM
LAOS
THAILAND
Bay of Bengal
Yining
Urumqi
Kashi
Lhasa
Xining
Lanzhou
Bautou
Beijing
Tianjin
Taiyuan
Jinan
Qingdao
Xi'an
Zhengzhou
Nanjing
Shanghai
Wuhan
Hangzhou
Chengdu
Chongking
Changsha
Nanchang
Fuzhou
Taipei
Kunming
Guangzhou
Shantou
Nanning
Hong Kong
Hainan
Hailar
Harbin
Jilin
Changchun
Shenyang
RUSSIA
NORTH KOREA
SOUTH KOREA
JAPAN
Sea of Japan (East Sea)
Yellow Sea
South China Sea
PACIFIC OCEAN
PHILIPPINES
Population Density of China
Persons per square kilometer
Uninhabited
0 1 10 100 200
0 2.6 26 260 520
Persons per square mile

Most of China's population lives in its eastern region, called China Proper, with fresh water and good soils. China Proper has dense population clusters that correspond to the areas of type C (temperate) climate that extend south from Shanghai to Hong Kong.

China Size and Population

China is roughly the same size as the USA; however, boasts a population more than 4x than that of the USA.

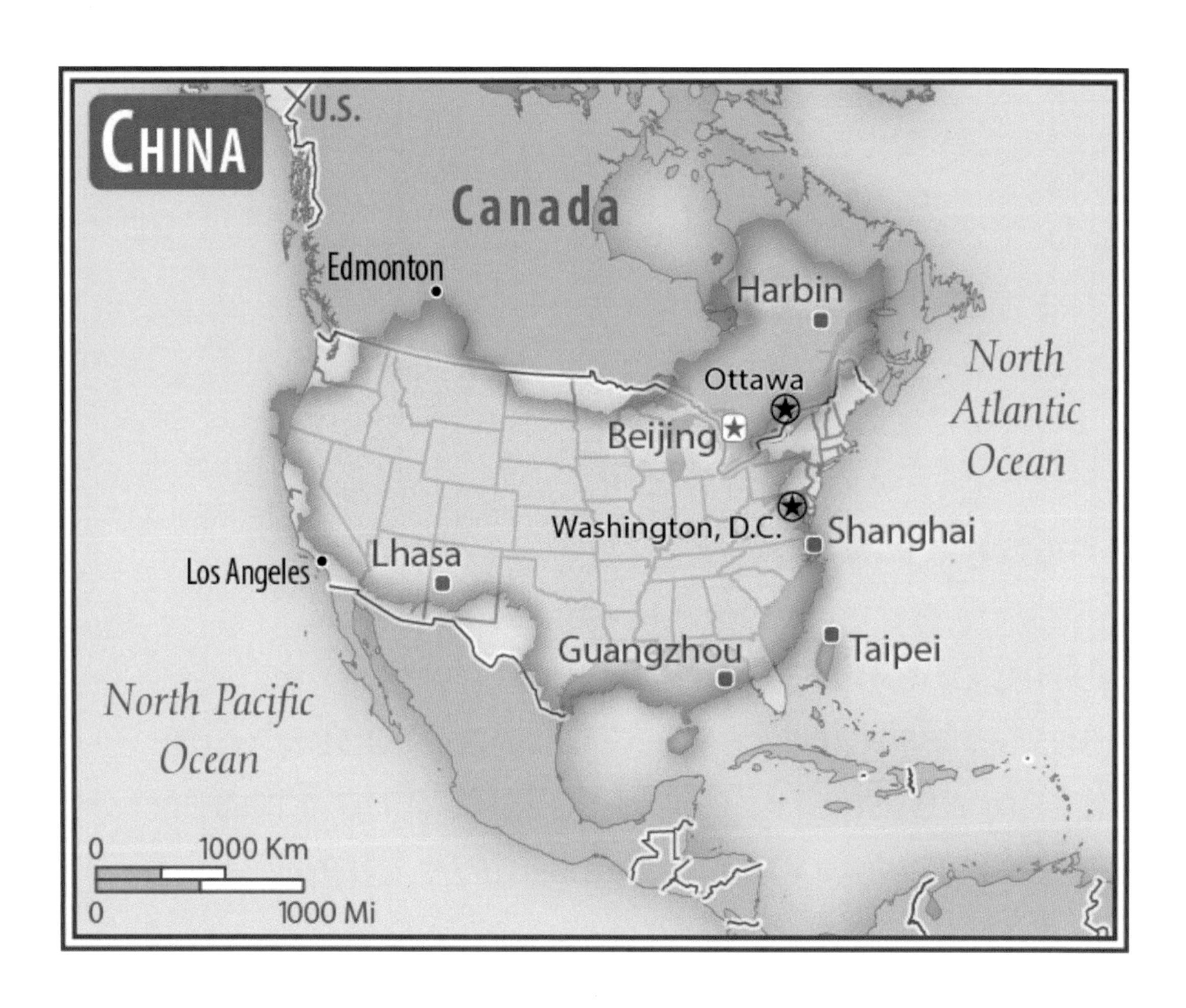
CHINA
U.S.
Canada
Edmonton
Harbin
Ottawa
Beijing
North
Atlantic
Ocean
Washington, D.C.
Shanghai
Lhasa
Los Angeles
Guangzhou
Taipei
North Pacific
Ocean
0
1000 Km
0
1000 Mi

China Population Shift

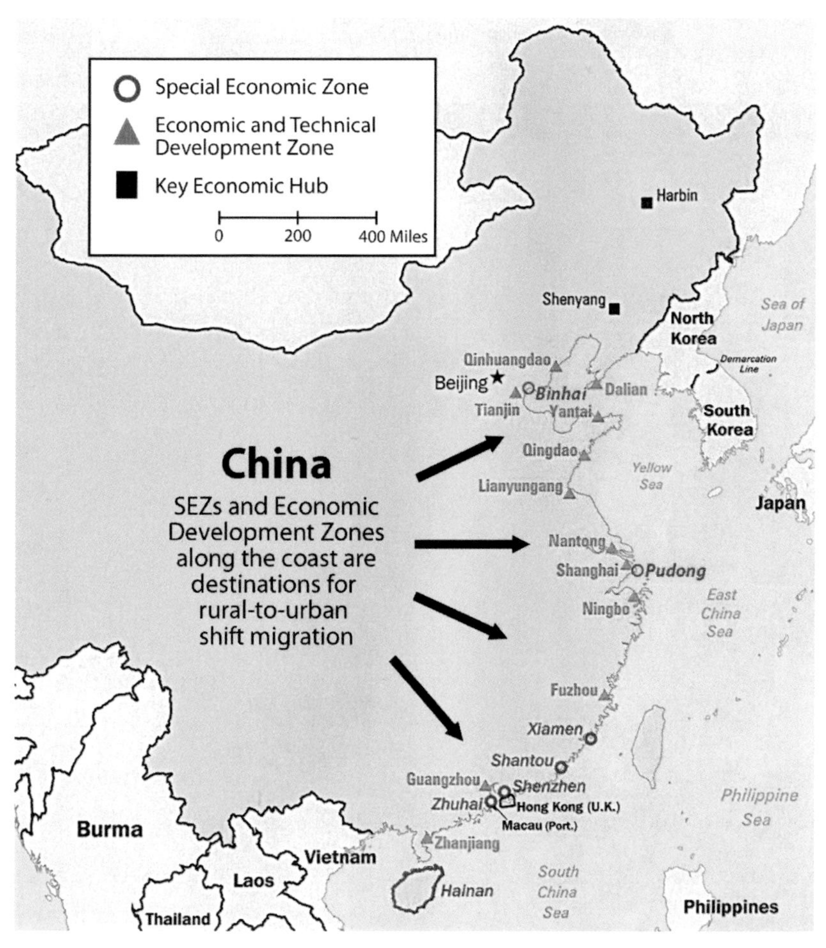

Special Economic Zone
Economic and Technical Development Zone
Key Economic Hub
0
200
400 Miles
Harbin
Shenyang
North Korea
Sea of Japan
Demarcation Line
South Korea
Japan
Qinhuangdao
Beijing
Binhai
Dalian
Tianjin
Yantai
Qingdao
Yellow Sea
Lianyungang
China
SEZs and Economic Development Zones along the coast are destinations for rural-to-urban shift migration
Nantong
Shanghai
Pudong
Ningbo
East China Sea
Fuzhou
Xiamen
Shantou
Guangzhou
Shenzhen
Zhuhai
Hong Kong (U.K.)
Macau (Port.)
Philippine Sea
Burma
Zhanjiang
Vietnam
Laos
Hainan
South China Sea
Thailand
Philippines

Coastal development and SEZs (Special Economic Zones) along the coast of China are prompting growth of the rural-to-urban shift.

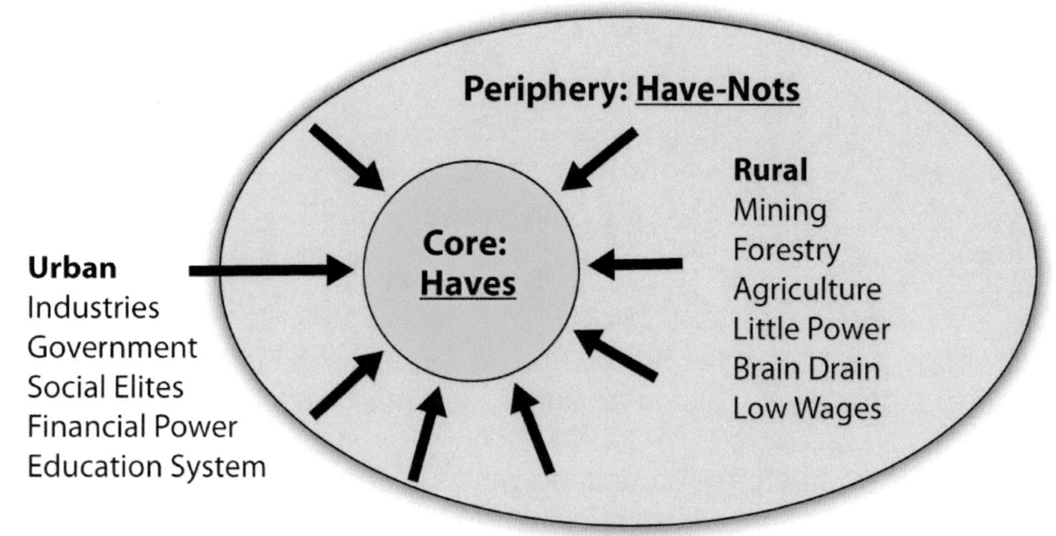

Periphery: Have-Nots
Core: Haves
Urban
Industries
Government
Social Elites
Financial Power
Education System
Rural
Mining
Forestry
Agriculture
Little Power
Brain Drain
Low Wages

People usually shift from periphery to core.

East Asia is home to one-fifth of the human population 21.8%

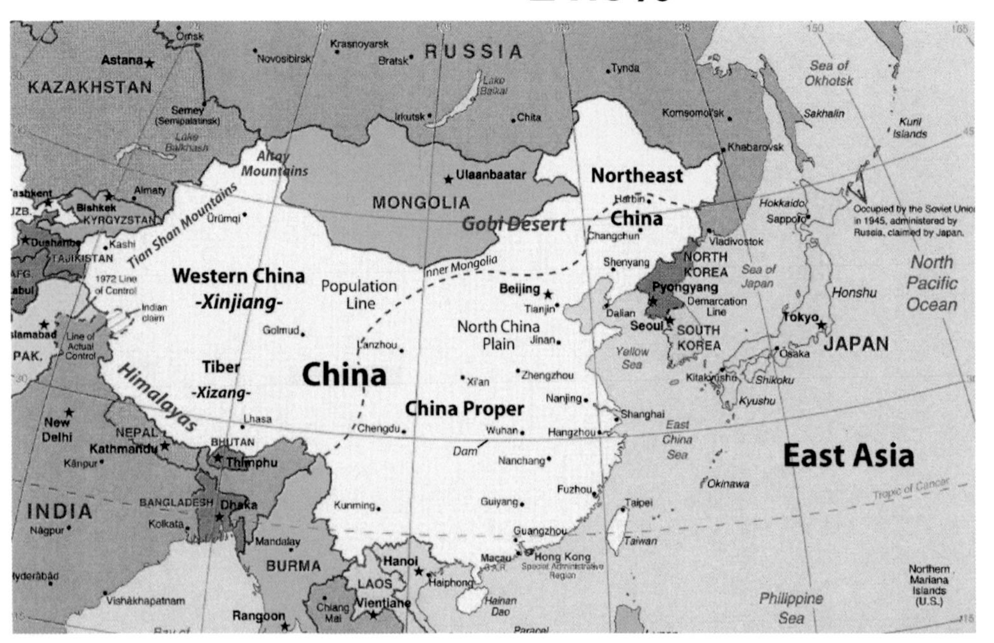

RUSSIA
KAZAKHSTAN
Astana
Novosibirsk
Krasnoyarsk
Bratsk
Irkutsk
Chita
Tynda
Lake Baikal
Sea of Okhotsk
Sakhalin
Kuril Islands
Komsomolsk
Khabarovsk
Semey (Semipalatinsk)
Lake Balkhash
Altay Mountains
Almaty
Bishkek
KYRGYZSTAN
Tian Shan Mountains
Ürümqi
Kashi
TAJIKISTAN
Ulaanbaatar
MONGOLIA
Gobi Desert
Northeast China
Harbin
Changchun
Vladivostok
Hokkaido
Sapporo
Occupied by the Soviet Union in 1945, administered by Russia, claimed by Japan.
Inner Mongolia
Shenyang
NORTH KOREA
Pyongyang
Sea of Japan
Demarcation Line
Honshu
North Pacific Ocean
Western China
-Xinjiang-
Population Line
Beijing
Tianjin
Dalian
Seoul
SOUTH KOREA
Tokyo
JAPAN
1972 Line of Control
Indian claim
Golmud
North China Plain
Jinan
Lanzhou
Yellow Sea
Osaka
Line of Actual Control
PAK.
Tibet
-Xizang-
China
Xi'an
Zhengzhou
Kitakyushu
Shikoku
Kyushu
Himalayas
Lhasa
China Proper
Nanjing
Shanghai
New Delhi
NEPAL
Kathmandu
BHUTAN
Thimphu
Chengdu
Wuhan
Hangzhou
East China Sea
Dam
Nanchang
Okinawa
East Asia
Kanpur
Fuzhou
Taipei
Tropic of Cancer
INDIA
BANGLADESH
Dhaka
Kolkata
Nagpur
Kunming
Guiyang
Guangzhou
Taiwan
Mandalay
BURMA
Hanoi
Macau
Hong Kong
LAOS
Haiphong
Northern Mariana Islands (U.S.)
Vishakhapatnam
Rangoon
Chiang Mai
Vientiane
Hainan Dao
Philippine Sea

Rural Mongolia – Tyrell Heaton

Small village just across the border from Eastern Russia into Mongolia. Even within what is seemingly a densely populated area there are many rural areas in between.

Notice the bright blue paint around the windows (and doors), I was told that they do this to protect themselves from evil spirits entering the house. There is a gradual transition from Mongolian to Russian, even place names such as Ulan Ude, Russia, resemble place names in Mongolia, remnants of a once powerful and expansive Mongolian empire.

South Asia Population Distribution

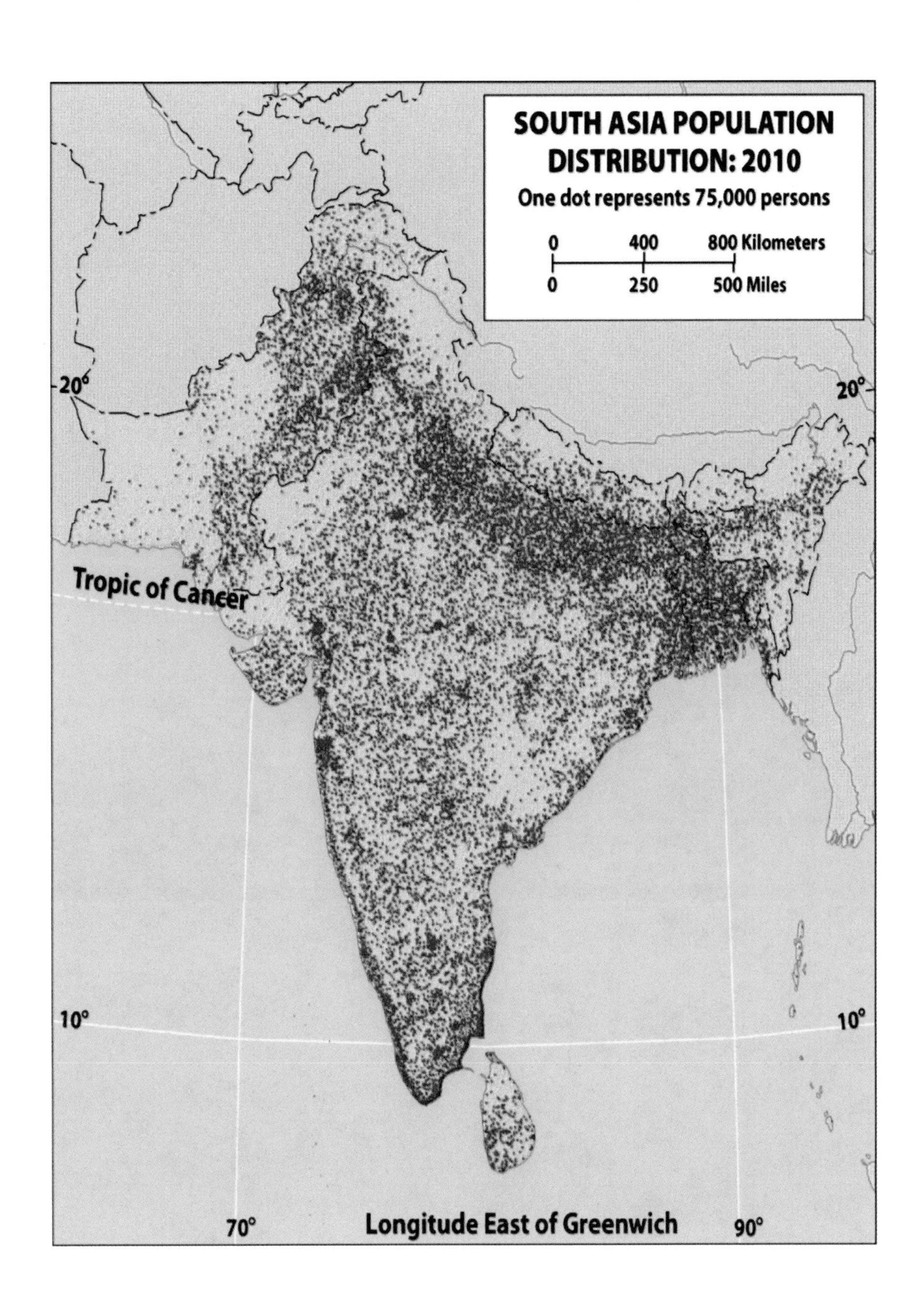
SOUTH ASIA POPULATION
DISTRIBUTION: 2010
One dot represents 75,000 persons
0 400 800 Kilometers
0 250 500 Miles
20°
20°
Tropic of Cancer
10°
10°
70°
Longitude East of Greenwich
90°

South Asia is home to nearly 25 percent (24.78%) of the human population.

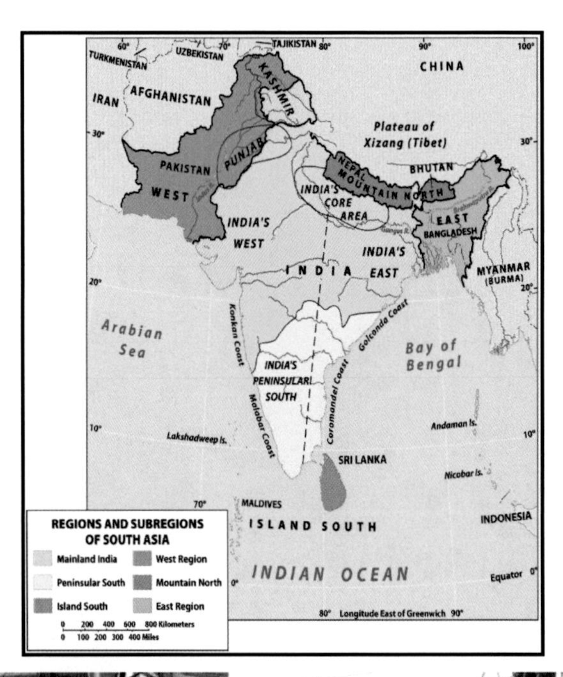
TURKMENISTAN
UZBEKISTAN
TAJIKISTAN
CHINA
IRAN
AFGHANISTAN
KASHMIR
Plateau of
Xizang (Tibet)
PAKISTAN
PUNJAB
WEST
NEPAL MOUNTAIN NORTH
BHUTAN
INDIA'S CORE AREA
INDIA'S WEST
EAST
BANGLADESH
INDIA'S EAST
INDIA
MYANMAR (BURMA)
Arabian Sea
Konkan Coast
Golconda Coast
Bay of Bengal
INDIA'S PENINSULAR SOUTH
Malabar Coast
Coromandel Coast
Andaman Is.
Lakshadweep Is.
SRI LANKA
Nicobar Is.
MALDIVES
ISLAND SOUTH
INDONESIA
INDIAN OCEAN
Equator
REGIONS AND SUBREGIONS OF SOUTH ASIA
Mainland India
West Region
Peninsular South
Mountain North
Island South
East Region
0 200 400 600 800 Kilometers
0 100 200 300 400 Miles
80° Longitude East of Greenwich 90°

Hotel Ganesh Himal
LAILAI
HOLIDAY INN P.LTD
ADMISSION
OPEN
+2 Level
Kathmandu, Nepal – Tyrell Heaton

Mass amounts of tangled electrical wires are everywhere throughout India, Nepal and Bangladesh; definitely not up to code.

India Population Growth

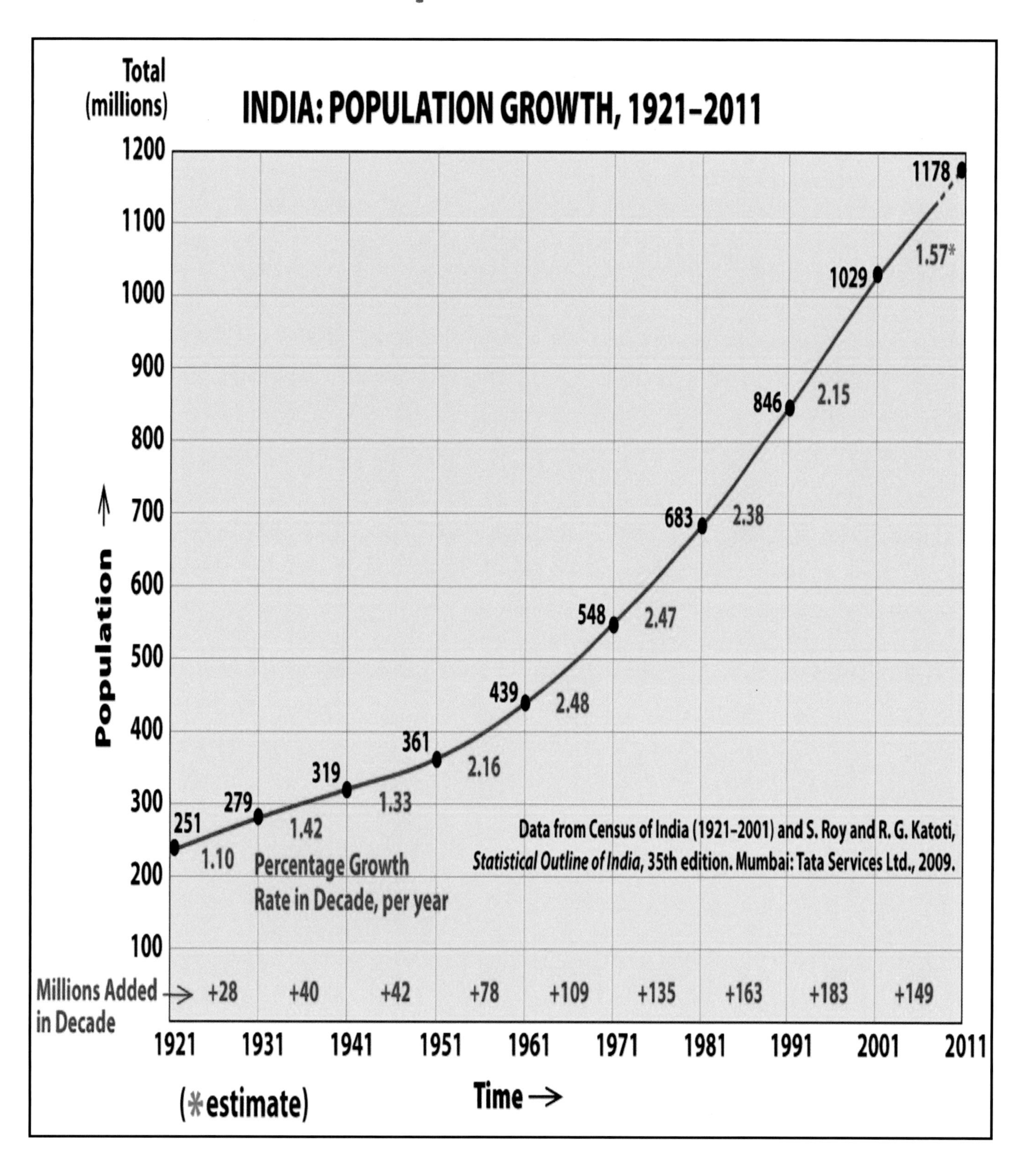

Total (millions)
INDIA: POPULATION GROWTH, 1921–2011
1200
1100
1000
900
800
700
600
500
400
300
200
100
Population →
1178
1.57*
1029
846
2.15
683
2.38
548
2.47
439
2.48
361
2.16
319
1.33
279
1.42
251
1.10
Percentage Growth Rate in Decade, per year
Data from Census of India (1921–2001) and S. Roy and R. G. Katoti, *Statistical Outline of India*, 35th edition. Mumbai: Tata Services Ltd., 2009.
Millions Added in Decade →
+28
+40
+42
+78
+109
+135
+163
+183
+149
1921
1931
1941
1951
1961
1971
1981
1991
2001
2011
(*estimate)
Time →

MAJOR CITIES OF THE REALM

City	Population* (in millions)
Ahmadabad, India	5.8
Bengaluru (Bangalore), India	7.2
Chennai (Madras), India	7.7
Colombo, Sri Lanka	0.7
Delhi–New Delhi, India	17.1
Dhaka, Bangladesh	14.6
Hyderabad, India	6.9
Karachi, Pakistan	13.3
Kathmandu, Nepal	1.0
Kolkata (Calcutta), India	15.8
Lahore, Pakistan	7.2
Mumbai (Bombay), India	20.2
Varanasi, India	1.5

*Based on 2010 estimates.

Children on the street in Chennai, India

India's Great Cities

Delhi

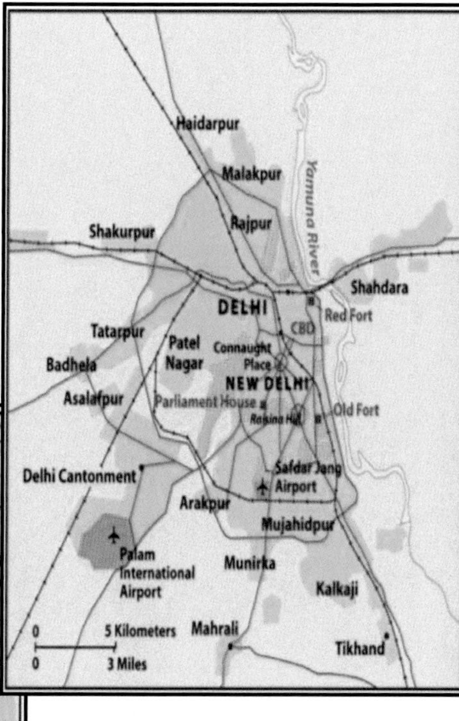
Haidarpur
Malakpur
Yamuna River
Rajpur
Shakurpur
Shahdara
DELHI
Red Fort
CBD
Tatarpur
Patel Nagar
Connaught Place
Badhela
NEW DELHI
Asalatpur
Parliament House
Old Fort
Raisina Hill
Delhi Cantonment
Safdar Jang Airport
Arakpur
Mujahidpur
Palam International Airport
Munirka
Kalkaji
0 5 Kilometers
0 3 Miles
Mahrali
Tikhand

Delhi (new and old)
- 16.4 million

Kolkata

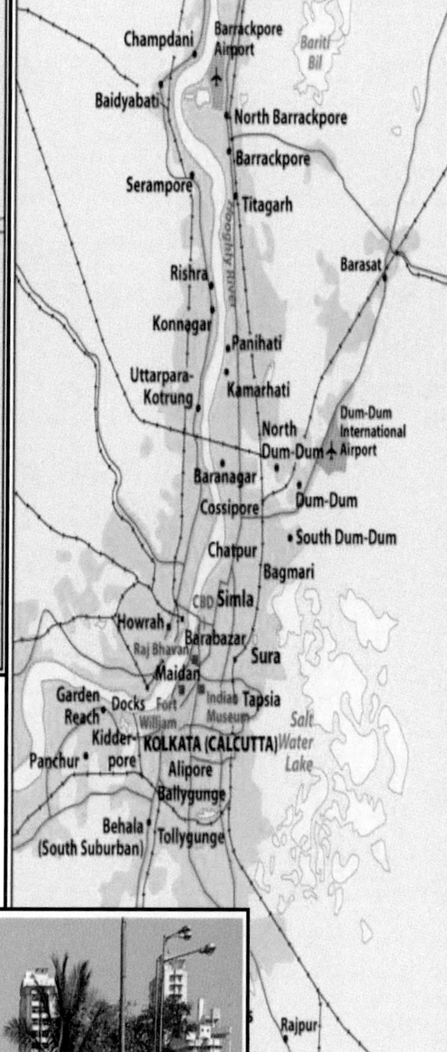
Champdani
Barrackpore Airport
Bariti Bil
Baidyabati
North Barrackpore
Barrackpore
Serampore
Titagarh
Hooghly River
Rishra
Barasat
Konnagar
Panihati
Uttarpara-Kotrung
Kamarhati
North Dum-Dum
Dum-Dum International Airport
Baranagar
Dum-Dum
Cossipore
South Dum-Dum
Chatpur
Bagmari
CBD
Simla
Howrah
Raj Bhavan
Barabazar
Sura
Maidan
Garden Reach
Docks
Fort William
Indian Museum
Tapsia
Salt Water Lake
Kidderpore
Panchur
KOLKATA (CALCUTTA)
Alipore
Ballygunge
Behala (South Suburban)
Tollygunge
Rajpur

Kolkata (Calcutta)
- 15 million

Mumbai

Mumbai (Bombay)
- 19.3 million

Southeast Asia Population

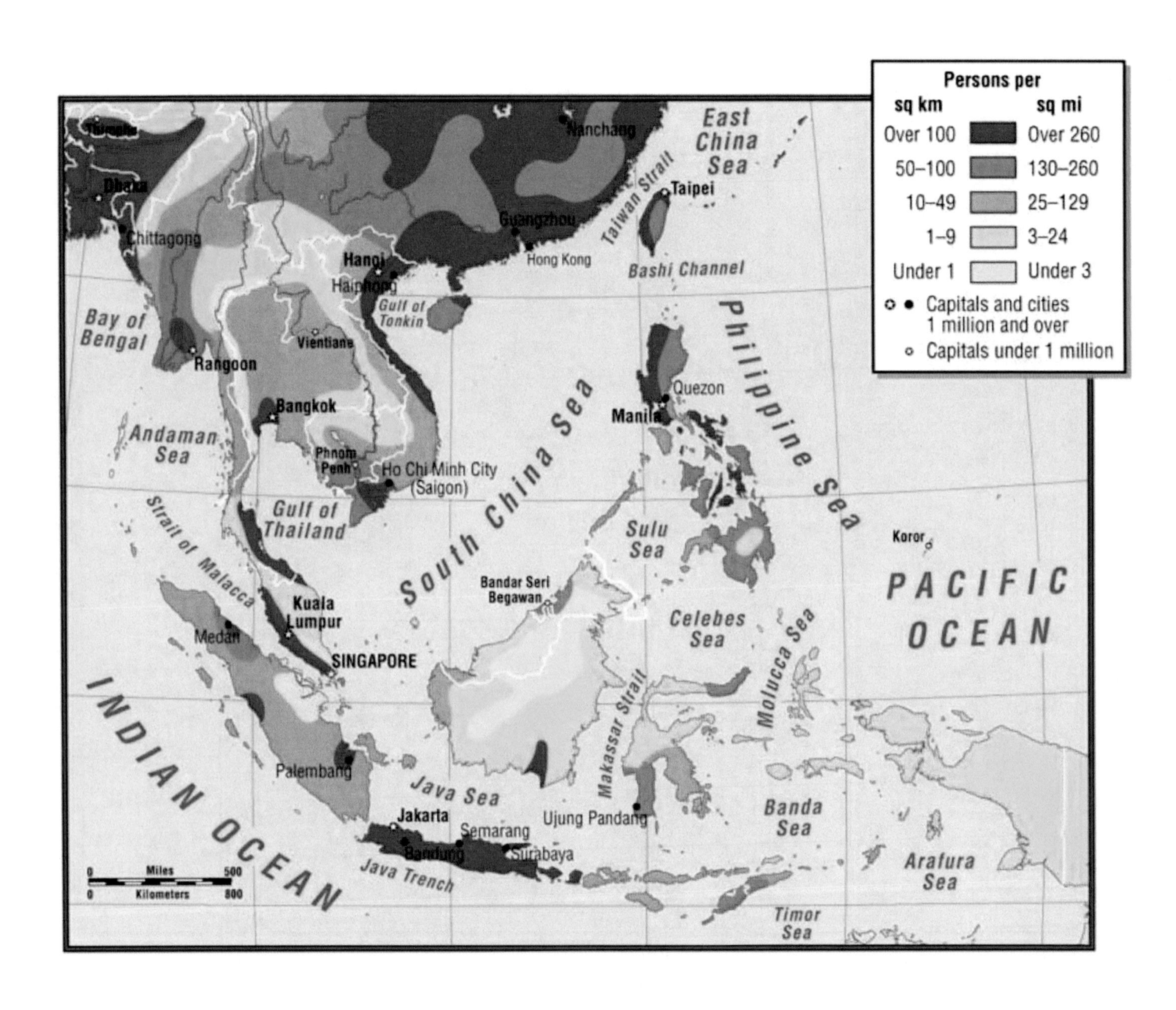

Persons per
sq km
sq mi
Over 100
Over 260
50–100
130–260
10–49
25–129
1–9
3–24
Under 1
Under 3
Capitals and cities 1 million and over
Capitals under 1 million
Nanchang
East China Sea
Taiwan Strait
Taipei
Dhaka
Chittagong
Guangzhou
Hong Kong
Bashi Channel
Hanoi
Haiphong
Gulf of Tonkin
Bay of Bengal
Vientiane
Rangoon
Philippine Sea
Quezon
Manila
Bangkok
Andaman Sea
South China Sea
Phnom Penh
Ho Chi Minh City (Saigon)
Gulf of Thailand
Strait of Malacca
Sulu Sea
Koror
PACIFIC OCEAN
Bandar Seri Begawan
Kuala Lumpur
Medan
SINGAPORE
Celebes Sea
Molucca Sea
Makassar Strait
INDIAN OCEAN
Palembang
Java Sea
Jakarta
Semarang
Bandung
Surabaya
Ujung Pandang
Banda Sea
Java Trench
Arafura Sea
Timor Sea
Miles
Kilometers
0
500
800

Africa Population Distribution

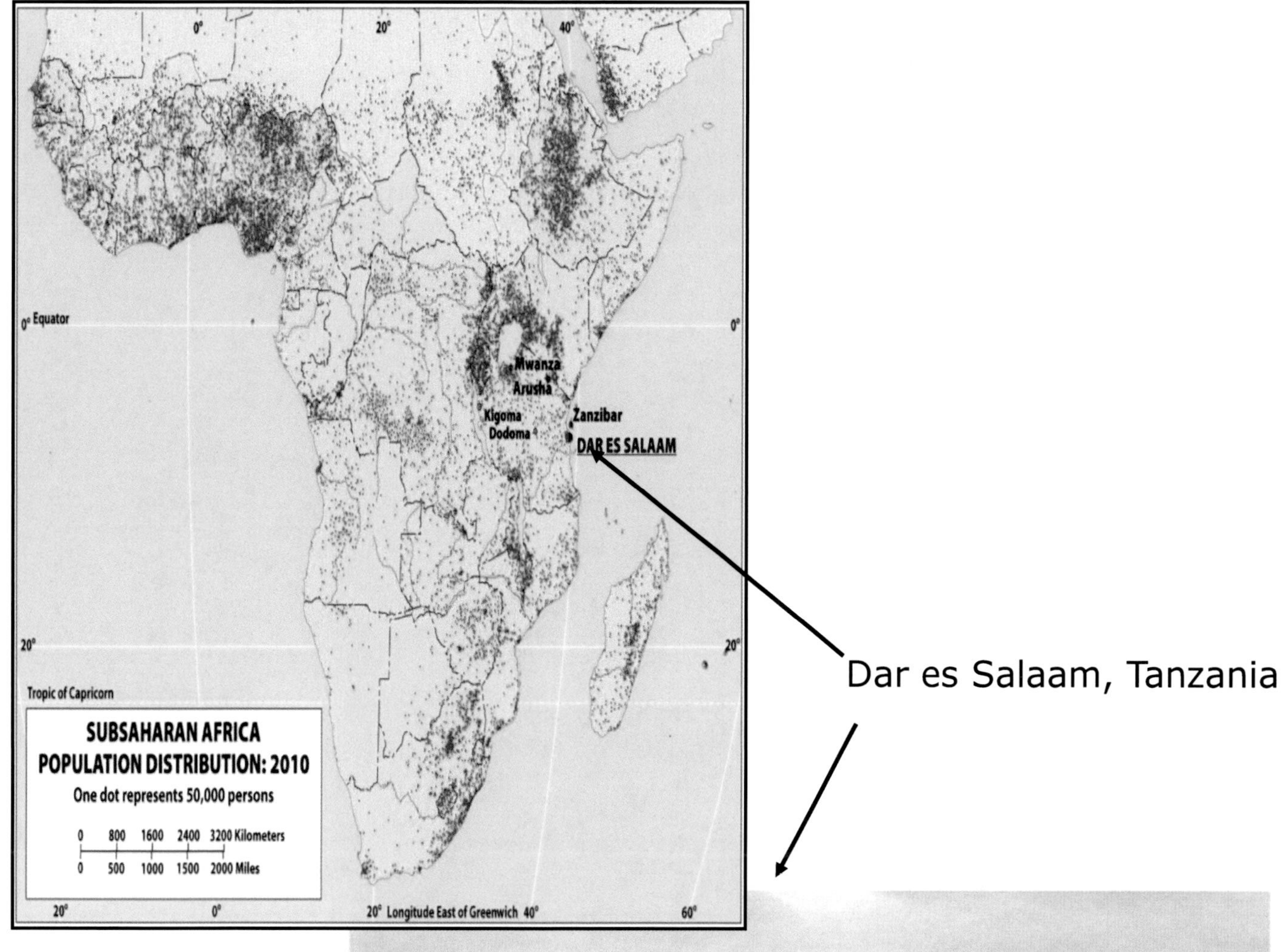
0°
20°
40°
0° Equator
Mwanza
Arusha
Kigoma
Dodoma
Zanzibar
DAR ES SALAAM
20°
Tropic of Capricorn
SUBSAHARAN AFRICA
POPULATION DISTRIBUTION: 2010
One dot represents 50,000 persons
0 800 1600 2400 3200 Kilometers
0 500 1000 1500 2000 Miles
20° Longitude East of Greenwich 40°
60°
Dar es Salaam, Tanzania

This port area in Dar es Salaam, Tanzania is packed with people

Urban Africa

- This is **not an urban realm** with relatively low overall urbanization (34%)
- changing rapidly as **rate of urbanization is high**
- City living is **harsh**
  - informal sector

MAJOR CITIES OF THE REALM

City	Population* (in millions)
Abidjan, Ivory Coast	4.3
Accra, Ghana	2.4
Adis Abeba, Ethiopia	3.6
Cape Town, South Africa	3.3
Dakar, Senegal	2.9
Dar es Salaam, Tanzania	3.4
Durban, South Africa	2.8
Harare, Zimbabwe	1.7
Ibadan, Nigeria	2.9
Johannesburg, South Africa	3.6
Kinshasa, The Congo	9.2
Lagos, Nigeria	10.6
Lusaka, Zambia	1.5
Mombasa, Kenya	1.0
Nairobi, Kenya	3.5

Knysna, South Africa – Tyrell Heaton

Europe Population

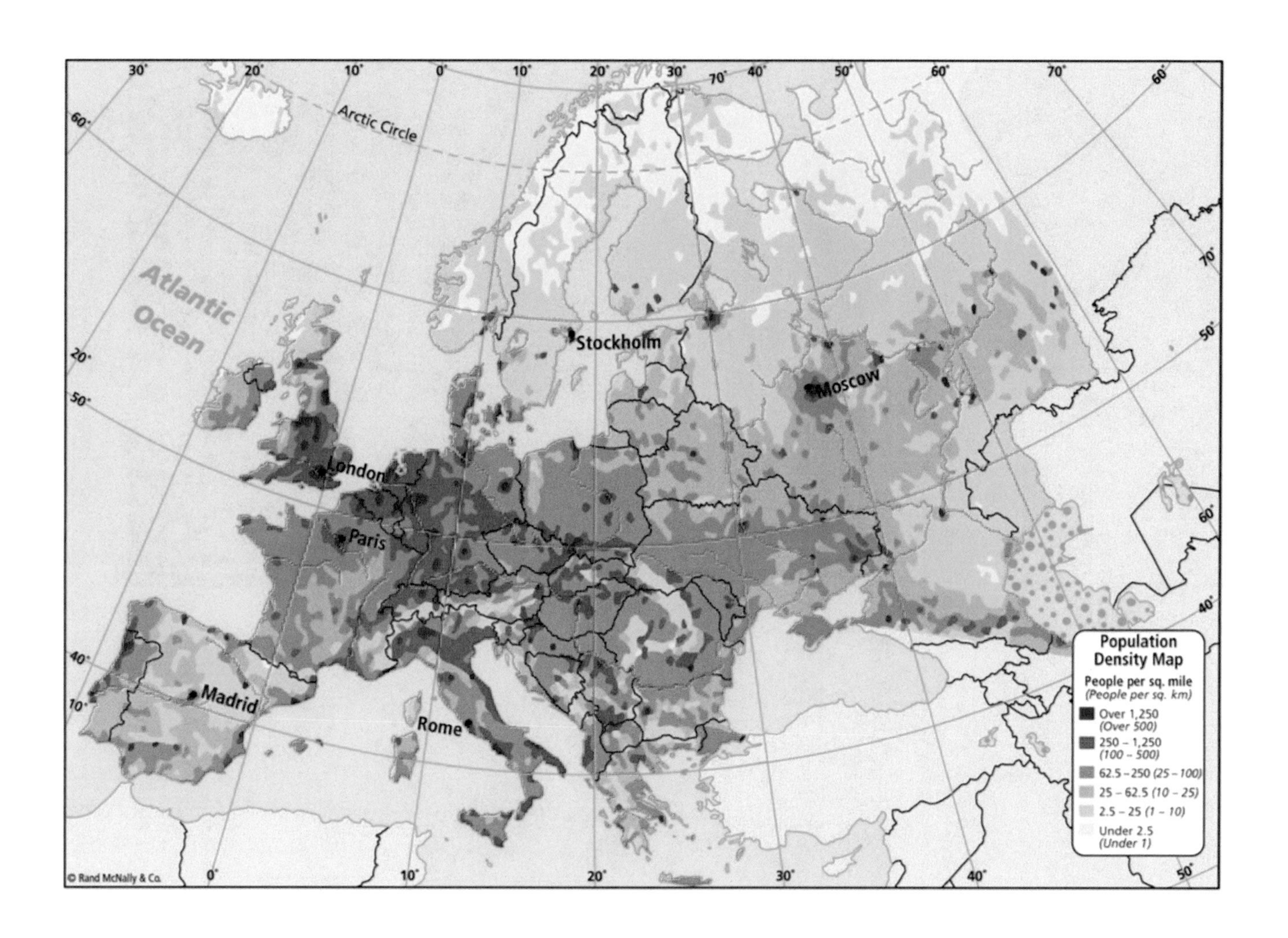
Arctic Circle
Atlantic Ocean
Stockholm
Moscow
London
Paris
Madrid
Rome
Population Density Map
People per sq. mile
(People per sq. km)
Over 1,250 (Over 500)
250 – 1,250 (100 – 500)
62.5 – 250 (25 – 100)
25 – 62.5 (10 – 25)
2.5 – 25 (1 – 10)
Under 2.5 (Under 1)
© Rand McNally & Co.

European Cities

In this version of the map, we can see significant differences between values for the most densely populated areas.
This adds another dimension of information that a conventional 2D choropleth cannot convey.
Berlin
London
Paris
Istanbul
Madrid
Athens

MAJOR CITIES OF THE REALM

City	Population* (in millions)
Amsterdam, Netherlands	1.0
Athens, Greece	3.2
Barcelona, Spain	5.0
Berlin, Germany	3.4
Brussels, Belgium	1.7
Frankfurt, Germany	3.7
London, UK	8.6
Lyon, France	1.4
Madrid, Spain	5.7
Milan, Italy	4.0
Paris, France	9.9
Prague, Czech Republic	1.2
Rome, Italy	3.3
Stuttgart, Germany	2.6
Vienna, Austria	2.3
Warsaw, Poland	1.7

*Based on 2010 estimates.

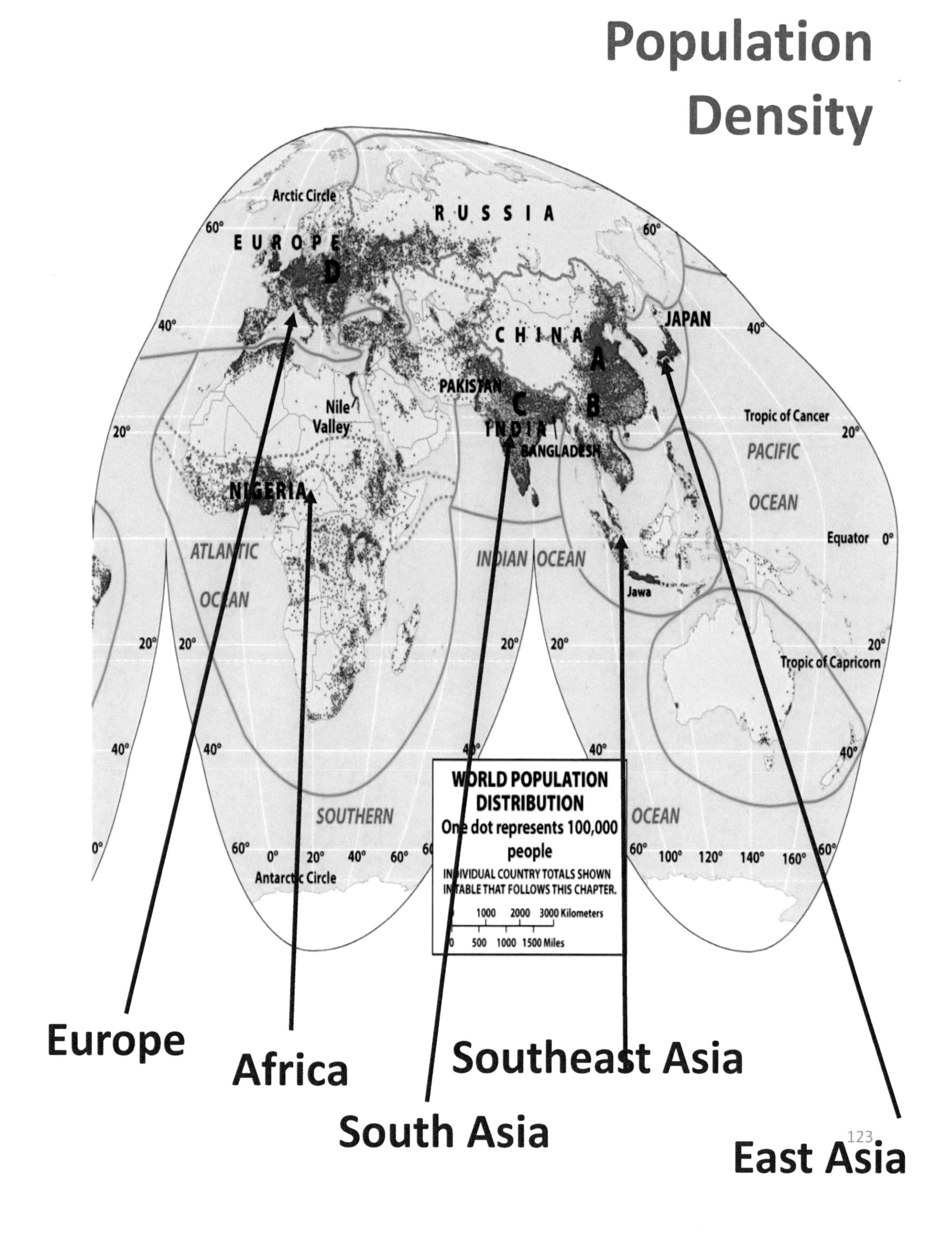

Population Density
Arctic Circle
RUSSIA
EUROPE
D
CHINA
A
B
C
JAPAN
PAKISTAN
INDIA
BANGLADESH
Nile Valley
NIGERIA
Tropic of Cancer
PACIFIC OCEAN
Equator 0°
ATLANTIC OCEAN
INDIAN OCEAN
Jawa
Tropic of Capricorn
SOUTHERN OCEAN
Antarctic Circle
WORLD POPULATION DISTRIBUTION
One dot represents 100,000 people
INDIVIDUAL COUNTRY TOTALS SHOWN IN TABLE THAT FOLLOWS THIS CHAPTER.
0 1000 2000 3000 Kilometers
0 500 1000 1500 Miles
Europe
Africa
Southeast Asia
South Asia
East Asia

North America Population

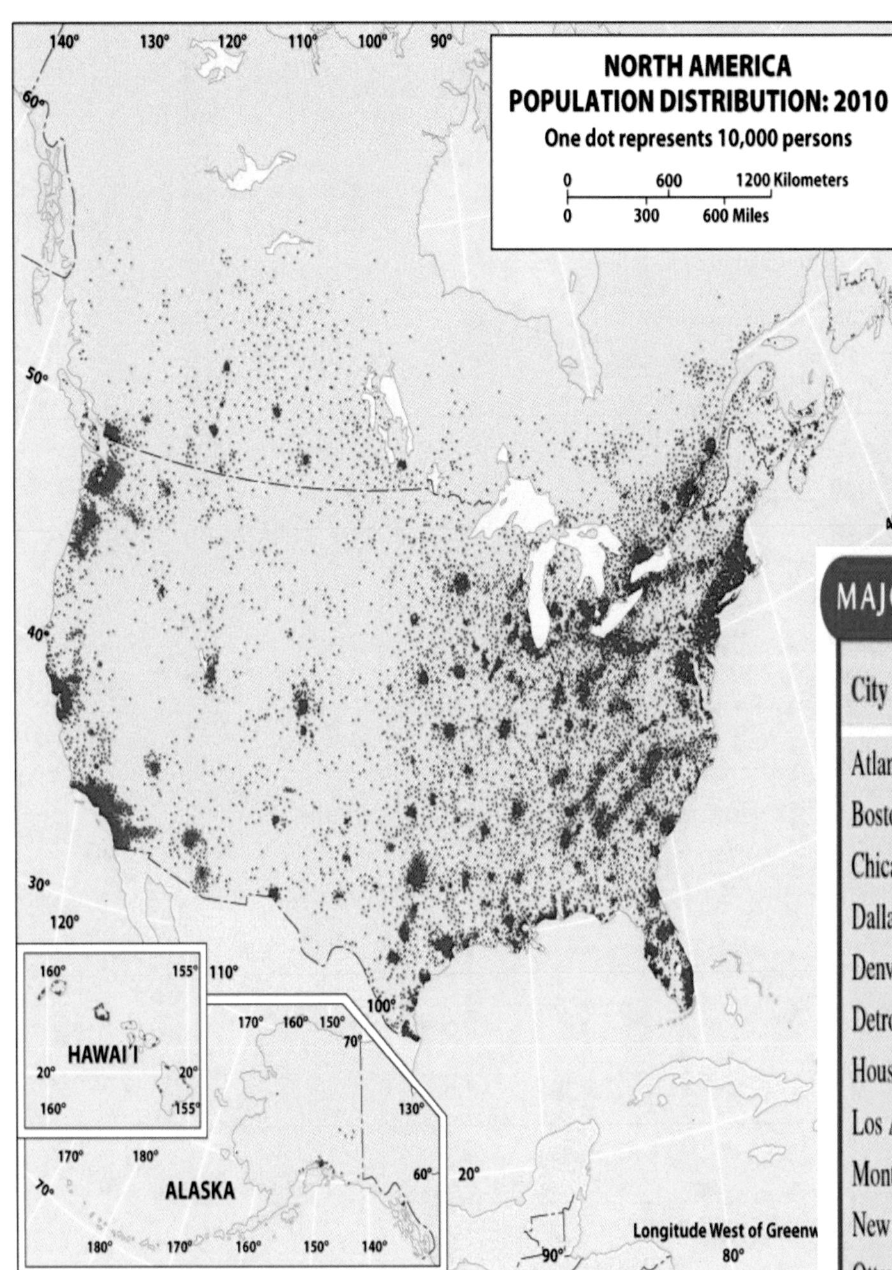
NORTH AMERICA
POPULATION DISTRIBUTION: 2010
One dot represents 10,000 persons
0 600 1200 Kilometers
0 300 600 Miles
HAWAI'I
ALASKA
Longitude West of Greenw

MAJOR CITIES OF THE REALM

City	Population (in millions)*
Atlanta	5.3
Boston	6.2
Chicago	10.2
Dallas—Ft. Worth	6.1
Denver	3.3
Detroit	5.4
Houston	5.6
Los Angeles	18.1
Montreal, Canada	3.7
New York	22.6
Ottawa, Canada	1.1
Philadelphia	6.4
San Diego	3.4
San Francisco	7.9
Seattle	4.1
Toronto, Canada	5.3
Vancouver, Canada	2.1
Washington, DC	5.8

*Based on 2010 estimates.

Canada's Main Street Cluster

Quebec City
Toronto
Montreal
Detroit
Windsor

Three other **clusters** are part of Canada's **ecumene**

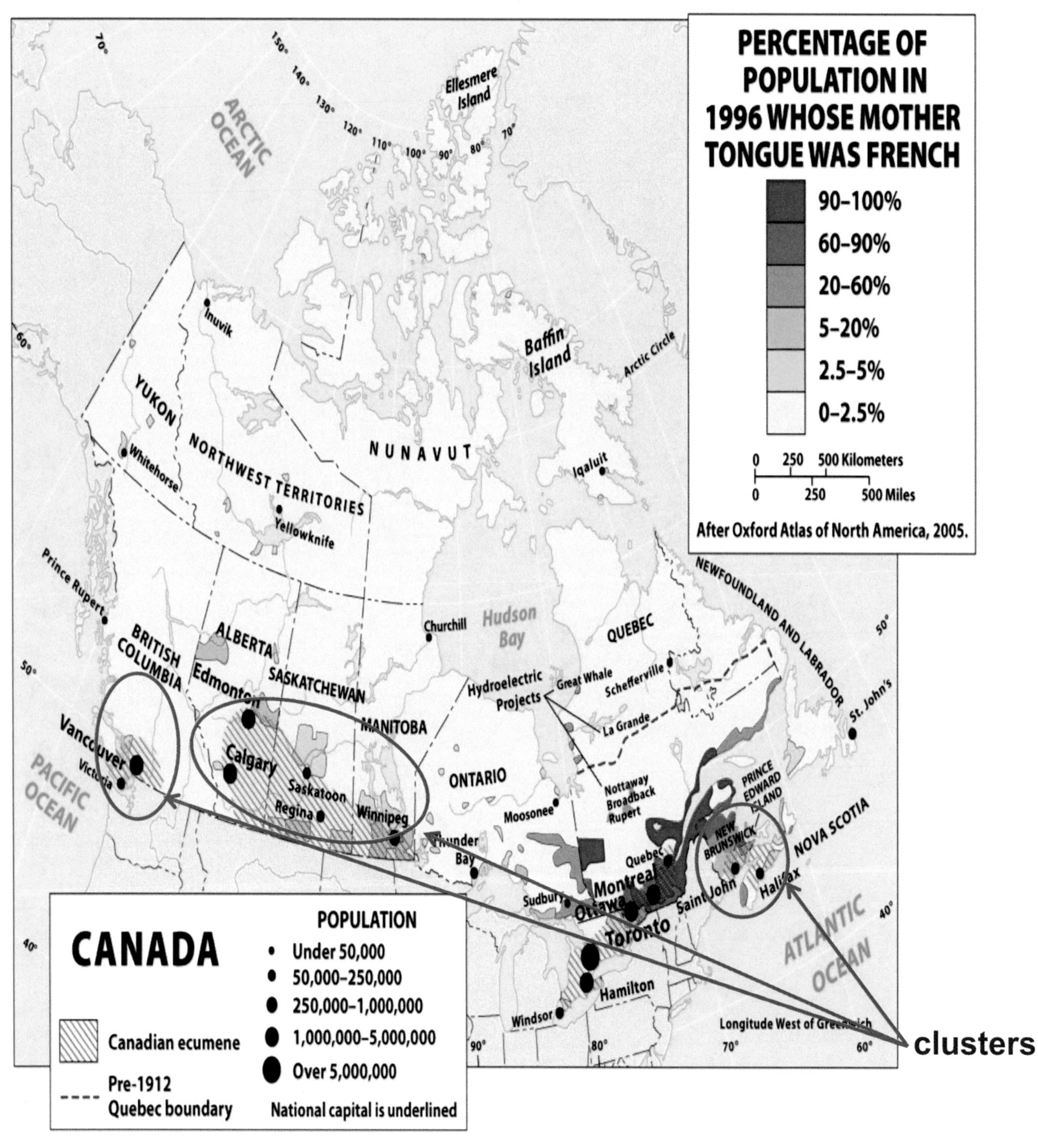
PERCENTAGE OF POPULATION IN 1996 WHOSE MOTHER TONGUE WAS FRENCH
90–100%
60–90%
20–60%
5–20%
2.5–5%
0–2.5%
0 250 500 Kilometers
0 250 500 Miles
After Oxford Atlas of North America, 2005.
ARCTIC OCEAN
Ellesmere Island
Baffin Island
Arctic Circle
Inuvik
YUKON
NORTHWEST TERRITORIES
NUNAVUT
Whitehorse
Yellowknife
Iqaluit
Prince Rupert
BRITISH COLUMBIA
ALBERTA
SASKATCHEWAN
MANITOBA
Edmonton
Calgary
Saskatoon
Regina
Winnipeg
Vancouver
Victoria
PACIFIC OCEAN
Churchill
Hudson Bay
QUEBEC
Hydroelectric Projects
Great Whale
Schefferville
La Grande
Nottaway Broadback Rupert
ONTARIO
Moosonee
Thunder Bay
Sudbury
Ottawa
Montreal
Quebec
Toronto
Hamilton
Windsor
NEWFOUNDLAND AND LABRADOR
St. John's
PRINCE EDWARD ISLAND
NEW BRUNSWICK
NOVA SCOTIA
Saint John
Halifax
ATLANTIC OCEAN
Longitude West of Greenwich
CANADA
POPULATION
Under 50,000
50,000–250,000
250,000–1,000,000
1,000,000–5,000,000
Over 5,000,000
Canadian ecumene
Pre-1912 Quebec boundary
National capital is underlined
clusters

POPULATION DENSITY OF MEXICO

People per sq. mi.
310+
186-310
124-186
31-124
0-31
UNITED STATES
Gulf of Mexico
CUBA
Mexico City
Pacific Ocean
BELIZE
GUATEMALA
HONDURAS
0 mi 200 400
Copyright STRATFOR 2010 www.STRATFOR.com

MAJOR CITIES OF THE REALM

City	Population* (in millions)
Ciudad Juárez, Mexico	1.4
Guadalajara, Mexico	4.3
Guatemala City, Guatemala	1.2
Havana, Cuba	2.2
Managua, Nicaragua	1.3
Mexico City, Mexico	28.8
Monterrey, Mexico	3.9
Panama City, Panama	1.4
Port-au-Prince, Haiti	2.2
Puebla, Mexico	2.3
San José, Costa Rica	1.4
San Juan, Puerto Rico	2.7
San Salvador, El Salvador	1.5
Santo Domingo, Dominican Rep.	2.3
Tegucigalpa, Honduras	1.0
Tijuana, Mexico	1.7

*Based on 2010 estimates.

Mexico City
Tlalnepantla
Villa Madero
Azcapotzalco
Three Cultures Plaza
Gran Canal del Desagüe
Guadalupe del Norte
Canal de Desfogue del Lago
Lake Texcoco (dry)
Zona Rosa
National Palace
MEXICO CITY
CBD
Chapultepec Castle
Zócalo (Plaza de la Constitución)
Benito Juárez International Airport
Ixtacalco
Ixtapalapa
Villa Obregón
Coyoacán
Tlapan
Xochimilco
0 5 Kilometers
0 3 Miles

South America Population

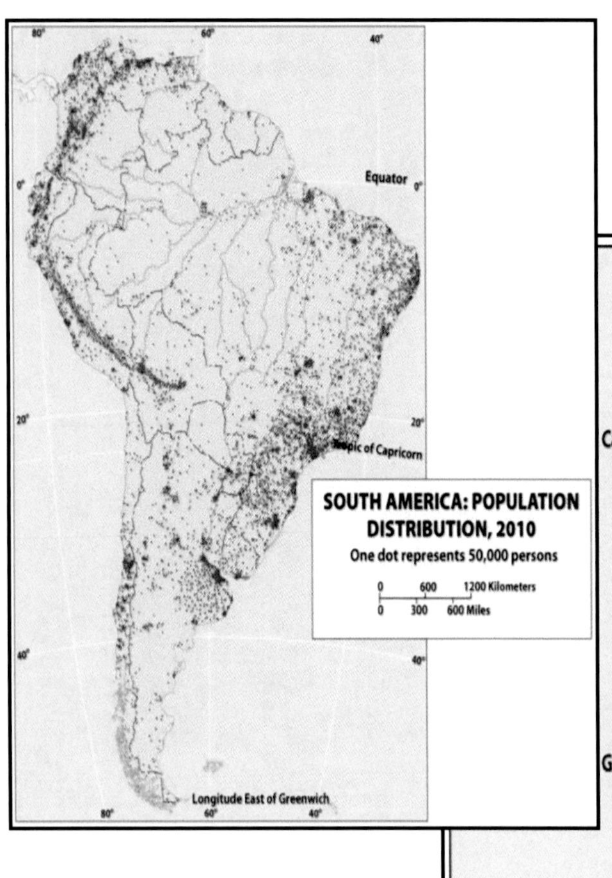

Equator
SOUTH AMERICA: POPULATION DISTRIBUTION, 2010
One dot represents 50,000 persons
0 600 1200 Kilometers
0 300 600 Miles
Longitude East of Greenwich

Population Cartogram

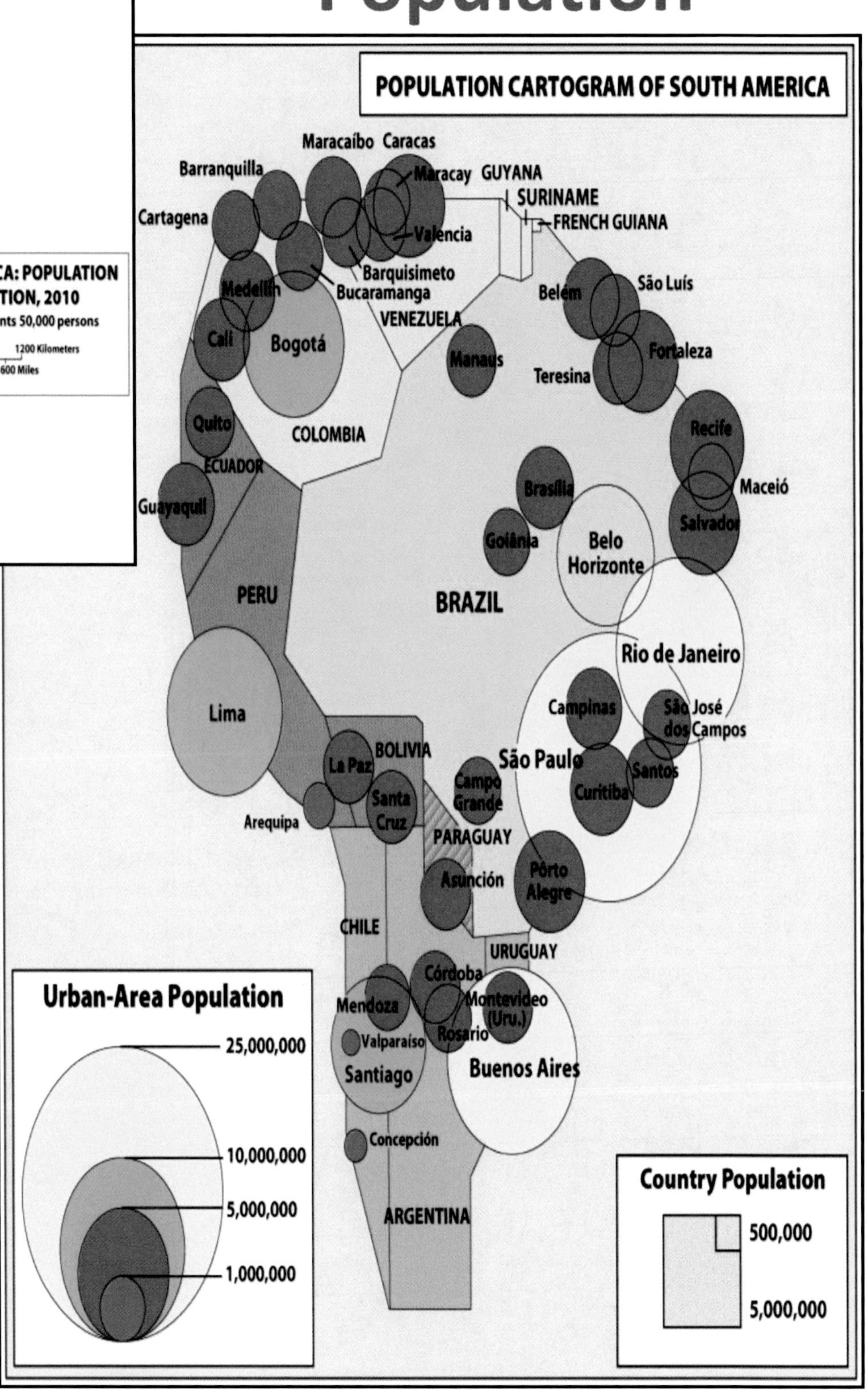

POPULATION CARTOGRAM OF SOUTH AMERICA
Maracaíbo
Caracas
Barranquilla
Maracay
GUYANA
SURINAME
FRENCH GUIANA
Cartagena
Valencia
Barquisimeto
Bucaramanga
Medellín
VENEZUELA
Belém
São Luís
Cali
Bogotá
Manaus
Teresina
Fortaleza
Quito
COLOMBIA
Recife
ECUADOR
Maceió
Guayaquil
Brasília
Salvador
Goiânia
Belo Horizonte
PERU
BRAZIL
Rio de Janeiro
Lima
Campinas
São José dos Campos
BOLIVIA
São Paulo
La Paz
Santa Cruz
Campo Grande
Curitiba
Santos
Arequipa
PARAGUAY
Asunción
Pôrto Alegre
CHILE
URUGUAY
Urban-Area Population
Córdoba
Mendoza
Montevideo (Uru.)
Valparaíso
Rosario
25,000,000
Santiago
Buenos Aires
10,000,000
Concepción
5,000,000
ARGENTINA
1,000,000
Country Population
500,000
5,000,000

Australia & New Zealand Population

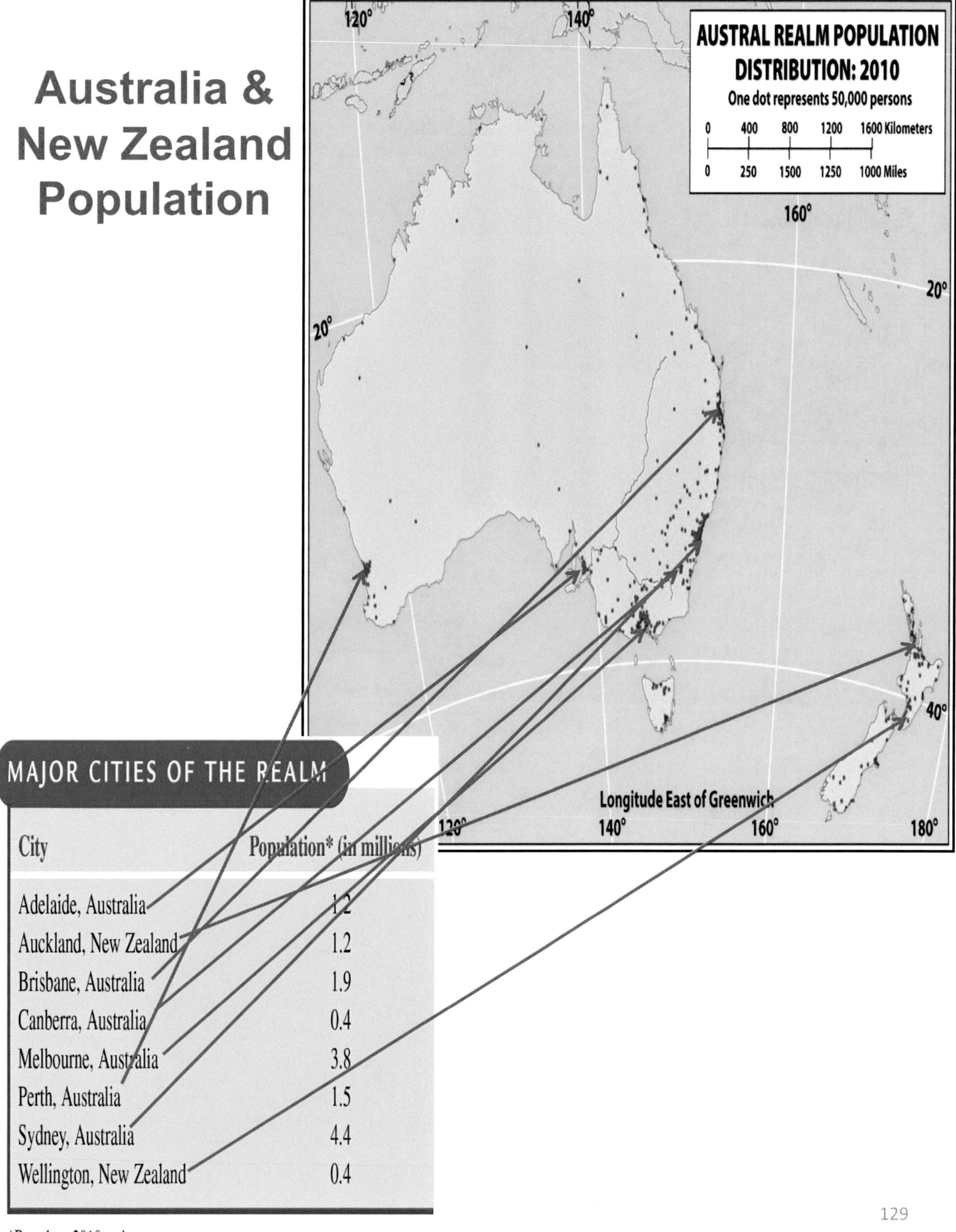

AUSTRAL REALM POPULATION DISTRIBUTION: 2010
One dot represents 50,000 persons
0 400 800 1200 1600 Kilometers
0 250 1500 1250 1000 Miles
120°
140°
160°
180°
20°
40°
Longitude East of Greenwich

MAJOR CITIES OF THE REALM

City	Population* (in millions)
Adelaide, Australia	1.2
Auckland, New Zealand	1.2
Brisbane, Australia	1.9
Canberra, Australia	0.4
Melbourne, Australia	3.8
Perth, Australia	1.5
Sydney, Australia	4.4
Wellington, New Zealand	0.4

*Based on 2010 estimates.

The Pacific Realm Population

MAJOR CITIES OF THE REALM

City	Population* (in millions)
Honolulu, Hawai'i (U.S.)	0.9
Nouméa, New Caledonia	0.2
Port Moresby, Papua New Guinea	0.3
Suva, Fiji	0.2

*Based on 2010 estimates.

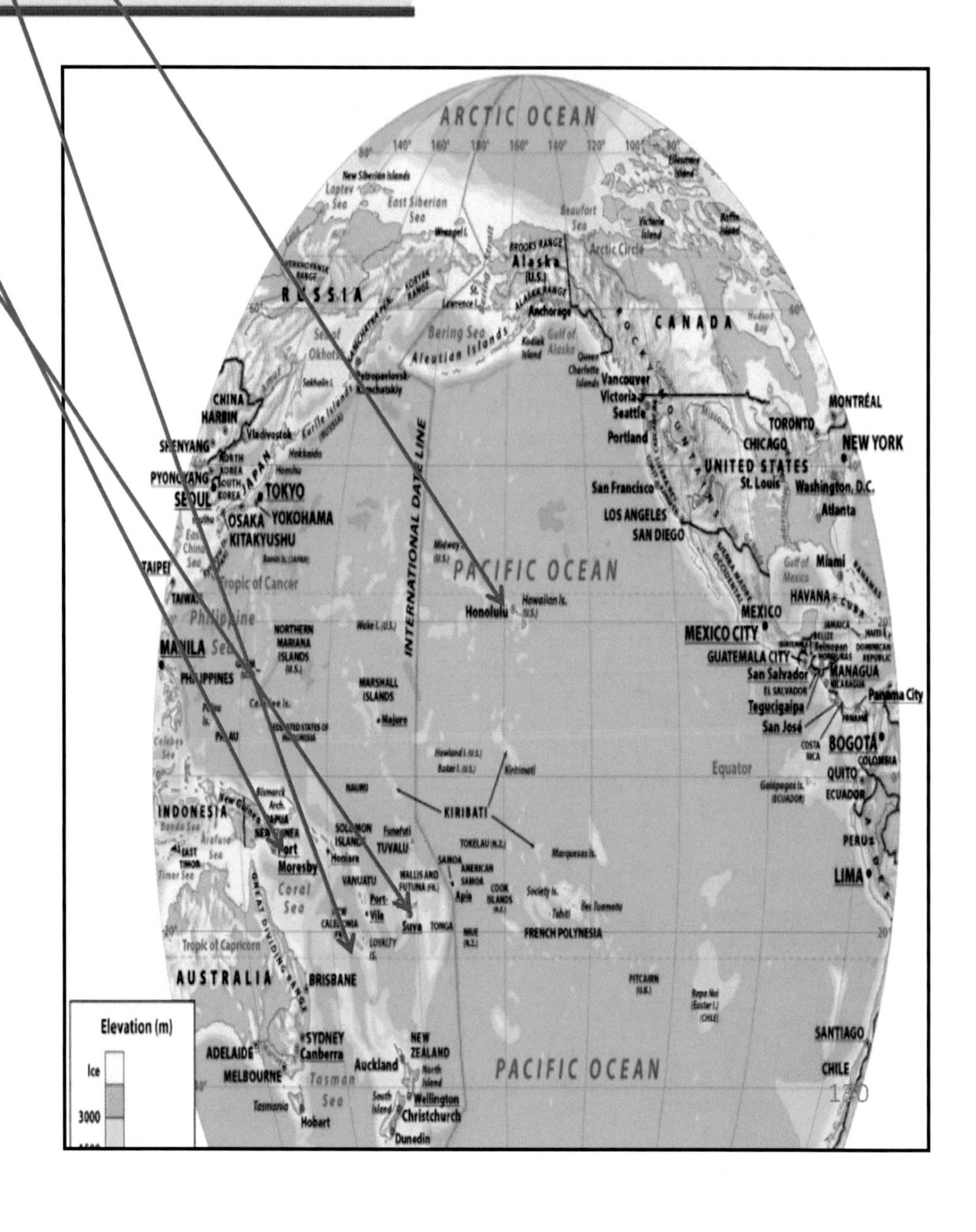
ARCTIC OCEAN
RUSSIA
Alaska (U.S.)
Anchorage
CANADA
Bering Sea
Aleutian Islands
CHINA
HARBIN
SHENYANG
PYONGYANG
SEOUL
JAPAN
TOKYO
YOKOHAMA
OSAKA
KITAKYUSHU
TAIPEI
MANILA
PHILIPPINES
Vancouver
Victoria
Seattle
Portland
San Francisco
LOS ANGELES
SAN DIEGO
UNITED STATES
CHICAGO
TORONTO
MONTRÉAL
NEW YORK
St. Louis
Washington, D.C.
Atlanta
Miami
HAVANA
MEXICO
MEXICO CITY
GUATEMALA CITY
San Salvador
MANAGUA
Tegucigalpa
San José
Panama City
BOGOTÁ
QUITO
ECUADOR
PERU
LIMA
INTERNATIONAL DATE LINE
PACIFIC OCEAN
Honolulu
Hawaiian Is.
Tropic of Cancer
NORTHERN MARIANA ISLANDS
MARSHALL ISLANDS
Equator
KIRIBATI
INDONESIA
Port Moresby
SOLOMON ISLANDS
TUVALU
VANUATU
Coral Sea
Suva
TONGA
FRENCH POLYNESIA
Tropic of Capricorn
AUSTRALIA
BRISBANE
SYDNEY
Canberra
ADELAIDE
MELBOURNE
Tasman Sea
Hobart
NEW ZEALAND
Auckland
Wellington
Christchurch
Dunedin
SANTIAGO
CHILE
Elevation (m)
Ice
3000

Human Geography

Abu Dhabi, U.A.E- Tyrell Heaton

Human Geography

Human geography is the study of the the relationship between people and places. Many cultural aspects found throughout the world and how they relate to the spaces and places where they originate and then travel as people continually move across various areas.

Tyrell Heaton - Blanket weaving in Qenqo, Peru

Human geography encompasses the diffusion of religions and languages, food production, and ways of living, population dynamics, and human-environmental interactions.

Tyrell Heaton - Skyline of Abu Dhabi, UAE

Human geography is concerned with making sense of people and the places they occupy through analyses of cultural processes, cultural landscapes, and cultural identities focusing on how cultures work in place and how they are embedded in everyday life.

"*Geographers see cultures and societies as developing out of their local landscapes but also shaping those landscapes,*" - Carl Sauer, 1925, The Morphology of Landscape.

Food and Culture

Every single culture and religion uses food as part of their celebrations … the celebratory nature of food is universal. Every season, every harvest, and every holiday has its own food… it helps define us.

The key driver for eating is of course hunger but what we choose to eat is not determined solely by physiological or nutritional needs. Some of the other factors that influence food choice include: Biological determinants such as hunger, appetite, and taste. Economic determinants such as cost, income, availability.

Tyrell Heaton - Bangkok, Thailand – *"the fresh aroma of street food blended with emanating smell of sewer, so beautifully orchestrated in the uniqueness unto your own... yet I am so content sitting on a small stool eating noodles on the street at Midnight."*

On a larger scale, food is an important part of culture. Traditional cuisine is passed down from one generation to the next. ... Immigrants bring the food of their countries with them wherever they go and cooking traditional food is a way of preserving their culture when they move to new places.

Tyrell Heaton – Antigua, Guatemala – my first meal in this city and $2.00 will get you a whole fish, rice and a salad.

"I think food, culture, people and landscape are all absolutely inseparable," – Anthony Bourdain

Tyrell Heaton – butcher shop in Basantapur Durbar Square, Kathmandu Nepal

Tyrell Heaton – Vilnius, Lithuania – garishly pink soup called, šaltibarščiai (beet-root soup)

Food has received attention from both the physical sciences and the social sciences because it is a bridge between the natural and social worlds. Some of the earliest numerical data about food production come from bureaucratic sources linked to the ancient civilizations of Ancient Egypt and the Roman Empire.

Tyrell Heaton - Buenos Aires, Argentina – meat cooking inside a restaurant

WENDY'S

Tyrell Heaton – Tokyo, Japan – line out the door at Wendy's

Daily diets from around the world

Minnesota, USA, The Mall of America Staffer
Student and part-time ride supervisor at Mall of America
Age: 21; Height: 5' 7"; Weight: 130 pounds
Caloric value of food this day: 1900 calories

Namibia, The Pastoralist, a Himba tribeswoman
Age: 23; Height: 5' 8"; Weight: 160 pounds
The caloric value of her food this day: 1500 calories

Yemen, The Home Maker
Age: 27; Height: 4' 11"
Weight: 98 pounds
2700 calories this day

China, The Teenaged Acrobat
Age: 16; Height: 5' 2"
Weight: 99 pounds
1700 calories this day

Ecuador, The Mountain Farmer
Age: 37; Height: 5' 3"; Weight: 119 pounds
Caloric value of food this day: 3800 calories

GMOs
Genetically Modified Organisms

Wild watermelon

This 17th-century painting by Giovanni Stanchi depicts a watermelon that looks strikingly different from modern melons. A cross-section of the one in the painting, which was made between 1645 and 1672, appears to have swirly shapes embedded in six triangular pie-shaped pieces.

Modern watermelon

Over time, humans have bred watermelons to have a red, fleshy interior that is actually the placenta — like the ones seen here. Some people think the watermelon in Stanchi's painting may just be unripe or un-watered, but the black seeds in the painting suggest that it was, in fact, ripe.

Wild Carrot

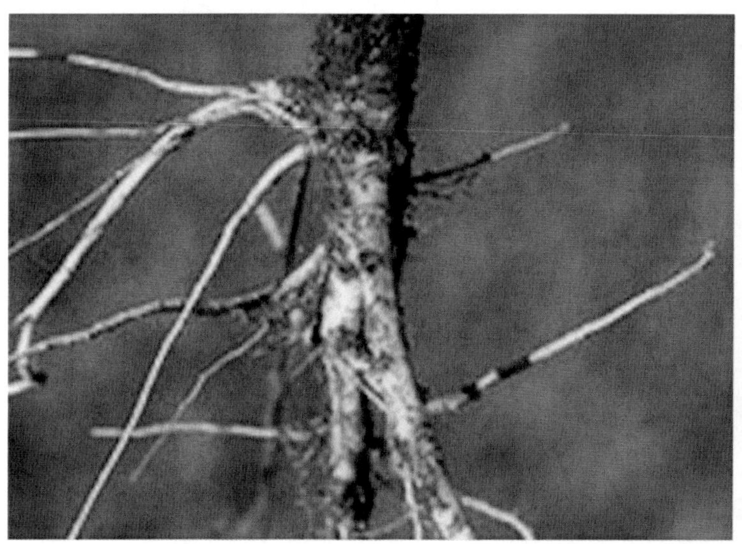

Modern Carrot

The earliest know carrots were grown in the 10th century in Persia and Asia Minor. These were thought to originally be purple or white with a thin, forked root — like those shown here — but they lost their purple pigment and became a yellow color. Farmers domesticated these thin, white roots, which had a strong flavor and annual biennial flower, into these large, tasty orange roots that are an annual winter crop.

NATURAL PEACH, 4000 B.C.

ARTIFICIAL PEACH, 2014

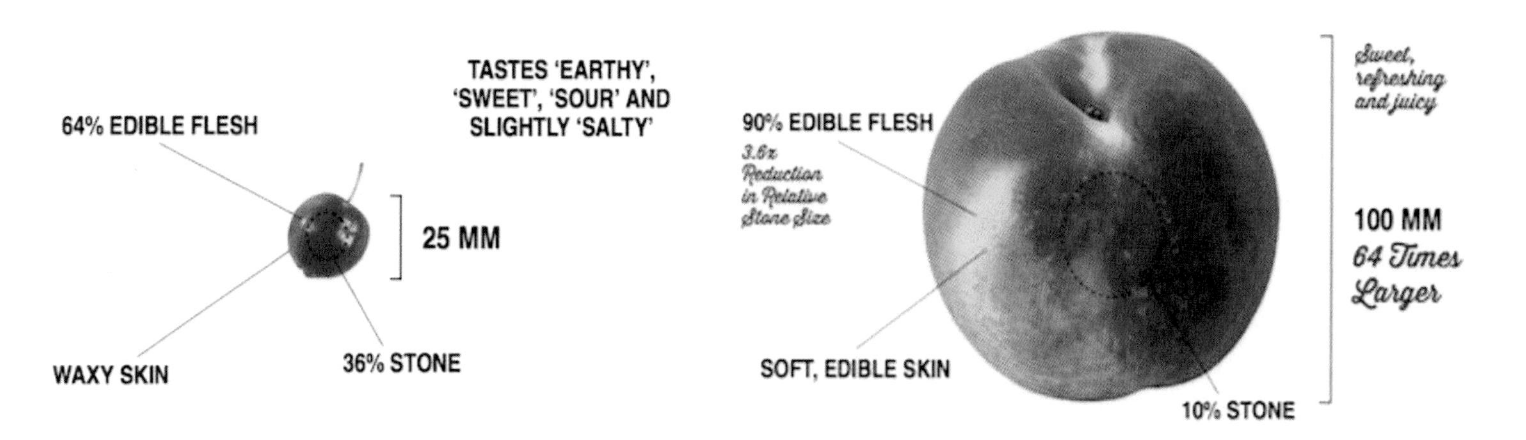

TASTES 'EARTHY', 'SWEET', 'SOUR' AND SLIGHTLY 'SALTY'
64% EDIBLE FLESH
25 MM
WAXY SKIN
36% STONE
90% EDIBLE FLESH
3.6x Reduction in Relative Stone Size
Sweet, refreshing and juicy
100 MM
64 Times Larger
SOFT, EDIBLE SKIN
10% STONE

Peaches used to be small, cherry-like fruits with little flesh. They were first domesticated around 4,000 BC by the ancient Chinese and tasted earthy and slightly salty like a lentil. But after thousands of years of farmers selectively breeding them, peaches are now 64 times larger, 27% juicier, and 4% sweeter.

Do you think we should continue to genetically modify food?

For nearly a billion people a glass of water means miles to walk

Tyrell Heaton – Annapurna region of Nepal - each village has several water spigots where they collect water.

We take for granted being able go to the faucet for a drink of water. Nearly one billion people worldwide have limited access to clean water and the crisis disproportionately affects women and girls.

On average, women in developing countries walk more than 3.5 miles a day to collect water because there is not enough of it nearby. The chore keeps girls out of school and women from more productive economic activities.

Girl fetching water in Cote D'Ivoire

Where is your water source?

A96

TyrellHeaton - Cape Town, South Africa. Women washing clothes; (left); woman collecting fresh water (right) in the Langa Township (200,000 people live in this township). Basically a suburb of Cape Town.

Tyrell Heaton – Woman washing clothes by hand in a stream in rural Guatemala.

Two side of Sierra Leone
Do you think one affects the other?

Water pollution (particularly drinking water) is a serious problem in Sierra Leone. Almost half of the population of Sierra Leone has no access to safe drinking water and only 13% of the population has access to improved non-shared sanitation facilities.

5:30pm Daily
BISHOP FRED ADDO &

Some 74% of urban dwellers have access to safe drinking water while only 46% of rural people use safe water. In the Northern Region, only 30% of residents have access to safe drinking water. According to the Sierra Leone Water Company, on average only 35% of rural residents have access to safe drinking water.

Environmental vs. Cultural Determinism

From a geographic perspective…

Environmental determinism is the belief that the environment (primarily physical factors such as landforms, location, and climate) determines the patterns of human culture and societal development.

Cultural determinism is the belief that the culture (learned human behavior passed along by communication and imitation from one generation to the next) defines how a collective society will develop.

For instance: both Haiti and the Dominican Republic share an island and they are very different. Look at the photo and read the caption below...

Along the political boundary between Haiti and the Dominican Republic you can see long stretches of the border marked by a stark contrast in vegetation, denudation prevails to the west in Haiti while the forest survives on the Dominican (eastern) side. Overpopulation, lack of governmental control, and mismanagement on the Haitian side combine to create this stark spatial contrast

Yes, we're discussing poop

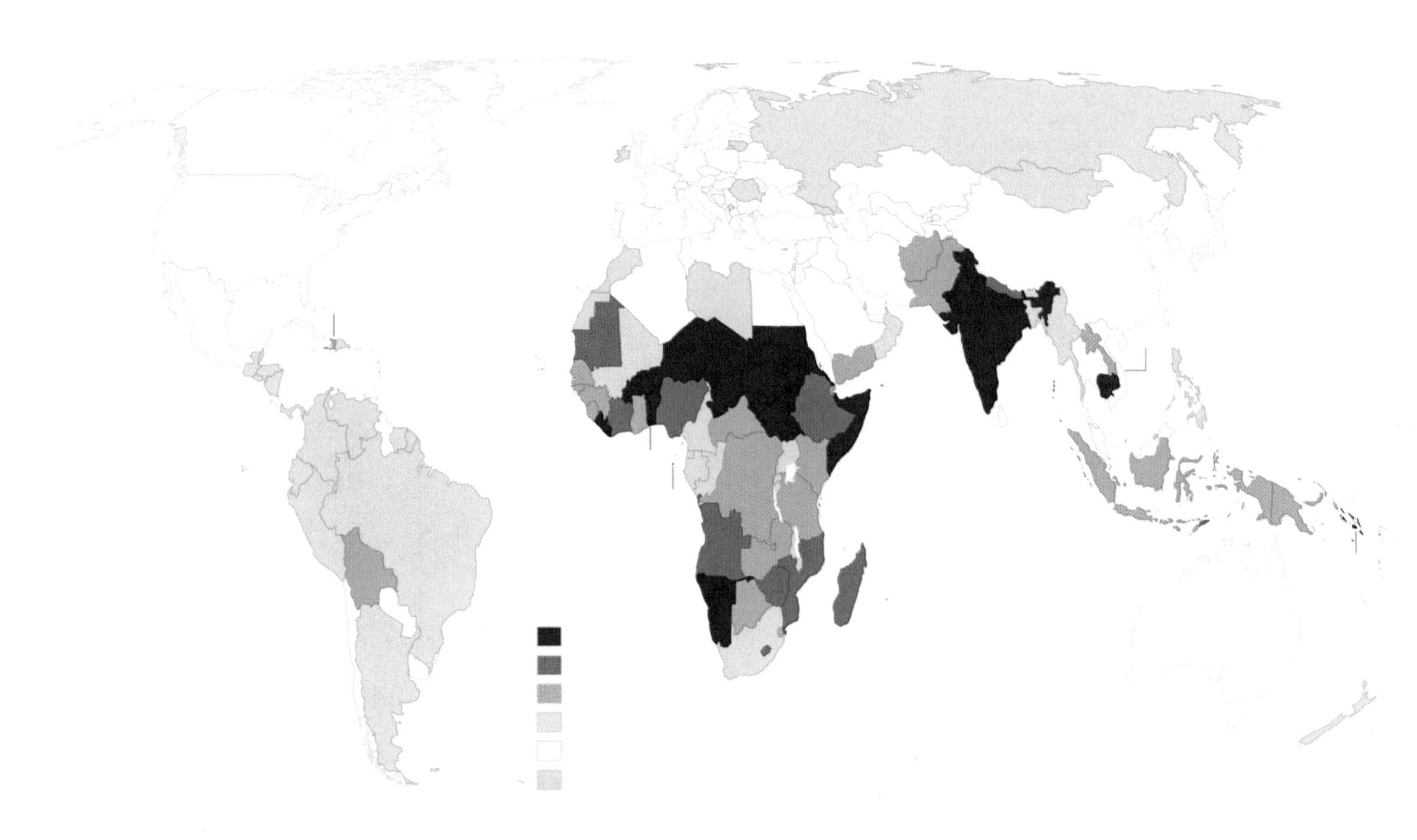

Roughly 2.6 billion people around the world lack any sanitation whatsoever.

More than 200 million tons of human waste goes untreated every year. In the developing world, 90 percent of sewage is discharged directly into lakes, rivers and oceans. In India alone roughly 570 million people practice open defecation - the current population of the USA is roughly 323 million.

The percentage of people defecating in the open air declined worldwide from 1990 to 2015, with the most dramatic reductions in some of the least developed countries. Yet nearly 950 million people still practice this public health hazard — a challenge augmented by population growth.

TUALET

Tyrell Heaton - Gas station toilet in Morin, Kukës, Albania

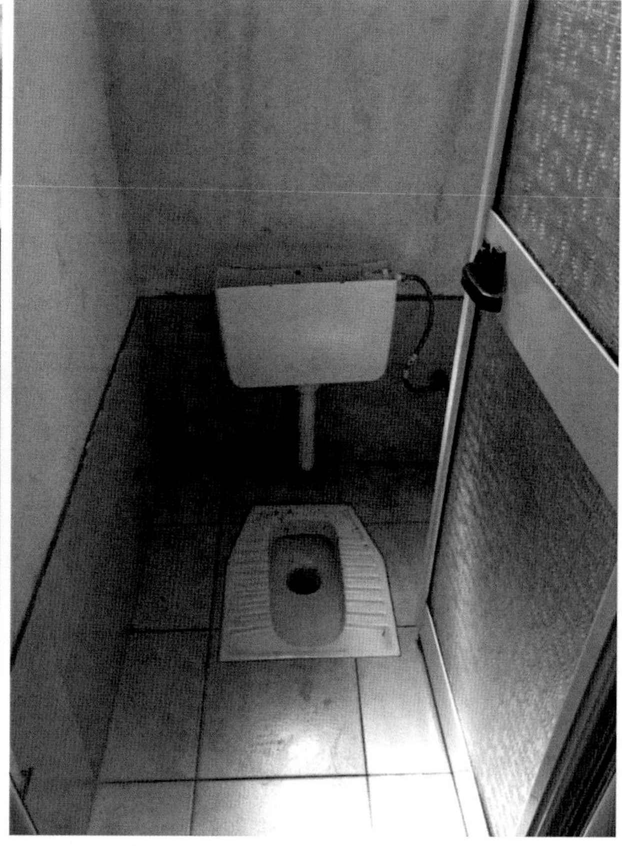

Toilet in the Albanian gas station bathroom (upper left)

Daily business is same-same but different all around the world

A makeshift latrine in Dhaka, Bangladesh.

Tyrell Heaton - Restaurant bathroom in rural China

Cultural Hearth

The Indus River Valley

- An early culture emerged and developed:
  - Arts and trade routes emerged from isolated tribes and villages to towns and beyond
  - **Hinduism** emerged from the beliefs and practices brought to India by the Indo-Europeans (Aryans) - (6th century BC)
  - **Buddhism** born of discontent; made the state religion of India in 3rd century BC
  - **Islam** swept through northern India in the late 10th century AD

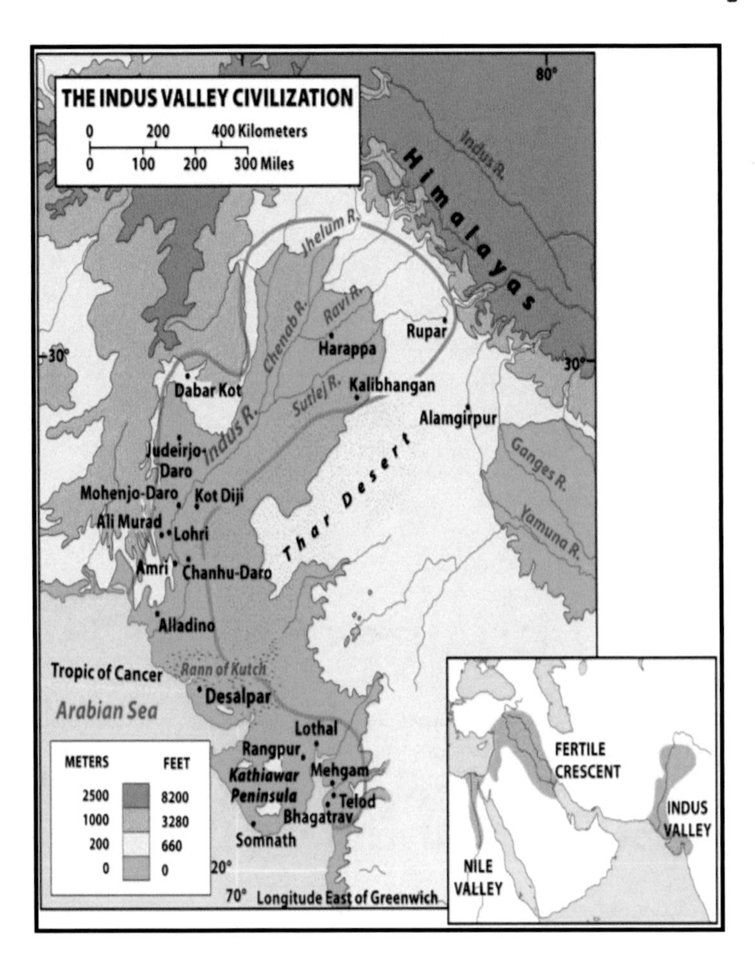
THE INDUS VALLEY CIVILIZATION
0 200 400 Kilometers
0 100 200 300 Miles
Himalayas
Indus R.
Jhelum R.
Chenab R.
Ravi R.
Sutlej R.
Indus R.
Ganges R.
Yamuna R.
Thar Desert
Harappa
Rupar
Kalibhangan
Alamgirpur
Dabar Kot
Judeirjo-Daro
Mohenjo-Daro
Kot Diji
Ali Murad
Lohri
Amri
Chanhu-Daro
Alladino
Tropic of Cancer
Rann of Kutch
Desalpar
Arabian Sea
Lothal
Rangpur
Kathiawar Peninsula
Mehgam
Telod
Bhagatrav
Somnath
METERS FEET
2500 8200
1000 3280
200 660
0 0
30°
80°
20°
70° Longitude East of Greenwich
FERTILE CRESCENT
INDUS VALLEY
NILE VALLEY

Culture Hearth

Source area from which radiated ideas, innovations, and ideologies that changed the world beyond

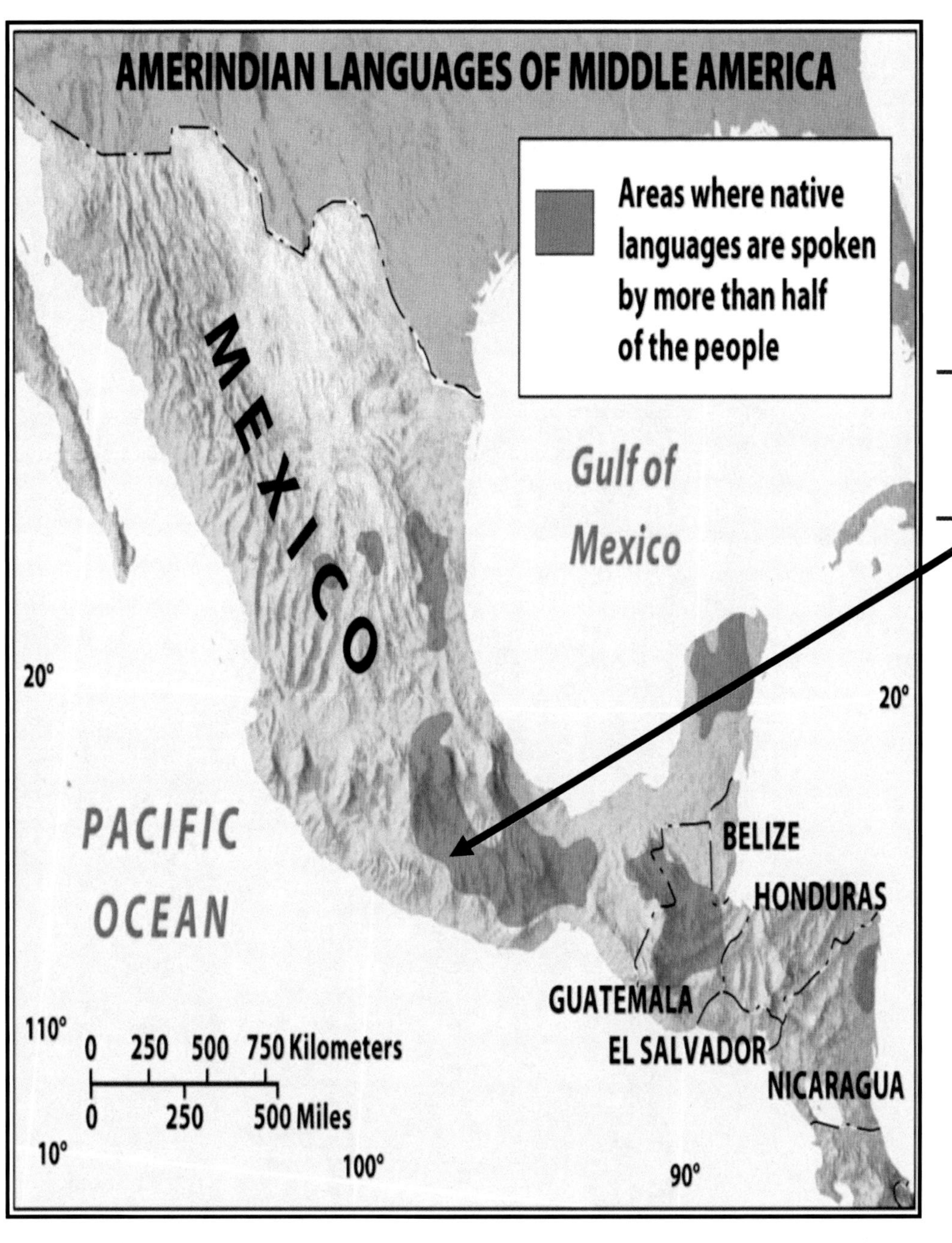

AMERINDIAN LANGUAGES OF MIDDLE AMERICA
Areas where native languages are spoken by more than half of the people
MEXICO
Gulf of Mexico
PACIFIC OCEAN
BELIZE
HONDURAS
GUATEMALA
EL SALVADOR
NICARAGUA
20°
20°
110°
10°
100°
90°
0 250 500 750 Kilometers
0 250 500 Miles

- Middle American Hearths
- **Aztecs** and their predecessors
  - Pinnacle of a long sequence of civilizations in the Valley of Mexico
  - 1300 AD
  - Tenochtitlan (>100,000 people)

Culture Hearth

- **Middle American Hearths**

- **Maya Civilization**
    - 3000 BP
    - Classic period 200-900 AD
    - Yucatan peninsula
    - Honduras, Guatemala, Belize;
    - Theocratic structure

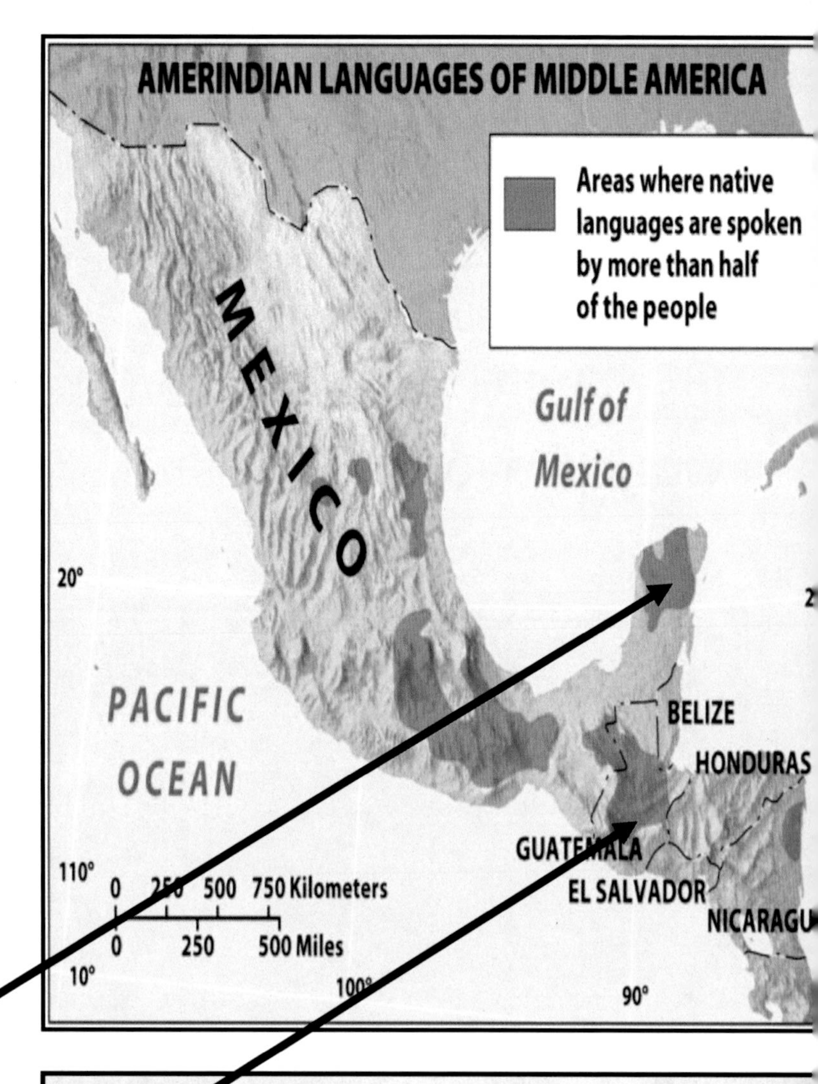
AMERINDIAN LANGUAGES OF MIDDLE AMERICA
Areas where native languages are spoken by more than half of the people
MEXICO
Gulf of Mexico
PACIFIC OCEAN
BELIZE
HONDURAS
GUATEMALA
EL SALVADOR
NICARAGU
0 250 500 750 Kilometers
0 250 500 Miles
20°
110°
10°
100°
90°

The Inca Empire

- A highly centralized state
- **<u>Culture hearth</u>** - intermontane basin around Cuzco (1200–1535 A.D.)
- ***<u>Altiplanos</u>*** were key to settlement patterns.
- 20 million subjects at its zenith
- Transportation networks and integration efforts were most impressive

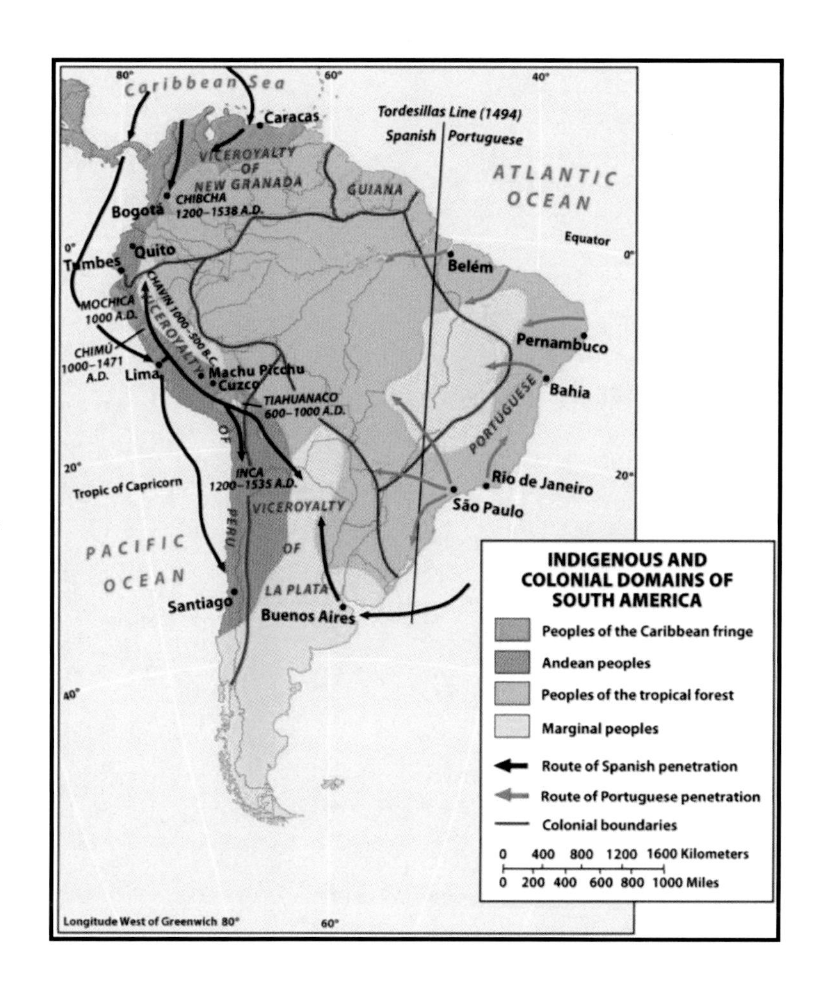

Caribbean Sea
Caracas
Tordesillas Line (1494)
Spanish
Portuguese
VICEROYALTY OF NEW GRANADA
GUIANA
ATLANTIC OCEAN
CHIBCHA 1200–1538 A.D.
Bogotá
Equator
Quito
Tumbes
Belém
MOCHICA 1000 A.D.
CHAVIN 1000–500 B.C.
CHIMÚ 1000–1471 A.D.
Lima
Machu Picchu
Cuzco
Pernambuco
Bahia
TIAHUANACO 600–1000 A.D.
PORTUGUESE
VICEROYALTY OF PERU
INCA 1200–1535 A.D.
Tropic of Capricorn
Rio de Janeiro
São Paulo
VICEROYALTY OF LA PLATA
PACIFIC OCEAN
Santiago
Buenos Aires
INDIGENOUS AND COLONIAL DOMAINS OF SOUTH AMERICA
Peoples of the Caribbean fringe
Andean peoples
Peoples of the tropical forest
Marginal peoples
Route of Spanish penetration
Route of Portuguese penetration
Colonial boundaries
0 400 800 1200 1600 Kilometers
0 200 400 600 800 1000 Miles
Longitude West of Greenwich 80°
80°
60°
40°
0°
20°
40°

Machu Picchu, Peru

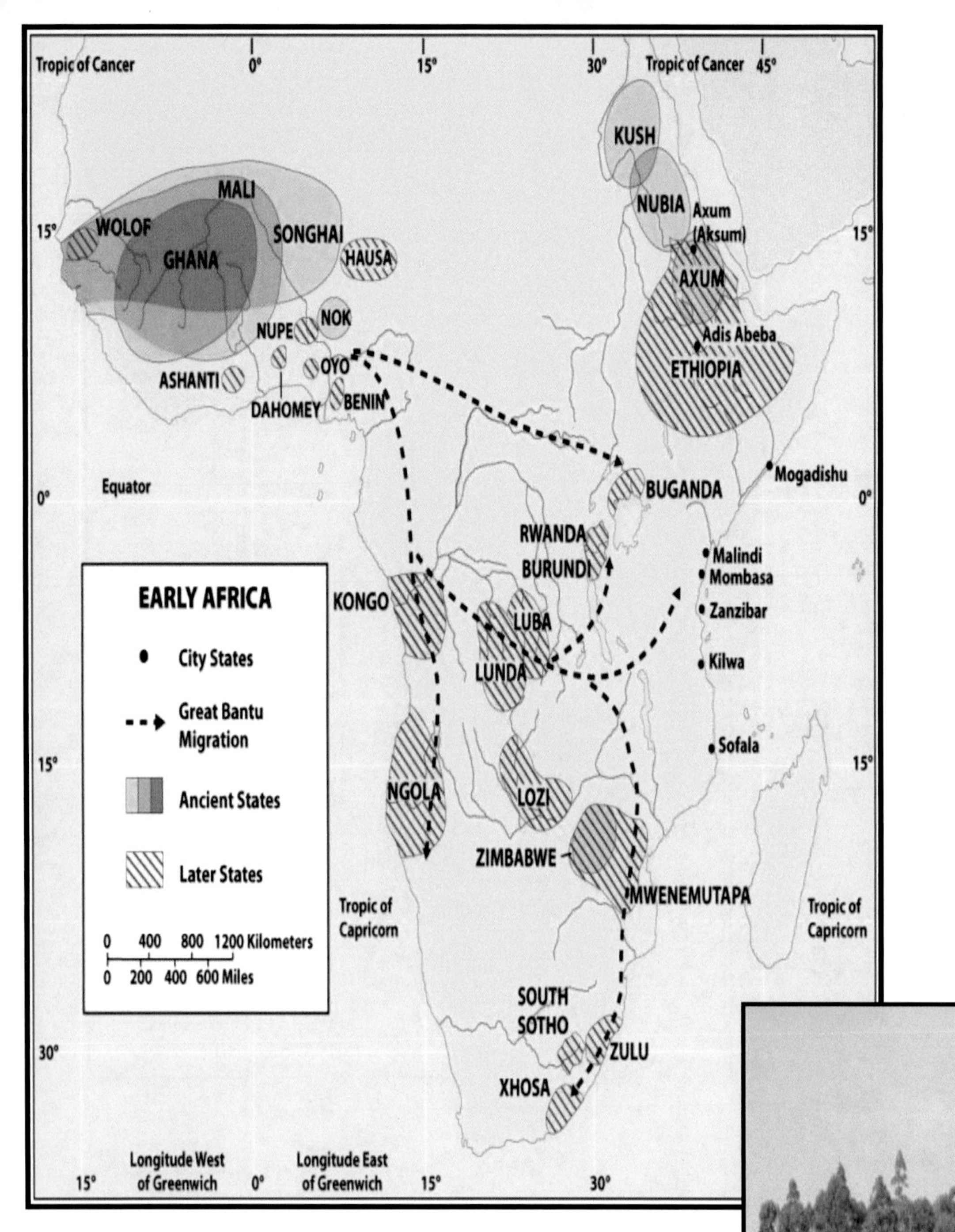
EARLY AFRICA
City States
Great Bantu Migration
Ancient States
Later States
0 400 800 1200 Kilometers
0 200 400 600 Miles
Tropic of Cancer
0°
15°
30°
45°
Equator
Tropic of Capricorn
Longitude West of Greenwich
Longitude East of Greenwich
KUSH
NUBIA
Axum (Aksum)
AXUM
Adis Abeba
ETHIOPIA
Mogadishu
MALI
WOLOF
GHANA
SONGHAI
HAUSA
NUPE
NOK
OYO
ASHANTI
DAHOMEY
BENIN
BUGANDA
RWANDA
BURUNDI
Malindi
Mombasa
Zanzibar
Kilwa
Sofala
KONGO
LUBA
LUNDA
NGOLA
LOZI
ZIMBABWE
MWENEMUTAPA
SOUTH SOTHO
ZULU
XHOSA

Early Kingdoms

South America's Ethnic Groups

80°
60°
40°
Caribbean Sea
ATLANTIC OCEAN
VENEZUELA
GUYANA
SURINAME
FRENCH GUIANA
COLOMBIA
Equator
0°
ECUADOR
BRAZIL
PERU
BOLIVIA
PACIFIC OCEAN
20°
Tropic of Capricorn
PARAGUAY
ARGENTINA
URUGUAY
CHILE
40°
Falkland Islands (U.K.)
B
100°
80°
60°
SOUTH AMERICA: DOMINANT ETHNIC GROUPS
African
Mestizo
White
Amerindian
0 400 800 1200 Kilometers
0 200 400 600 Miles

Longitude West of Greenwich

Ethnic Patterns in Southeast Asia

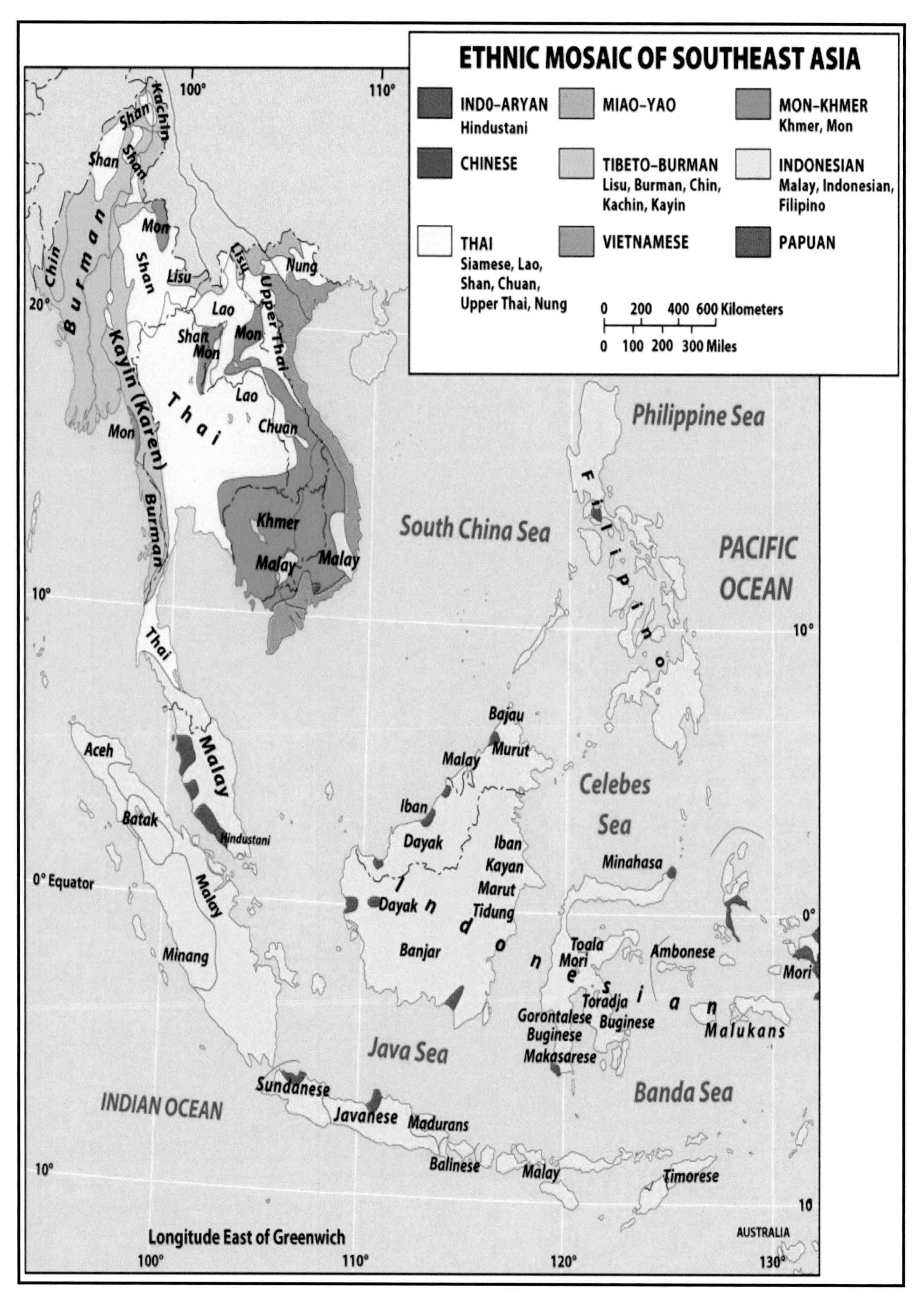
ETHNIC MOSAIC OF SOUTHEAST ASIA
INDO-ARYAN Hindustani
MIAO-YAO
MON-KHMER Khmer, Mon
CHINESE
TIBETO-BURMAN Lisu, Burman, Chin, Kachin, Kayin
INDONESIAN Malay, Indonesian, Filipino
THAI Siamese, Lao, Shan, Chuan, Upper Thai, Nung
VIETNAMESE
PAPUAN
0 200 400 600 Kilometers
0 100 200 300 Miles
Philippine Sea
South China Sea
PACIFIC OCEAN
Celebes Sea
Java Sea
Banda Sea
INDIAN OCEAN
Filipino
Indonesian
Kachin
Shan
Chin
Burman
Mon
Lisu
Nung
Upper Thai
Lao
Kayin (Karen)
Thai
Chuan
Khmer
Malay
Aceh
Batak
Hindustani
Minang
Bajau
Murut
Iban
Dayak
Kayan
Marut
Tidung
Banjar
Minahasa
Toala
Mori
Ambonese
Toradja
Gorontalese
Buginese
Makasarese
Malukans
Sundanese
Javanese
Madurans
Balinese
Timorese
AUSTRALIA
0° Equator
Longitude East of Greenwich
100°
110°
120°
130°
10°
20°

Colonial Spheres

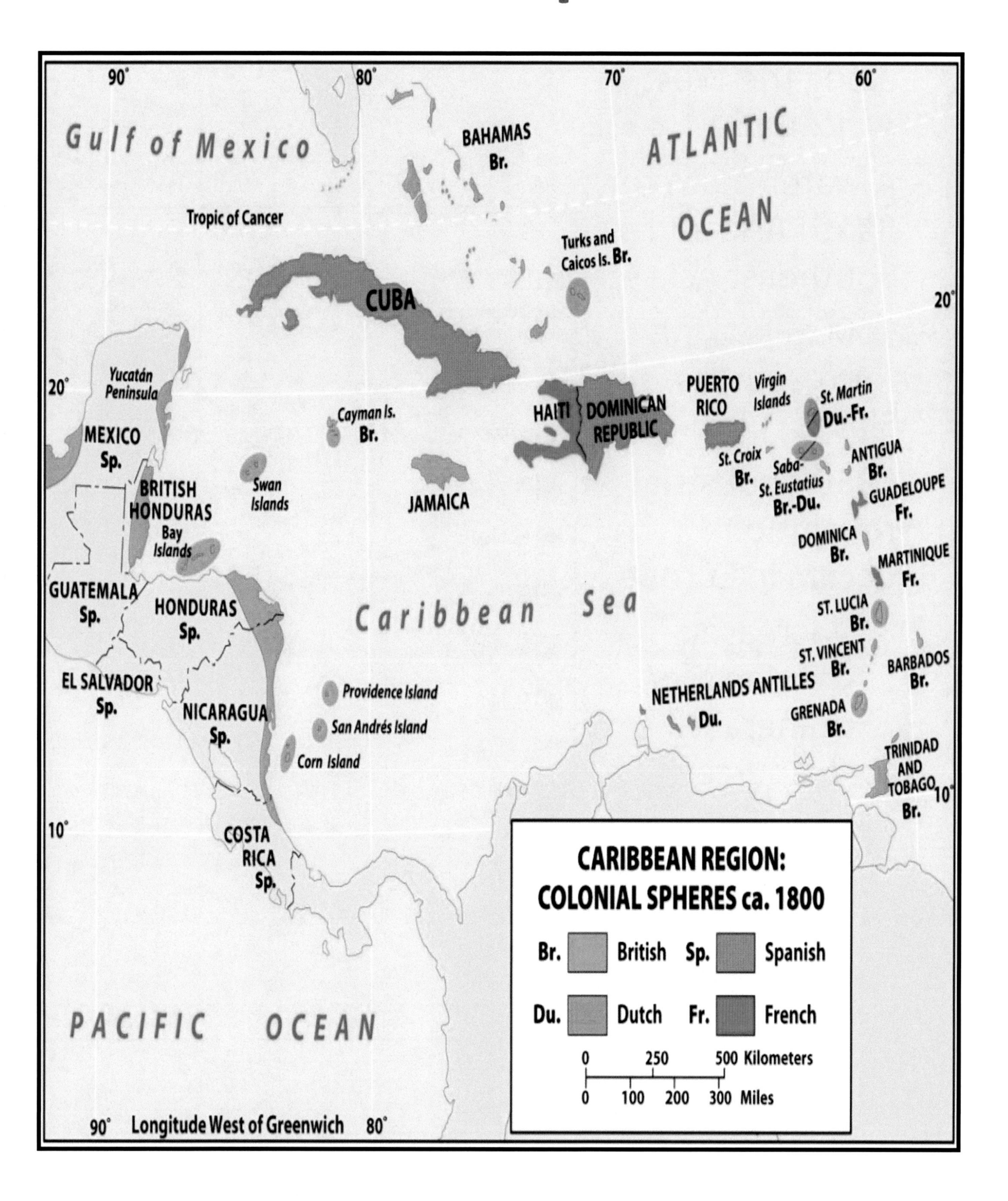

90°
80°
70°
60°
Gulf of Mexico
ATLANTIC
OCEAN
BAHAMAS
Br.
Tropic of Cancer
Turks and Caicos Is. Br.
CUBA
20°
Yucatán Peninsula
MEXICO
Sp.
Cayman Is.
Br.
HAITI
DOMINICAN REPUBLIC
PUERTO RICO
Virgin Islands
St. Martin
Du.-Fr.
St. Croix
Br.
Saba-St. Eustatius
Br.-Du.
ANTIGUA
Br.
GUADELOUPE
Fr.
BRITISH HONDURAS
Swan Islands
JAMAICA
Bay Islands
DOMINICA
Br.
MARTINIQUE
Fr.
GUATEMALA
Sp.
HONDURAS
Sp.
Caribbean Sea
ST. LUCIA
Br.
ST. VINCENT
Br.
BARBADOS
Br.
EL SALVADOR
Sp.
NICARAGUA
Sp.
Providence Island
San Andrés Island
Corn Island
NETHERLANDS ANTILLES
Du.
GRENADA
Br.
TRINIDAD AND TOBAGO
Br.
10°
COSTA RICA
Sp.
CARIBBEAN REGION: COLONIAL SPHERES ca. 1800
Br. British
Sp. Spanish
Du. Dutch
Fr. French
0 250 500 Kilometers
0 100 200 300 Miles
PACIFIC OCEAN
90° Longitude West of Greenwich 80°

Colonialism

- **European colonial objectives**
  - Supply ports along the West African coast
  - A water route to South Asia and Southeast Asia
  - 1500s- looking for resources; Slaves
  - 1850- industrial revolution occurs in Europe
    - Increased demand for mineral resources
    - Need to expand agricultural production

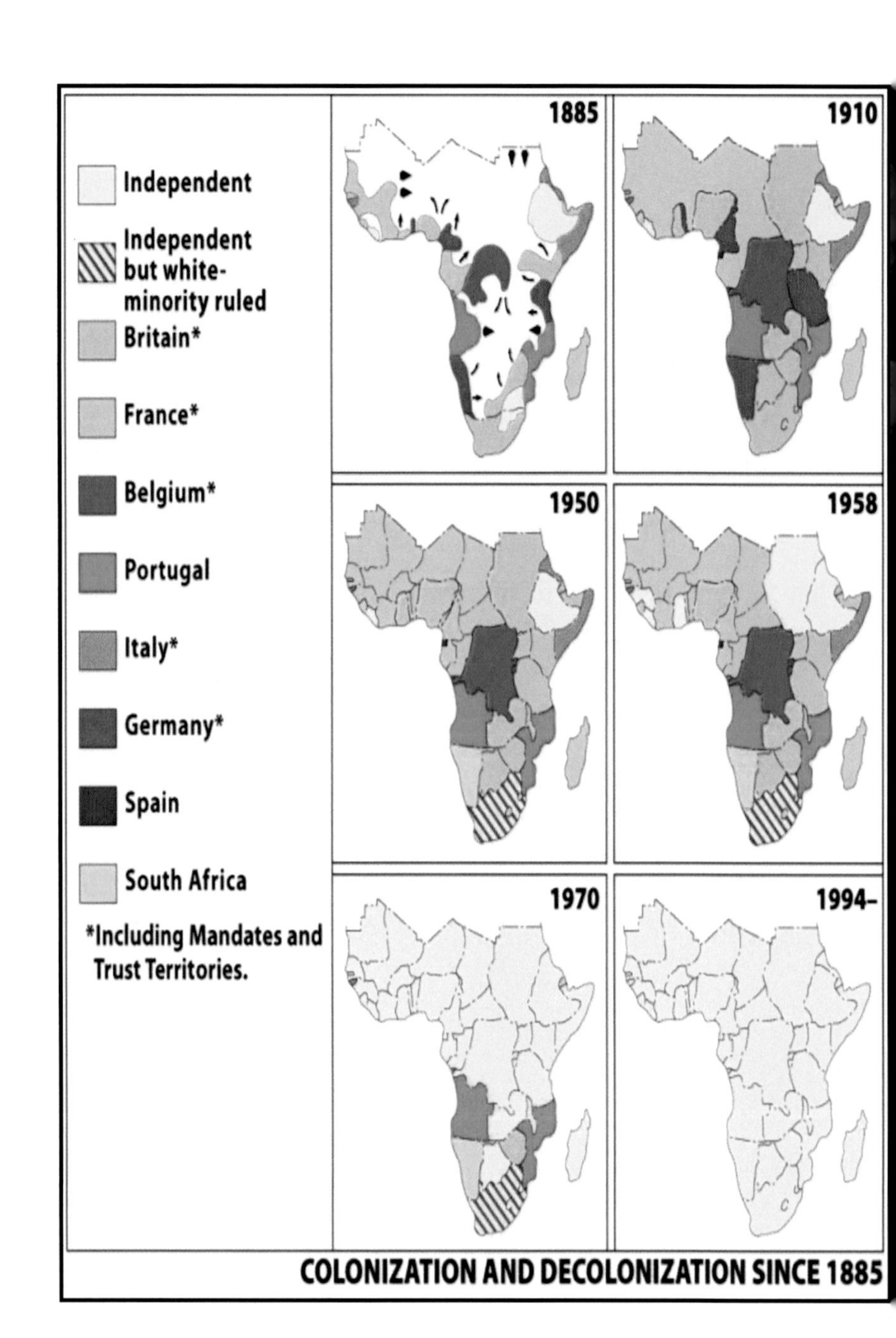

1885
1910
1950
1958
1970
1994–
Independent
Independent but white-minority ruled
Britain*
France*
Belgium*
Portugal
Italy*
Germany*
Spain
South Africa
*Including Mandates and Trust Territories.
COLONIZATION AND DECOLONIZATION SINCE 1885

Colonial Policies

<u>Portugal</u>: "Exploitation" (Guinea-Bissau, Angola, Mozambique)

- First to enslave and colonize and one of the last to grant independence
- Maintained rigid control; raw resource oriented

<u>Belgium</u>: "Paternalistic" (Rwanda, Zaire, Burundi)

- Treated Africans as though they where children who needed to be tutored in western ways; did not try to make them Belgium
- Raw resource oriented; ignored the development of natives

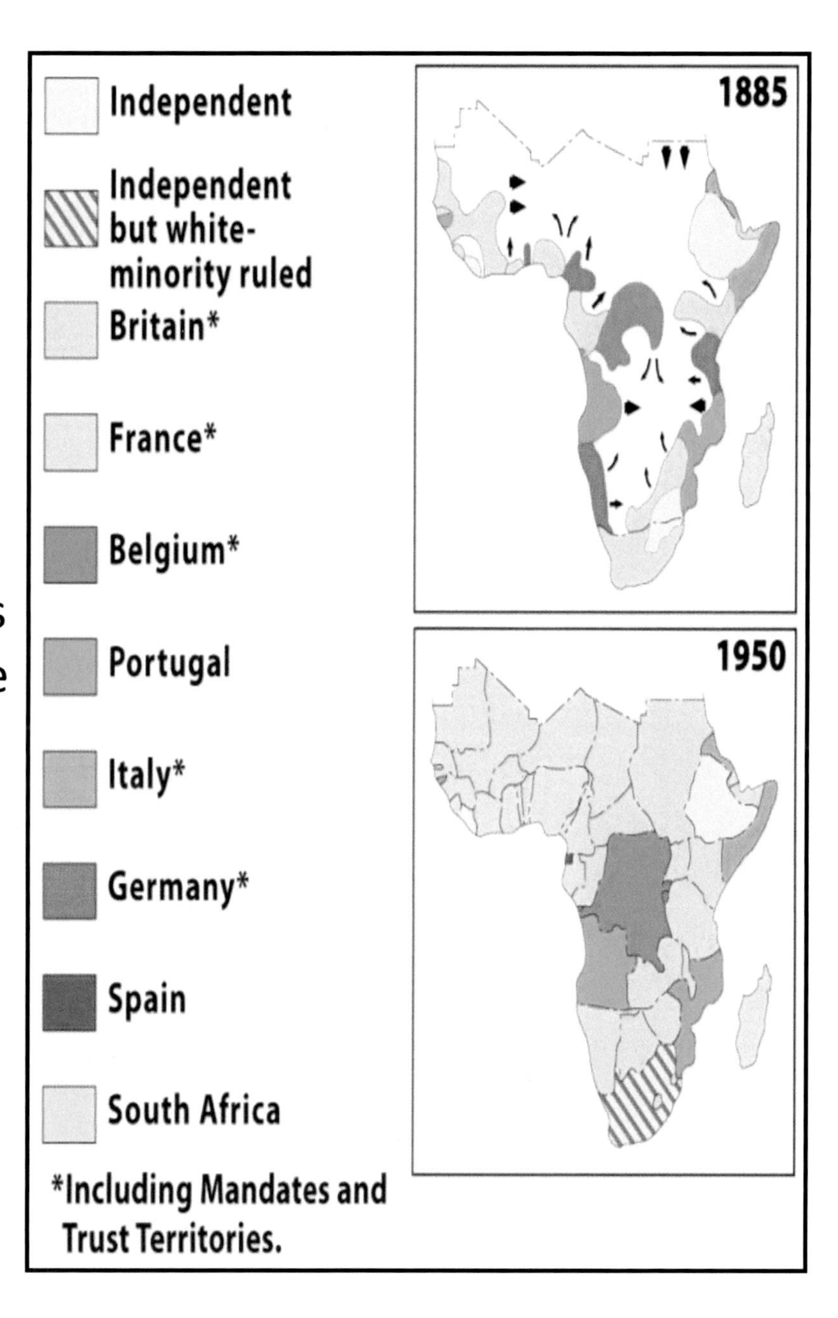

Independent
Independent but white-minority ruled
Britain*
France*
Belgium*
Portugal
Italy*
Germany*
Spain
South Africa
*Including Mandates and Trust Territories.
1885
1950

The Colonial Imprint

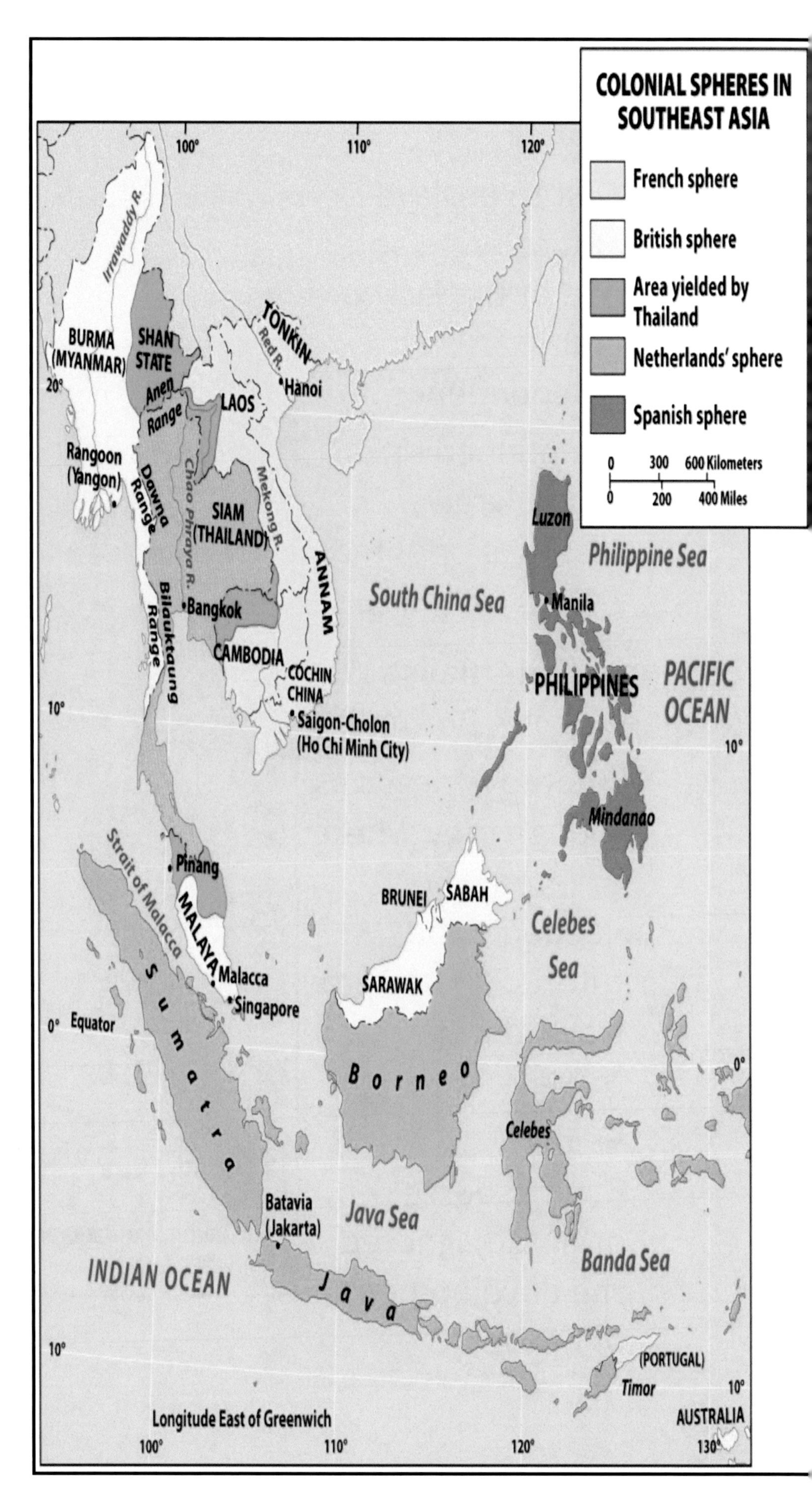

COLONIAL SPHERES IN SOUTHEAST ASIA
French sphere
British sphere
Area yielded by Thailand
Netherlands' sphere
Spanish sphere
0 300 600 Kilometers
0 200 400 Miles
100°
110°
120°
Irrawaddy R.
BURMA (MYANMAR)
SHAN STATE
Anen Range
TONKIN
Red R.
Hanoi
LAOS
Rangoon (Yangon)
Dawna Range
Chao Phraya R.
Mekong R.
SIAM (THAILAND)
ANNAM
Bilauktaung Range
Bangkok
CAMBODIA
COCHIN CHINA
Saigon-Cholon (Ho Chi Minh City)
South China Sea
Luzon
Philippine Sea
Manila
PHILIPPINES
PACIFIC OCEAN
Mindanao
Strait of Malacca
Pinang
MALAYA
Malacca
Singapore
BRUNEI
SABAH
SARAWAK
Celebes Sea
Equator
Sumatra
Borneo
Celebes
Batavia (Jakarta)
Java Sea
INDIAN OCEAN
Java
Banda Sea
(PORTUGAL)
Timor
AUSTRALIA
Longitude East of Greenwich
20°
10°
0°
130°

Aboriginal Claims

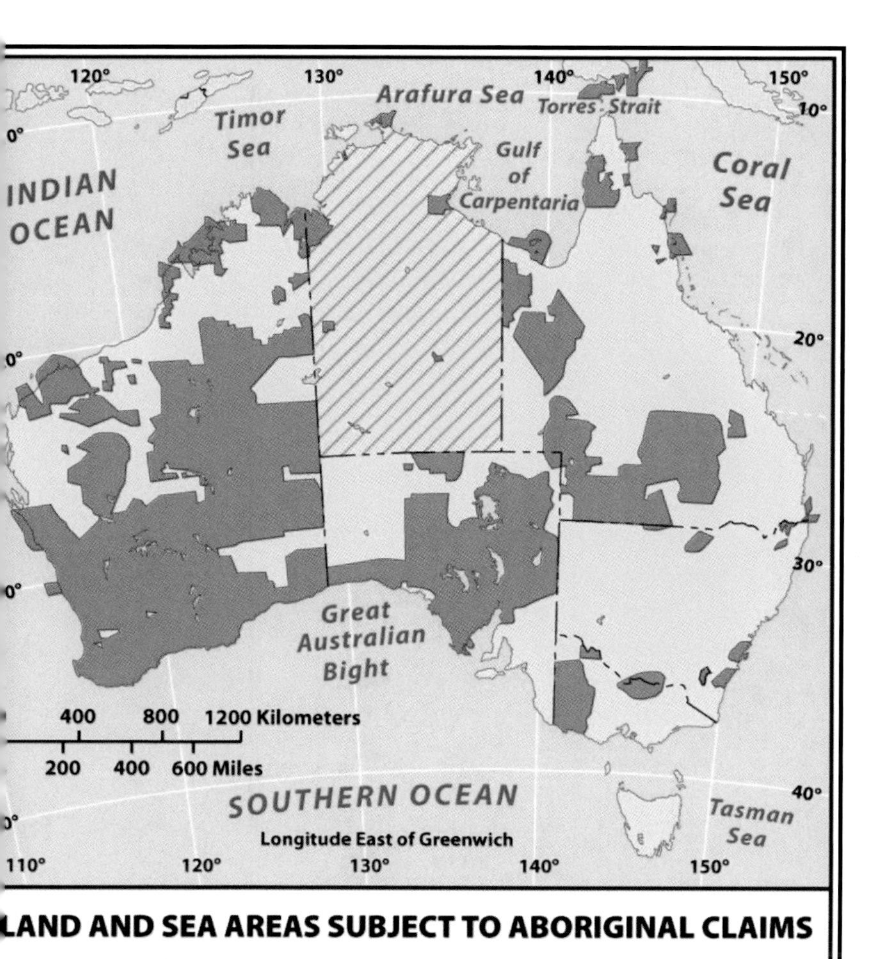

Arafura Sea
Torres Strait
Timor Sea
Gulf of Carpentaria
Coral Sea
INDIAN OCEAN
Great Australian Bight
400 800 1200 Kilometers
200 400 600 Miles
SOUTHERN OCEAN
Tasman Sea
Longitude East of Greenwich
110° 120° 130° 140° 150°
10° 20° 30° 40°
LAND AND SEA AREAS SUBJECT TO ABORIGINAL CLAIMS
Aboriginal claims
Other land
Northern Territory already Aboriginal land

Australia's **indigenous** population dates from **50,00-60,000 years ago**; very different way of life

British colonists assumed Australia was 'empty'

Independent states in Africa

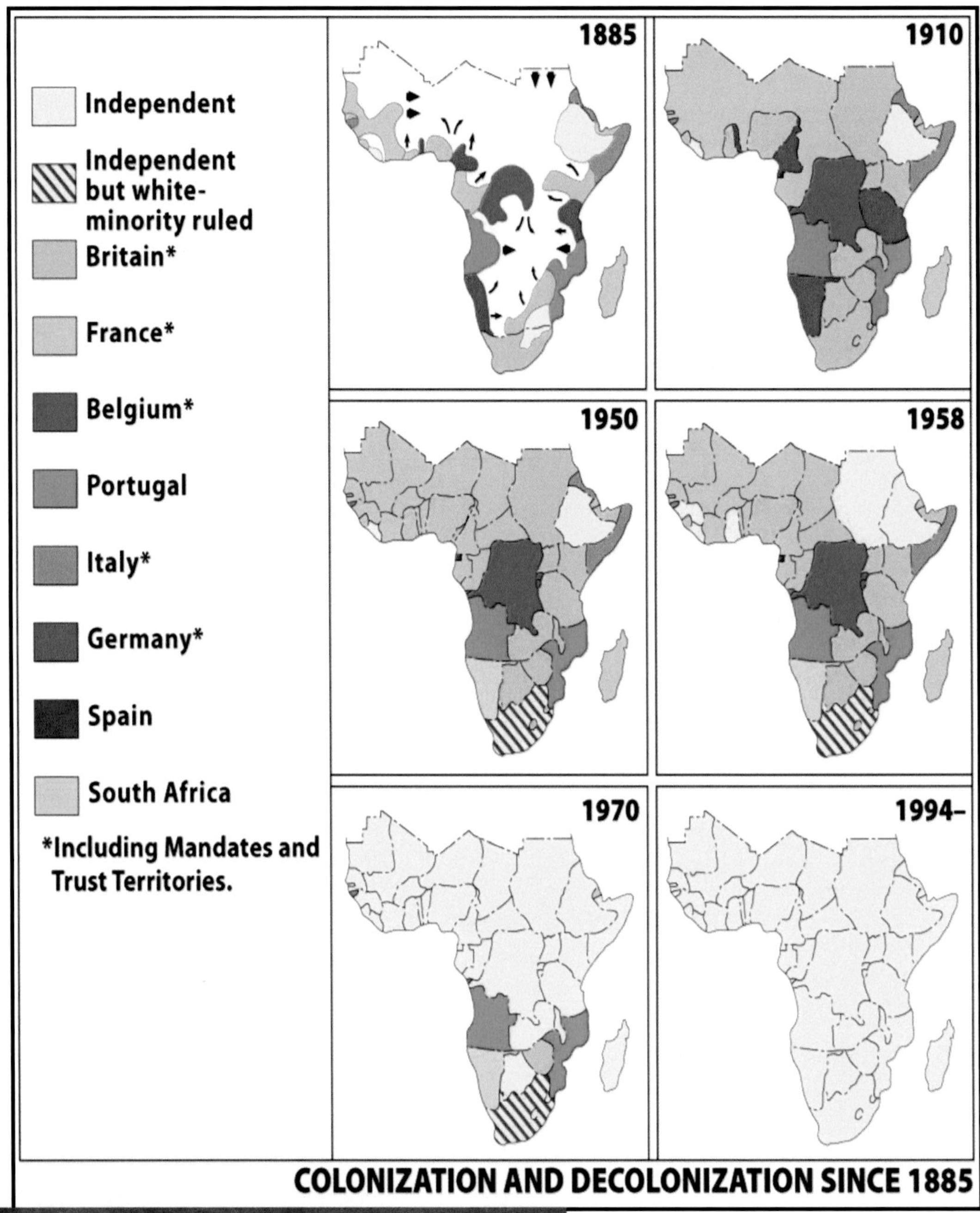
1885
1910
1950
1958
1970
1994–
Independent
Independent but white-minority ruled
Britain*
France*
Belgium*
Portugal
Italy*
Germany*
Spain
South Africa
*Including Mandates and Trust Territories.
COLONIZATION AND DECOLONIZATION SINCE 1885

LEERDAM

The six historical flags of South Africa at the Castle of Good Hope; the prince's flag, Great Britain, Batavian, UK, the old South African flag and the current South African flag.
– Tyrell Heaton

The Legacy

- Several hundred languages are spoken
- Antagonism between tribes (e.g., Rwanda)
- Low level of development is linked to colonization
  - **Transportation facilities** - Movement of goods is from the interior to coastal outlets.
  - **Communication** within Africa is impeded by desert, dense forest, and lack of navigable rivers in certain regions.
  - **Dual economy** remains intact; most states rely on a single crop or mineral and are vulnerable to world markets.

The Legacy of Colonialism

- Land was **appropriated** - colonial commercial interests
- Lands devoted to food crops for local consumption were **converted** to **cash cropping** for **export**
- **Land alienation** induced:
  - Famine
  - Poverty
  - Migration
  - Decreasing agricultural diversity

Human migration due to conflict

Refugees fleeing the violence in Syria arrive on the craggy shore of Lesbos, Turkey. More than 2,500 people died the year this photo was taken on over crowded flimsy rubber dinghies and rickety fishing boats.

Migrants fleeing the violence in Honduras just across the border into Guatemala.

A record 68.5 million people forcibly displaced last year. Record high numbers of men, women and children were driven from their homes across the world last year due to war, violence and persecution, according to a new report by the United Nations' refugee agency (2018). Countries such as Syria, Myanmar, the Democratic Republic of Congo and Sudan are where some of the worst violence is occurring.

Migration to North America

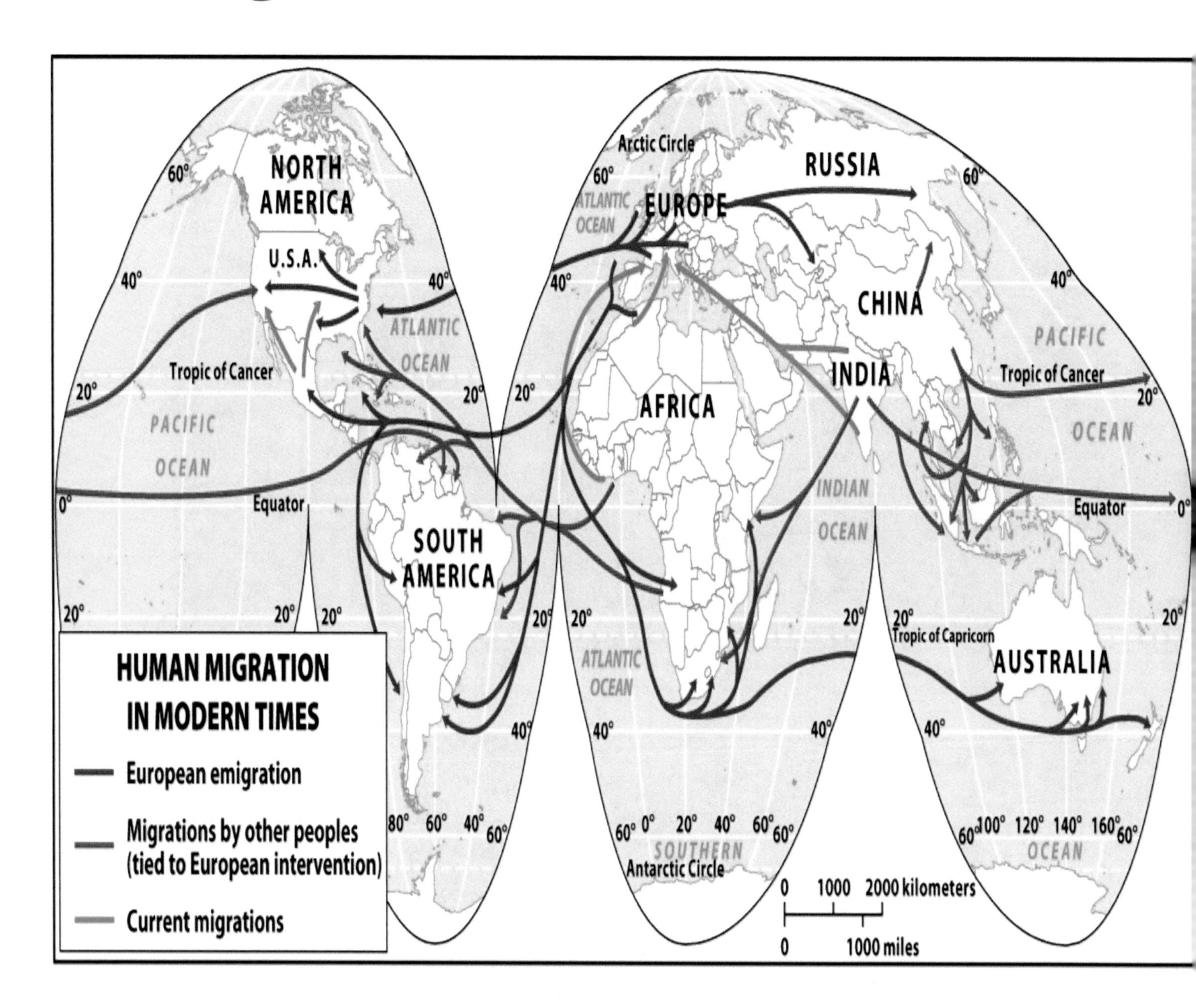
NORTH AMERICA
U.S.A.
SOUTH AMERICA
EUROPE
RUSSIA
CHINA
INDIA
AFRICA
AUSTRALIA
ATLANTIC OCEAN
PACIFIC OCEAN
INDIAN OCEAN
SOUTHERN OCEAN
Arctic Circle
Tropic of Cancer
Equator
Tropic of Capricorn
Antarctic Circle
HUMAN MIGRATION IN MODERN TIMES
European emigration
Migrations by other peoples (tied to European intervention)
Current migrations
0 1000 2000 kilometers
0 1000 miles

A realm of **immigrants**

Push factors: famine, war / conflict, religious persecution, etc.

Pull factors: security, economic opportunity, etc.

Long-term **Chinese immigrants** form a significant part of the cultural landscape of SE Asia

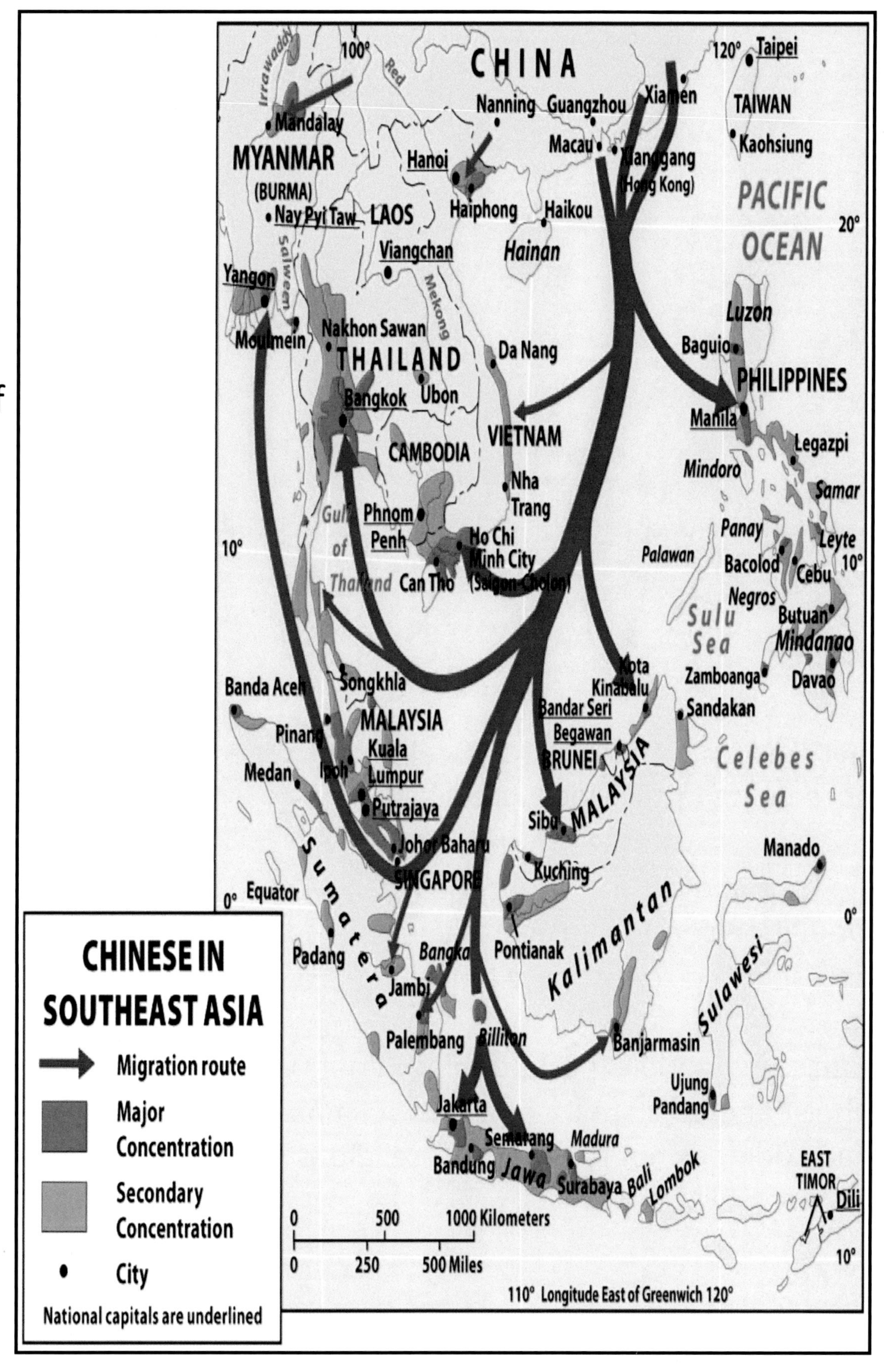
CHINESE IN SOUTHEAST ASIA
Migration route
Major Concentration
Secondary Concentration
City
National capitals are underlined
CHINA
MYANMAR (BURMA)
LAOS
THAILAND
CAMBODIA
VIETNAM
MALAYSIA
BRUNEI
PHILIPPINES
TAIWAN
SINGAPORE
EAST TIMOR
PACIFIC OCEAN
Sulu Sea
Celebes Sea
Gulf of Thailand
Mandalay
Nay Pyi Taw
Yangon
Moulmein
Hanoi
Haiphong
Nanning
Guangzhou
Xiamen
Macau
Xianggang (Hong Kong)
Taipei
Kaohsiung
Haikou
Hainan
Viangchan
Nakhon Sawan
Bangkok
Ubon
Da Nang
Nha Trang
Phnom Penh
Ho Chi Minh City (Saigon-Cholon)
Can Tho
Luzon
Baguio
Manila
Mindoro
Legazpi
Samar
Leyte
Panay
Palawan
Bacolod
Cebu
Negros
Butuan
Mindanao
Zamboanga
Davao
Sandakan
Kota Kinabalu
Bandar Seri Begawan
Banda Aceh
Songkhla
Pinang
Medan
Ipoh
Kuala Lumpur
Putrajaya
Johor Baharu
Sibu
Kuching
Pontianak
Kalimantan
Sumatera
Padang
Bangka
Jambi
Palembang
Billiton
Banjarmasin
Sulawesi
Manado
Ujung Pandang
Jakarta
Semarang
Madura
Bandung
Jawa
Surabaya
Bali
Lombok
Dili
Irrawaddy
Salween
Mekong
Red
Equator
0 500 1000 Kilometers
0 250 500 Miles
110° Longitude East of Greenwich 120°

Religions around the world

gp
United States
Christian 78.5%
(51% Protestant)
Mexico
Brazil
Roman Catholic
64.6%
Kazakhstan
Muslim 70.2%
Mongolia
Buddhist 53%
Iran
Algeria
Libya
Egypt
Saudi Arabia
Sudan
Chad
Muslim
53.1%
Mali
Niger
Nigeria
India
Hindu
Indonesia
Muslim 87.2%
Malaysia
Democratic Republic of the Congo
Colombia
Venezuela
Peru
Bolivia
Chile
Argentina
50-75% 75-90% > 90%
: Christianity
: Islam
: Buddhism
: Hinduism
: Judaism
Source: CIA Factbook
Simran Khosla / Global Post

There are an estimated 4,200 religions in the world today with roughly 12 of those being most widely practiced.

The map above shows countries in the world where more than half the population considers themselves religiously affiliated. The darker shades represent the countries with the highest percentages of religious citizens.

Notice the world's most populous country, China, is blank. In China, 47% are Atheist and 30% are listed as not religious. An Atheist believes affirmatively that God does not exist. A non-religious person has no opinion on whether there is a God or not.

Religious Contrasts

- **ISLAM**
  - Monotheistic
  - No idols
  - One sacred book (Koran)
  - Uniform dogma - 5 pillars
  - Intolerant (of other religions)
  - Eat beef/Sacrifice cows
  - Bury Dead
  - Social Equality (in theory)
  - Theocratic society
- **HINDUISM**
  - Polytheistic
  - Many idols
  - Various sacred writings
  - Varying beliefs
  - Absorbed other religions
  - Venerate cows
  - Burn dead
  - Caste system
  - 'State' of secondary importance

Languages around the world

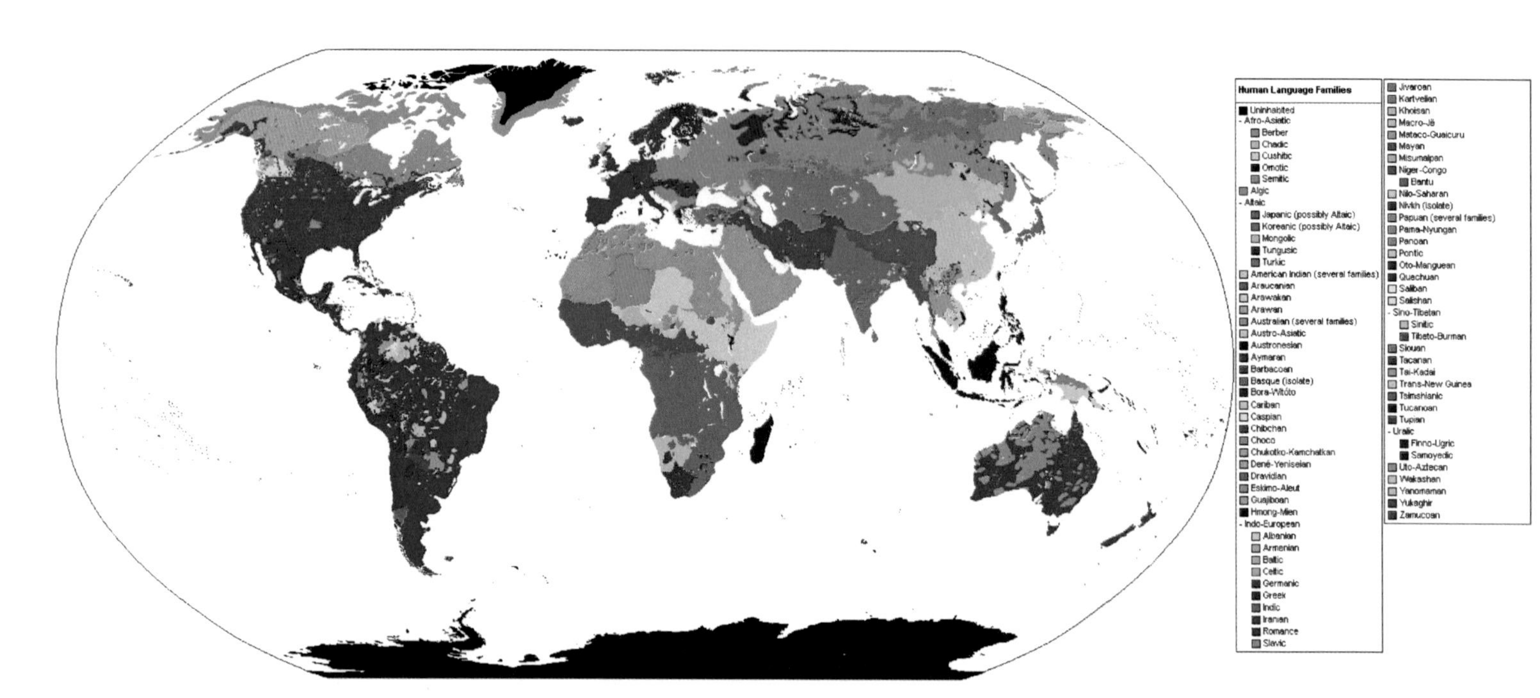
Human Language Families
Uninhabited
- Afro-Asiatic
Berber
Chadic
Cushitic
Omotic
Semitic
Algic
- Altaic
Japanic (possibly Altaic)
Koreanic (possibly Altaic)
Mongolic
Tungusic
Turkic
American Indian (several families)
Araucanian
Arawakan
Arawan
Australian (several families)
Austro-Asiatic
Austronesian
Aymaran
Barbacoan
Basque (isolate)
Bora-Witóto
Cariban
Caspian
Chibchan
Choco
Chukotko-Kamchatkan
Dené-Yeniseian
Dravidian
Eskimo-Aleut
Guajiboan
Hmong-Mien
- Indo-European
Albanian
Armenian
Baltic
Celtic
Germanic
Greek
Indic
Iranian
Romance
Slavic
Jivaroan
Kartvelian
Khoisan
Macro-Jë
Mataco-Guaicuru
Mayan
Misumalpan
Niger-Congo
Bantu
Nilo-Saharan
Nivkh (isolate)
Papuan (several families)
Pama-Nyungan
Panoan
Pontic
Oto-Manguean
Quechuan
Saliban
Salishan
- Sino-Tibetan
Sinitic
Tibeto-Burman
Siouan
Tacanan
Tai-Kadai
Trans-New Guinea
Tsimshianic
Tucanoan
Tupian
- Uralic
Finno-Ugric
Samoyedic
Uto-Aztecan
Wakashan
Yanomaman
Yukaghir
Zamucoan

There are roughly 6,500 spoken languages in the world today. However, about 2,000 of those languages have fewer than 1,000 speakers. The most popular language in the world is Mandarin Chinese.

Most Spoken Languages in the World:

Mandarin Chinese (1.1 billion speakers)
English (983 million speakers)
Hindustani (544 million speakers)
Spanish (527 million speakers)
Arabic (422 million speakers)
Malay (281 million speakers)
Russian (267 million speakers)
Bengali (261 million speakers)
Portuguese (229 million speakers)
French (229 million speakers)

Medical Geography

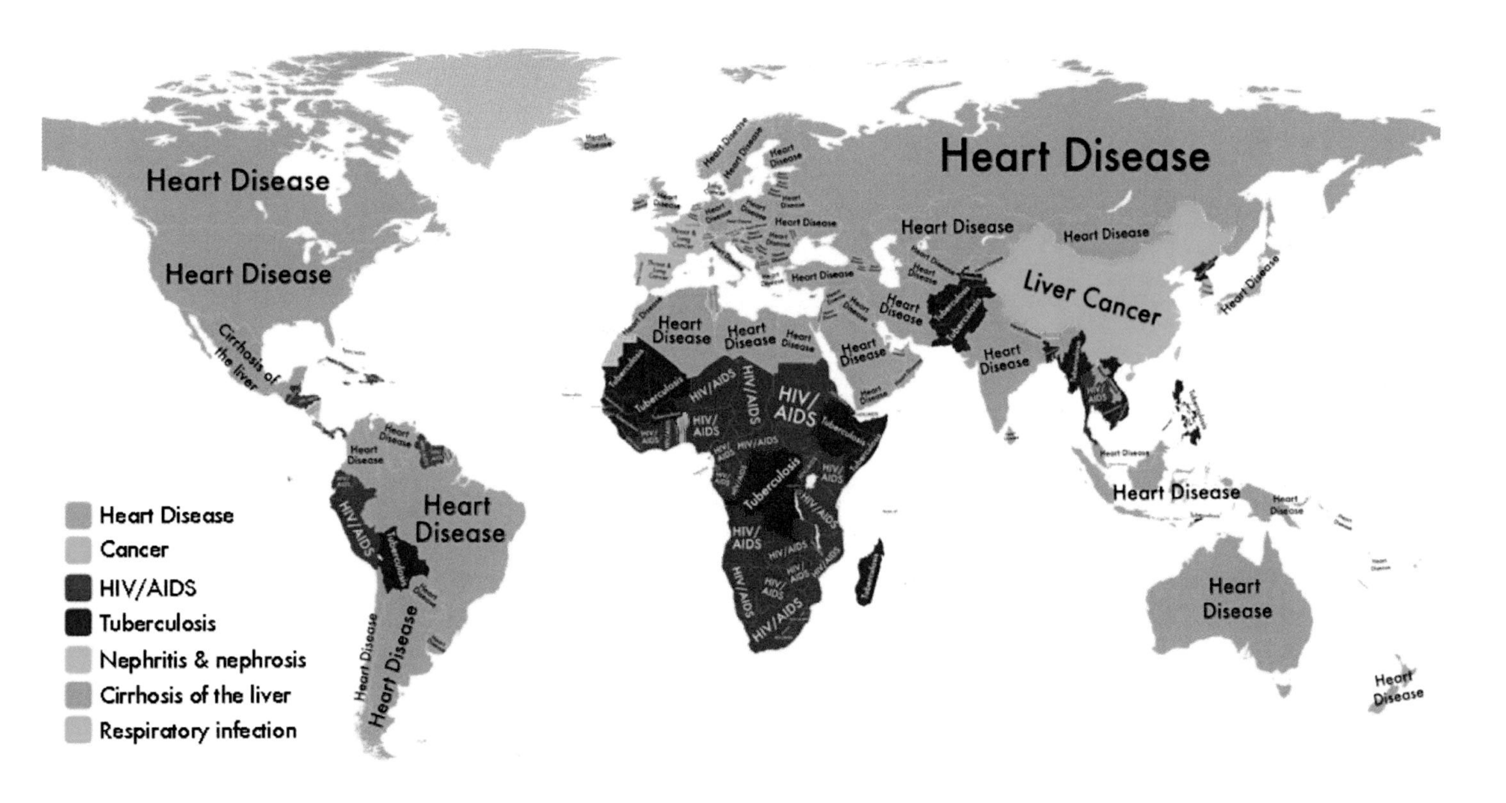

Heart Disease
Heart Disease
Heart Disease
Heart Disease
Heart Disease
Liver Cancer
Cirrhosis of the liver
Heart Disease
Heart Disease
HIV/AIDS
Tuberculosis
Heart Disease
Heart Disease
Heart Disease
Heart Disease
Heart Disease
Heart Disease
Heart Disease
HIV/AIDS
Heart Disease
Cancer
HIV/AIDS
Tuberculosis
Nephritis & nephrosis
Cirrhosis of the liver
Respiratory infection

- Medical Geography studies spatial aspects of disease and health
- Africa is an extraordinary laboratory
  - Disease incidence and diffusion
  - Widespread nutritional deficiencies
- Where most of the world suffers from Heart Disease, in Africa millions suffer from:
  - **Malaria**
  - **River Blindness**
  - **Yellow Fever**
  - **Sleeping Sickness**
  - **AIDS**
  - **Bilharzia**
  - **Tuberculosis**

Medical Geography

- **Endemic**
  - Exists in equilibrium with the population
  - Many develop an immunity of sorts
  - Saps energy, lowers resistance, shortens lives
- **Epidemic**
  - Sudden outbreak at local, regional scale
- **Pandemic**
  - Worldwide spread

Spread of Disease

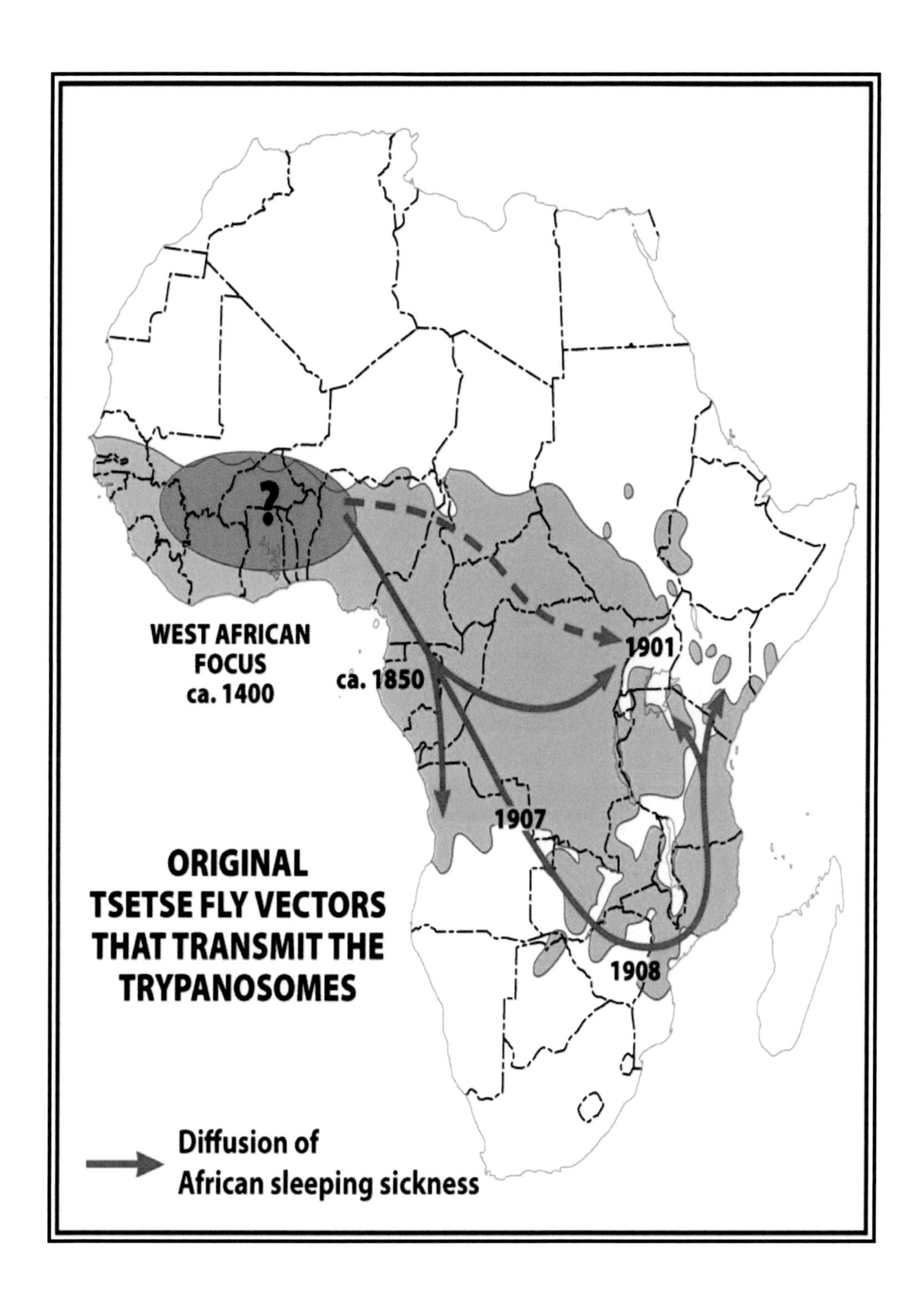
?
WEST AFRICAN
FOCUS
ca. 1400
ca. 1850
1901
1907
1908
ORIGINAL
TSETSE FLY VECTORS
THAT TRANSMIT THE
TRYPANOSOMES
Diffusion of
African sleeping sickness

A Global View of HIV infection

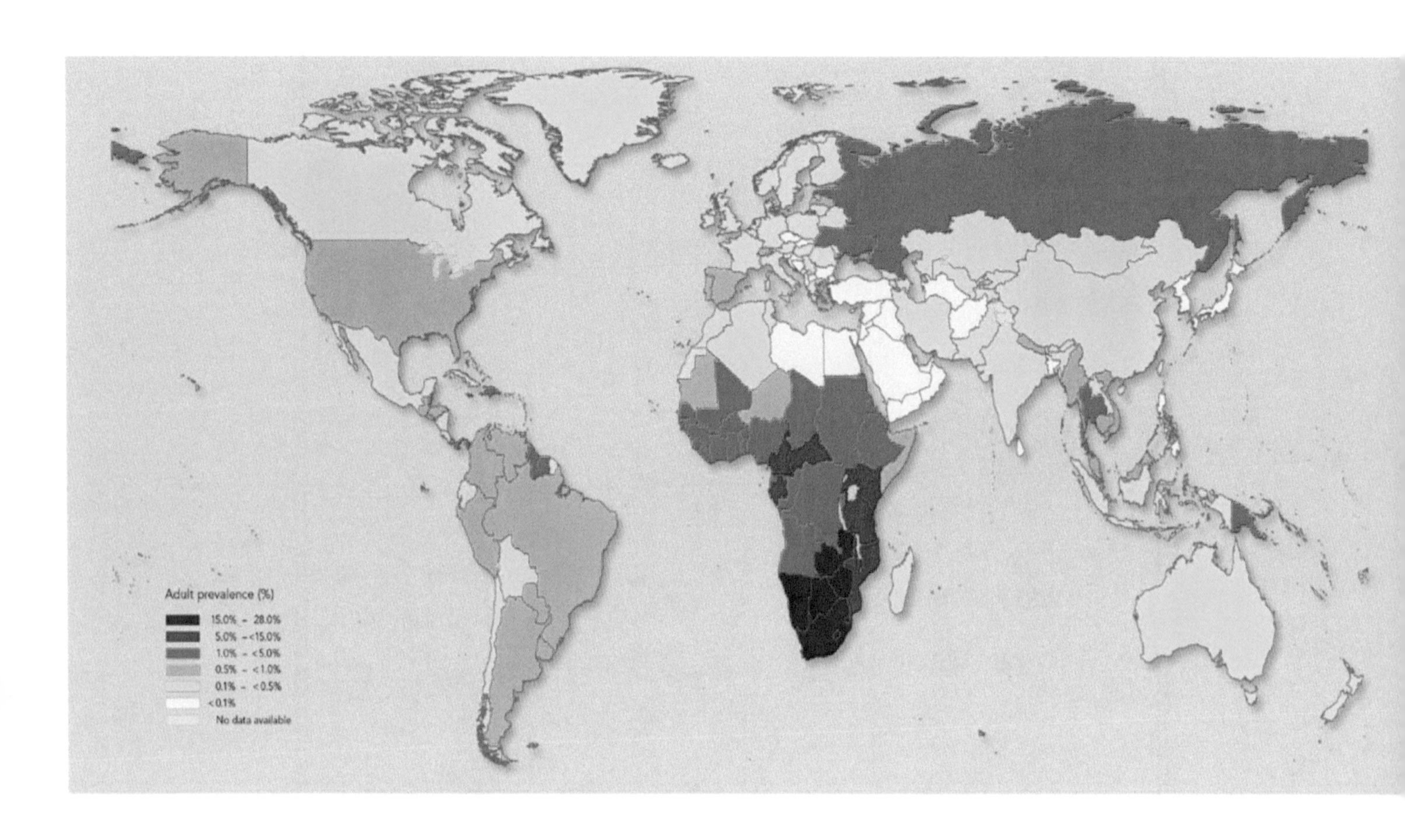
Adult prevalence (%)
15.0% - 28.0%
5.0% -<15.0%
1.0% - <5.0%
0.5% - <1.0%
0.1% - <0.5%
<0.1%
No data available

What can be done about AIDS ?

- **Awareness** and acceptance of the problem
- Political **will**
- Lowering of **cost of drugs**
- Success in lower rates in Uganda and Kenya

"STOP, THINK AND THINK AGAIN"
THINK CONDOMS
REMEMBER THE SIMPLE ACT OF PUTTING ON A CONDOM CAN SAVE YOUR LIFE AND THAT OF MANY PEOPLE.
TRUST NO ONE, USE A CONDOM EVERY TIME YOU HAVE SEX
HERE
"STOP, THINK AND THINK AGAIN"
THINK CONDOMS
REMEMBER THE SIMPLE ACT OF PUTTING ON A CONDOM CAN SAVE YOUR LIFE AND THAT OF MANY PEOPLE.
TRUST NO ONE, USE A CONDOM EVERY TIME YOU HAVE SEX
HERE

Tyrell Heaton - Free Condoms at the border crossing of Swaziland and South Africa

The Next World Power

The United States of America is commonly held by some as the current world power; however, as history has proven, one country's reign will expire with a rising nation waiting in the wings to take over. Will history repeat itself? Who will be the next world power?

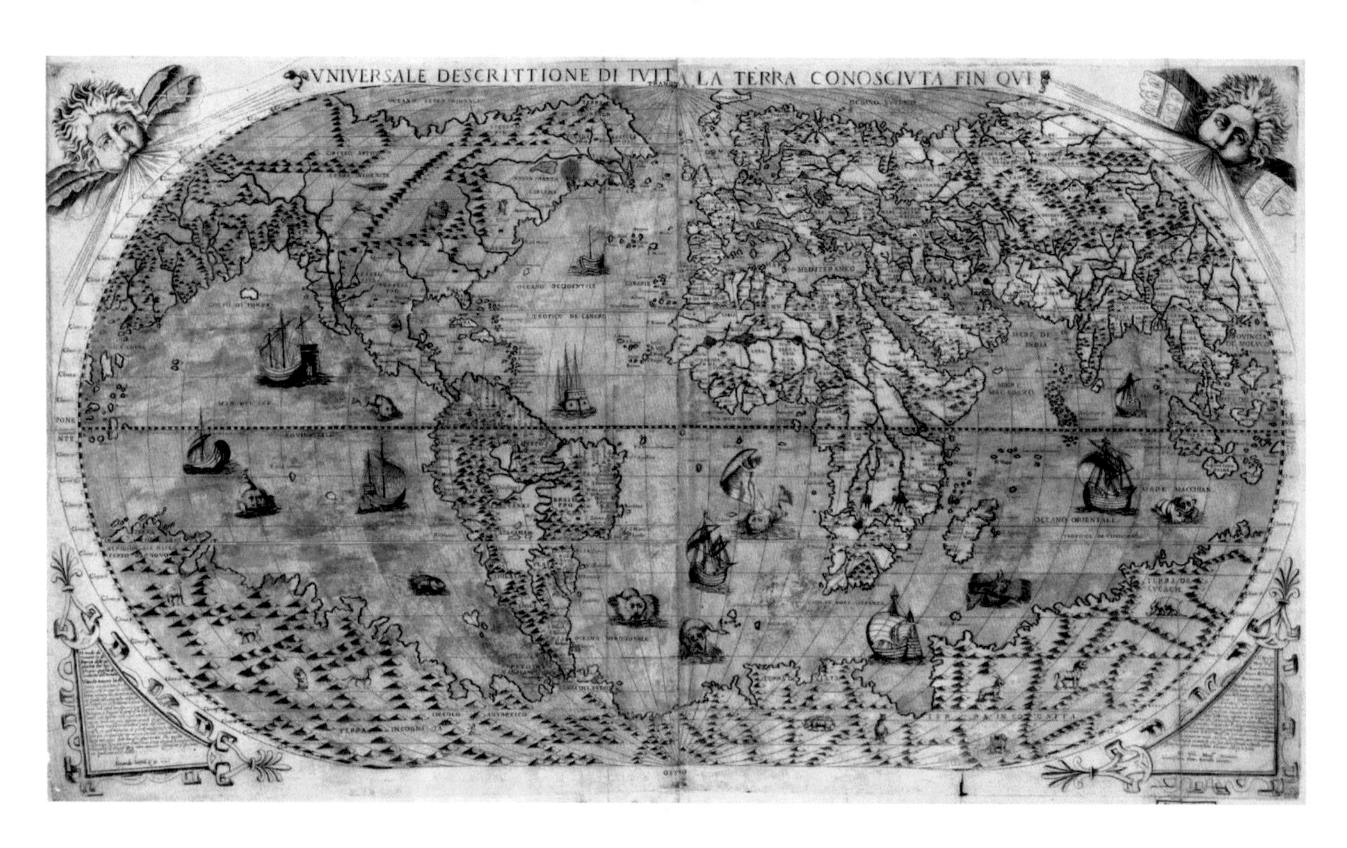
VNIVERSALE DESCRITTIONE DI TVTTA LA TERRA CONOSCIVTA FIN QVI

WESTWARD DRIFT OF WESTERN CIVILIZATION

Civilization	Time Frame	Span	Source of Power
Mesopotamia (Harness/wheel)	10,000 BC – 1,000 BC	(9000)	Agriculture, Animal Power
Greece	1,000 BC – 146 BC	(850)	Thinkers /Philosophers
Italy (Romans)	31 BC – 476 AD	(500)	Political Organizers & Military Strategists
Iberia (Portugal-Spain)	1492-17	(250)	Exploration & Exploitation
Britain	1750-1900	(150)	Industrialization & Colonization
United States	1900-????	(100+)	Abundant Natural Resources & Land

Early Man
IDEA: Ability to "use" the environment
POWERS: Those who possessed "power traits"
DEFINITION OF POWER: ability to better feed populace, protect and expand living and resource base
ARCHTYPE: more successful hunters, fishers & gatherers; stone, fire, etc...
RESULTS: Population growth, environmental knowledge, economic provision

Agricultural Revolution
IDEA: Plant & Animal domestication
POWERS: Farmers & Herders
DEFINITION OF POWER: some domination over nature; increase in economic base
ARCHTYPE: Village farmers; pastoral nomads
RESULTS: Beginnings of "civilization," urbanization; territorial expansion & conquest

Classic Greece
IDEA: Philosophy/Cosmography
POWERS: Aegean Hearth
DEFINITION OF POWER: Science, technology, and philosophical inquiry
ARCHTYPE: Philosophers/Astronomers
RESULTS: Expansion of Knowledge

15th Century
IDEA: Exploration
POWERS: Portugal & Spain
DEFINITION OF POWER: Expansion of Territory
ARCHTYPE: Explorers
RESULTS: Dimensions of the world are better known

16th Century
IDEA: Colonization
POWERS: Portugal & Spain
DEFINITION OF POWER: Recreation of European culture elsewhere
ARCHTYPE: Colonizer
RESULTS: Whole world is brought into contact with Western ideas

17th Century
IDEA: Commercialization
POWERS: England & Holland
DEFINITION OF POWER: Trade = Wealth = Power
ARCHTYPE: Trader
RESULTS: Much of the world brought into one economic community

18th Century
IDEA: Militarization
POWERS: England & France
DEFINITION OF POWER: Military Strength
ARCHTYPE: Soldier
RESULTS: Whole world is brought into one military community

19th Century
IDEA: Imperialism
POWERS: England, France & Germany
DEFINITION OF POWER: Colonies to provide raw materials for industry
ARCHTYPE: Imperialist
RESULTS: Whole world is brought into one industrial community

20th Century
IDEA: Ideology
POWERS: USA, USSR, Germany & Japan
DEFINITION OF POWER: control of minds (Ideology)
ARCHTYPE: Ideologue
RESULTS: Whole world is subjected to ideological conflicts

21st Century
IDEA: ???
POWERS: ???
DEFINITION OF POWER: ???
ARCHTYPE: ???
RESULTS: ???

World Views on Gay Marriage

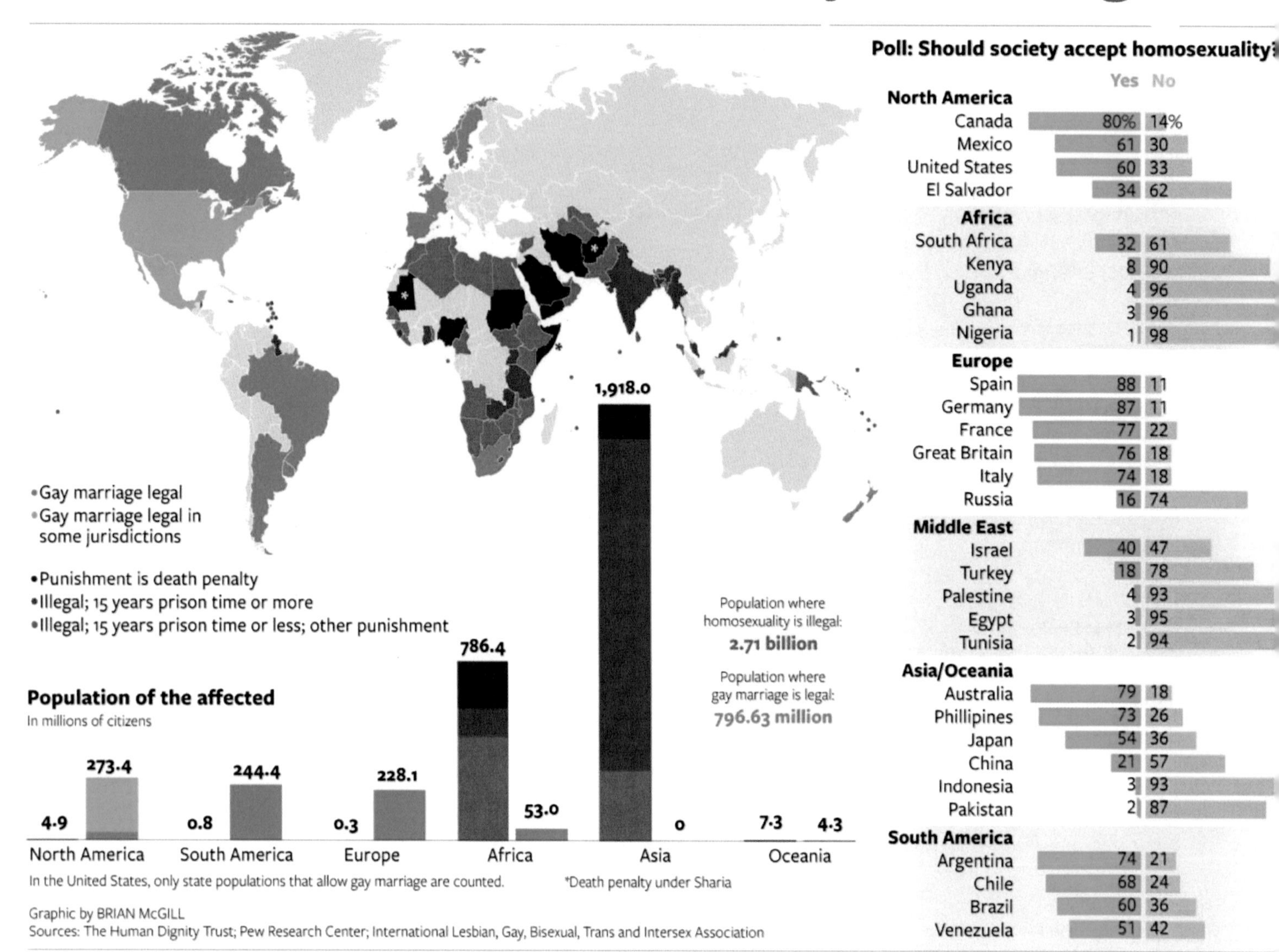
Poll: Should society accept homosexuality?
Yes No
North America
Canada 80% 14%
Mexico 61 30
United States 60 33
El Salvador 34 62
Africa
South Africa 32 61
Kenya 8 90
Uganda 4 96
Ghana 3 96
Nigeria 1 98
Europe
Spain 88 11
Germany 87 11
France 77 22
Great Britain 76 18
Italy 74 18
Russia 16 74
Middle East
Israel 40 47
Turkey 18 78
Palestine 4 93
Egypt 3 95
Tunisia 2 94
Asia/Oceania
Australia 79 18
Phillipines 73 26
Japan 54 36
China 21 57
Indonesia 3 93
Pakistan 2 87
South America
Argentina 74 21
Chile 68 24
Brazil 60 36
Venezuela 51 42
•Gay marriage legal
•Gay marriage legal in some jurisdictions
•Punishment is death penalty
•Illegal; 15 years prison time or more
•Illegal; 15 years prison time or less; other punishment
Population of the affected
In millions of citizens
4.9
273.4
0.8
244.4
0.3
228.1
786.4
53.0
1,918.0
0
7.3
4.3
North America
South America
Europe
Africa
Asia
Oceania
Population where homosexuality is illegal: 2.71 billion
Population where gay marriage is legal: 796.63 million
In the United States, only state populations that allow gay marriage are counted.
*Death penalty under Sharia
Graphic by BRIAN McGILL
Sources: The Human Dignity Trust; Pew Research Center; International Lesbian, Gay, Bisexual, Trans and Intersex Association

The wave of acceptance for same-sex couples that has washed through some Western countries has not reached all shores. Many countries still punish homosexual acts with prison time, torture and even death.

Africa and the Middle East are particularly strict with homosexuality

Country	Same-sex sexual activity
Benin	✓ Legal (No laws against same-sex sexual activity have ever existed in the country).[1][69] (Age of consent discrepancy)[1]
Burkina Faso	✓ Legal (No laws against same-sex sexual activity have ever existed in the country).[1]
Cape Verde	✓ Legal since 2004 + UN decl. sign.[1]
Gambia	✗ Illegal since 1888 (as Gambia Colony and Protectorate) Penalty: Up to life imprisonment.[1][70][44]
Ghana	✗ Male illegal since 1860s (as Gold Coast) Penalty: 10 years imprisonment or more ✓ Female always legal.[1][71][44]
Guinea	✗ Illegal since 1988 Penalty: 6 months to 3 years imprisonment.[1][72]
Guinea-Bissau	✓ Legal since 1993[1] + UN decl. sign.
Ivory Coast	✓ Legal (No laws against same-sex sexual activity have ever existed in the country). (Age of consent discrepancy)[1]
Liberia	✗ Illegal since 1976 Penalty: 1 year imprisonment.[1][73]
Mali	✓ Legal (No laws against same-sex sexual activity have ever existed in the country).[1]
Mauritania	☠ ✗ Illegal since 1983 Penalty: Death by stoning[1][74]
Niger	✓ Legal (No laws against same-sex sexual activity have ever existed in the country). (Age of consent discrepancy)[1]
Nigeria	✗ Illegal under federal law since 1901 (as Northern Nigeria Protectorate and Southern Nigeria Protectorate) Penalty: Up to 14 years imprisonment ☠ ✗ Illegal in the states of Bauchi, Borno, Gombe, Jigawa, Kaduna, Kano, Katsina, Kebbi, Niger, Sokoto, Yobe, and Zamfara Penalty: Death penalty for men. Whipping and/or imprisonment for women.[1][75][44]
Senegal	✗ Illegal since 1966 Penalty: 1 to 5 years imprisonment.[1][76]
Sierra Leone	✗ Male illegal since 1861 (as Sierra Leone Colony and Protectorate) Penalty: Up to life imprisonment (Not enforced) ✓ Female always legal + UN decl. sign.[1]

LGBT rights in:	Same-sex sexual activity
Algeria	✗ Illegal (Penalty: Fine - Up to 2 years prison)[37]
Spain (Canary Islands, Ceuta, Melilla)	✓ Legal since 1979 + UN decl. sign.
Egypt	✓ Not specifically outlawed
Libya	✗ Illegal (Penalty: Up to 5 years prison).[37]
Morocco (incl. Western Sahara)	✗ Illegal (Penalty: Up to 3 years)
South Sudan	✗ Illegal (Penalty: Up to 10 years.)
Sudan	✗ Illegal (Penalty: Corporal Punishment. Death penalty for men on third offense. Death penalty on fourth offense for women)
Tunisia	✗ Illegal (Penalty: Fine - 3 years)
Burundi	✗ Illegal since 2009 (Penalty: 3 months to 2 years imprisonment and/or fine) [40]
Djibouti	✓ Legal[37]
Eritrea	✗ Illegal (Penalty: Up to 3 years imprisonment) [37]
Ethiopia	✗ Illegal[37]
Kenya	✗ Male illegal (Penalty: up to 14 years imprisonment) ✗ Female presumed to be illegal.
Rwanda	✓ Legal[37] + UN decl. sign.
Somalia	✗ Illegal[37]
Uganda	✗ Male Illegal (Penalty: Up to life imprisonment) ✗ Female Illegal since 2000. (Penalty: Up to 7 years imprisonment)
Tanzania	✗ Illegal (Penalty: Up to life imprisonment)[37]

LGBT rights in:	Same-sex sexual activity
Angola	✗ Illegal[37]
Botswana	✗ Illegal (Penalty: Fine - 7 years, Though never enforced)
Lesotho	✗ Male illegal ✓ Female legal[37]
Malawi	✗ Illegal (Penalty: Up to 14 years imprisonment and/or whippings)
Mozambique	✓ Legal[45]
Namibia	✗ Illegal (not enforced)[37][46]
South Africa	✓ Male legal since 1998 (retroactive to 1994) Female always legal + UN decl. sign.
Swaziland	✗ Male illegal ✓ Female legal Pending law includes outlawing lesbian sex conduct.[37]
Zambia	✗ Illegal (Penalty: up to 14 years imprisonment)
Zimbabwe	✗ Male illegal ✓ Female legal[37]

LGBT rights in:	Same-sex sexual activity
Cameroon	✗ Illegal (Penalty: Fine to 5 years prison)
Central African Republic	✓ Legal[37] + UN decl. sign.
Chad	✓ Legal since 1967
Democratic Republic of the Congo (formerly Zaire)	✓ Legal[37]
Equatorial Guinea	✓ Legal[37]
Gabon	✓ Legal[37] + UN decl. sign.
Republic of the Congo	✓ Legal[37]
Saint Helena, Ascension and Tristan da Cunha (Overseas territory of the UK)	✓ Legal[37]
São Tomé and Príncipe	✓ Since 2012 + UN decl. sign.[39]

Gender inequality across the globe

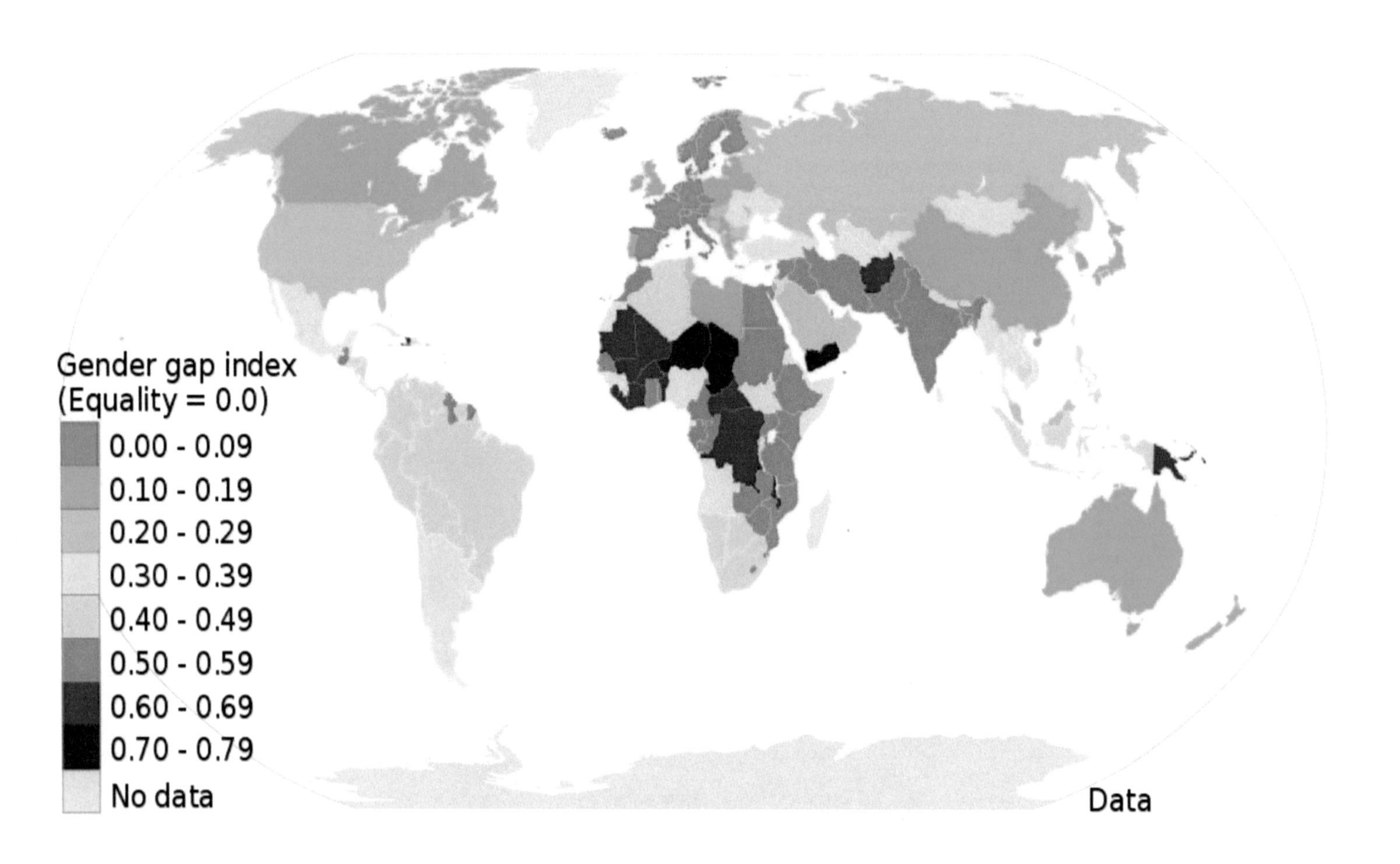
Gender gap index
(Equality = 0.0)
0.00 - 0.09
0.10 - 0.19
0.20 - 0.29
0.30 - 0.39
0.40 - 0.49
0.50 - 0.59
0.60 - 0.69
0.70 - 0.79
No data
Data

It ranges from 0, which indicates that women and men fare equally, to 1, which indicates that women fare as poorly as possible in all measured dimensions.

The unequal treatment of individuals based on their gender is a deeply rooted problem in most societies. While gender inequality remains a problem even in the more equal societies, it is a major barrier to human development in others, with the worst performing in the two highest quintiles of the data (having index values of 0.45 and above) covering a substantial part of the global population, most notably the African continent and the Indian subcontinent.

Gender Inequality Index

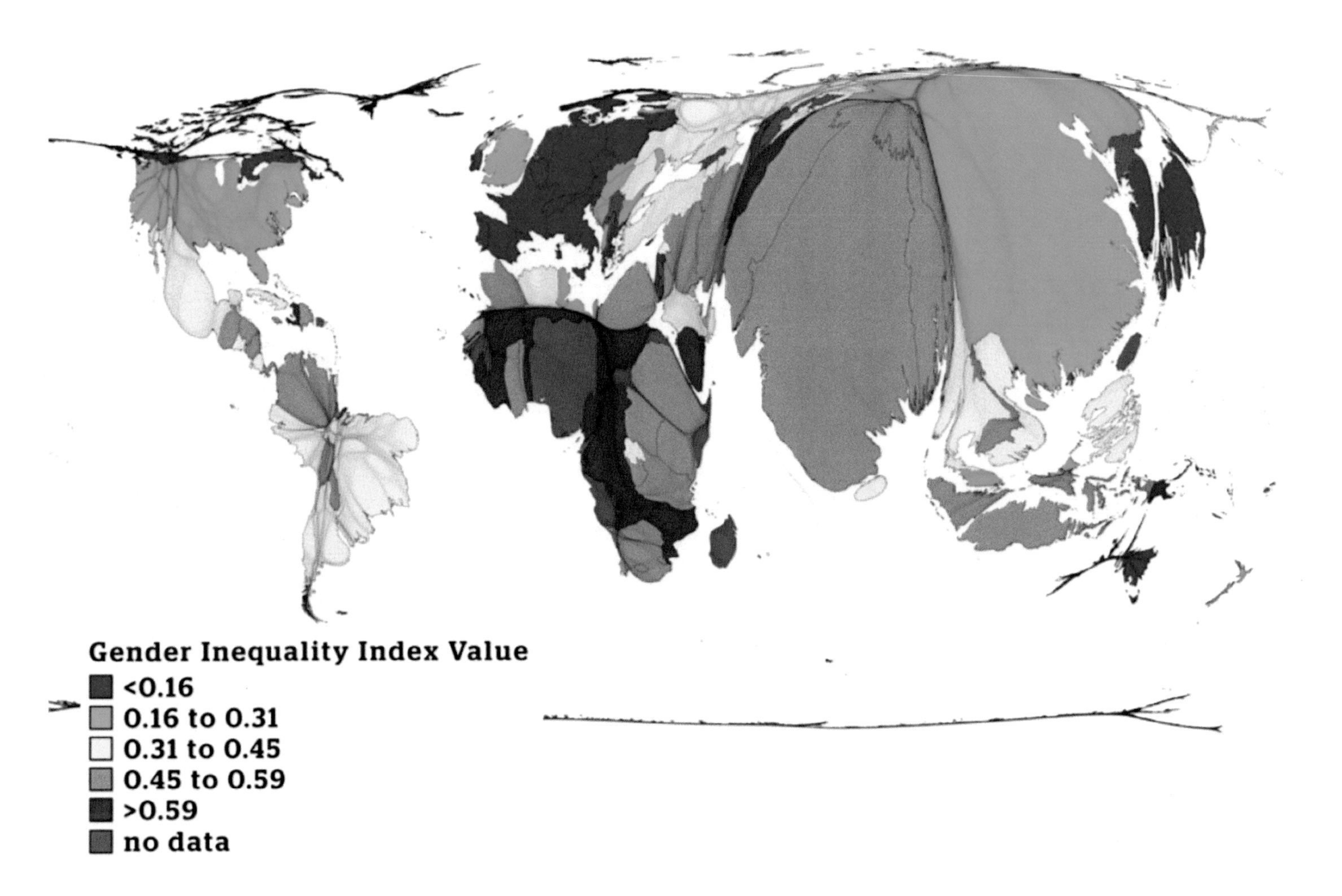

Gender Inequality Index Value
<0.16
0.16 to 0.31
0.31 to 0.45
0.45 to 0.59
>0.59
no data

The Gender Inequality Index (GII) reflects women's disadvantage in three dimensions—reproductive health, empowerment and the labor market—for as many countries as data of reasonable quality allow. The index shows the loss in human development due to inequality between female and male achievements in these dimensions.

The cartogram above shows this in its real human dimensions. The map is a gridded population cartogram in which every square of land is resized according to the total number of people living in that space. The transformed map therefore shows the gender inequality index on an equal population projection, emphasizing where and how many people live in the more equal or unequal societies. This highlights the high need for action combating gender gaps for a large share of the world's population in order to overcome systematic disadvantages of women.

Tourism: A Mixed Blessing?

- **Advantages**
  - State and regional economic options
  - A clean industry
  - Educational

Tyrell Heaton - Bay of Kotor, Montenegro

- **Disadvantages**
  - Disjunctive development
  - Degrades fragile environmental resources
  - Inauthentic representations of native cultures

Tyrell Heaton - Cruise ships pull into the Bay of Kotor and offload thousands of tourists into the small town. Tourism is a mixed blessing as it brings outside money to the area, yet the cruise ships are unsightly, loud, pollute, and the added tourists create congestion and more waste in the town. I drove to Kotor from Sofia, Bulgaria, roughly a 10-hour drive through Serbia, Kosovo and Albania to get to the coast of Montenegro only to be overrun by cruise-boat tourists.

Political Geography

Mexico City, Mexico– Tyrell Heaton

State, Nation and Nation-State

A State is an independent, sovereign government exercising control over a certain spatially defined and bounded area, whose borders are usually clearly defined and internationally recognized by other states.

A Nation is a group of people who see themselves as a cohesive and coherent unit based on shared cultural or historical criteria. Nations are socially constructed units, not given by nature. Their existence, definition, and members can change dramatically based on circumstances. Nations in some ways can be thought of as "imagined communities" that are bound together by notions of unity that can pivot around religion, ethnic identity, language, cultural practice and so forth. The concept and practice of a nation work to establish who belongs and who does not (insider vs. outsider). Such conceptions often ignore political boundaries such that a single nation may "spill over" into multiple states. Furthermore, states ≠ nations: not every nation has a state (e.g., Kurds; Roma; Palestine). Some states may contain all or parts of multiple nations.

A Nation-State is the idea of a homogenous nation governed by its own sovereign state—where each state contains one nation. This idea is almost never achieved.

Types of relationships between states and nations:

- **Nation-States** – Poland and Slovenia are examples of states occupied by a distinct nation, or people.
- **A Multinational State** –Switzerland shows that a common ethnicity, language, or religion is not necessary for a strong sense of nationalism.
- **A Part-Nation State –** The Arab nation extends across and dominates many states in northern Africa and the Middle East.
- **A Stateless Nation** – Kurds are concentrated in Turkey, Iran, and Iraq. Smaller numbers live in Syria, Armenia, and Azerbaijan.

Boundary Classifications

The national boundaries of a country are the different borders that outline its territory. ... They are usually the result of political decision or agreements between different countries. Geopolitics refer to the physical and human geographic influences on political and international relations.

Antecedent - a political boundary that existed before the cultural landscape emerged and stayed in a place while people moved into occupy the surroundings.

Boundary Classifications in SE Asia

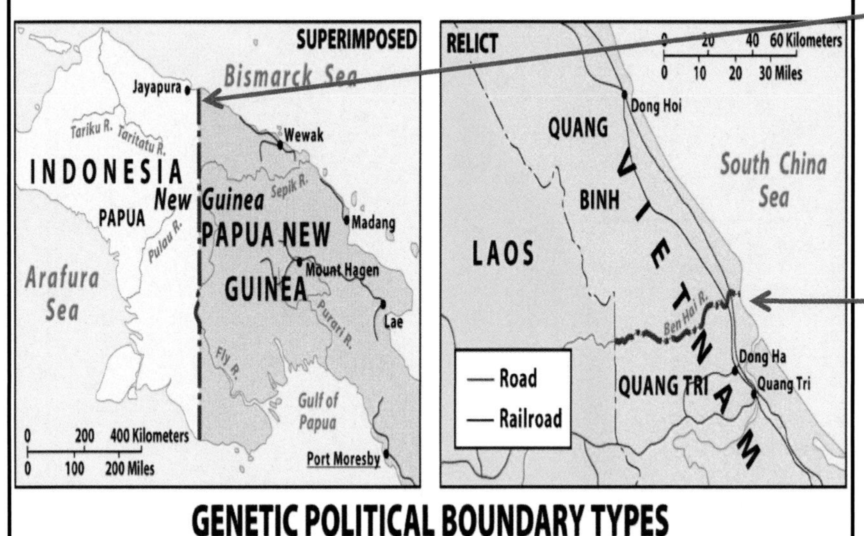
ANTECEDENT
0 200 400 Kilometers
0 100 200 Miles
Kota Kinabalu
PHILIPPINES
Bandar Seri Begawan
SABAH
South China Sea
BRUNEI
MALAYSIA
SARAWAK
Borneo
Celebes Sea
Kuching
INDONESIA
KALIMANTAN
Pontianak
Samarinda
SUBSEQUENT
Wenshan
CHINA
Hu Giang
Nanning
Lao Cai
Pingxiang
Lang Son
VIETNAM
Hanoi
Haiphong
LAOS
0 50 100 Kilometers
0 50 Miles
Nam Dinh
Gulf of Tonkin
SUPERIMPOSED
Jayapura
Bismarck Sea
Wewak
INDONESIA
New Guinea
PAPUA
PAPUA NEW GUINEA
Madang
Mount Hagen
Lae
Arafura Sea
Gulf of Papua
Port Moresby
0 200 400 Kilometers
0 100 200 Miles
RELICT
0 20 40 60 Kilometers
0 10 20 30 Miles
Dong Hoi
QUANG BINH
South China Sea
LAOS
VIETNAM
Dong Ha
Quang Tri
QUANG TRI
Road
Railroad
GENETIC POLITICAL BOUNDARY TYPES

Subsequent - is drawn after the cultural landscape has been developed.

Superimposed - is a boundary that has been imposed on an area by an outside or conquering power.

Relict - a former boundary, which may no longer be a legal boundary at all. However, the former presence of the boundary can still be seen in the landscape.

Territorial Morphology

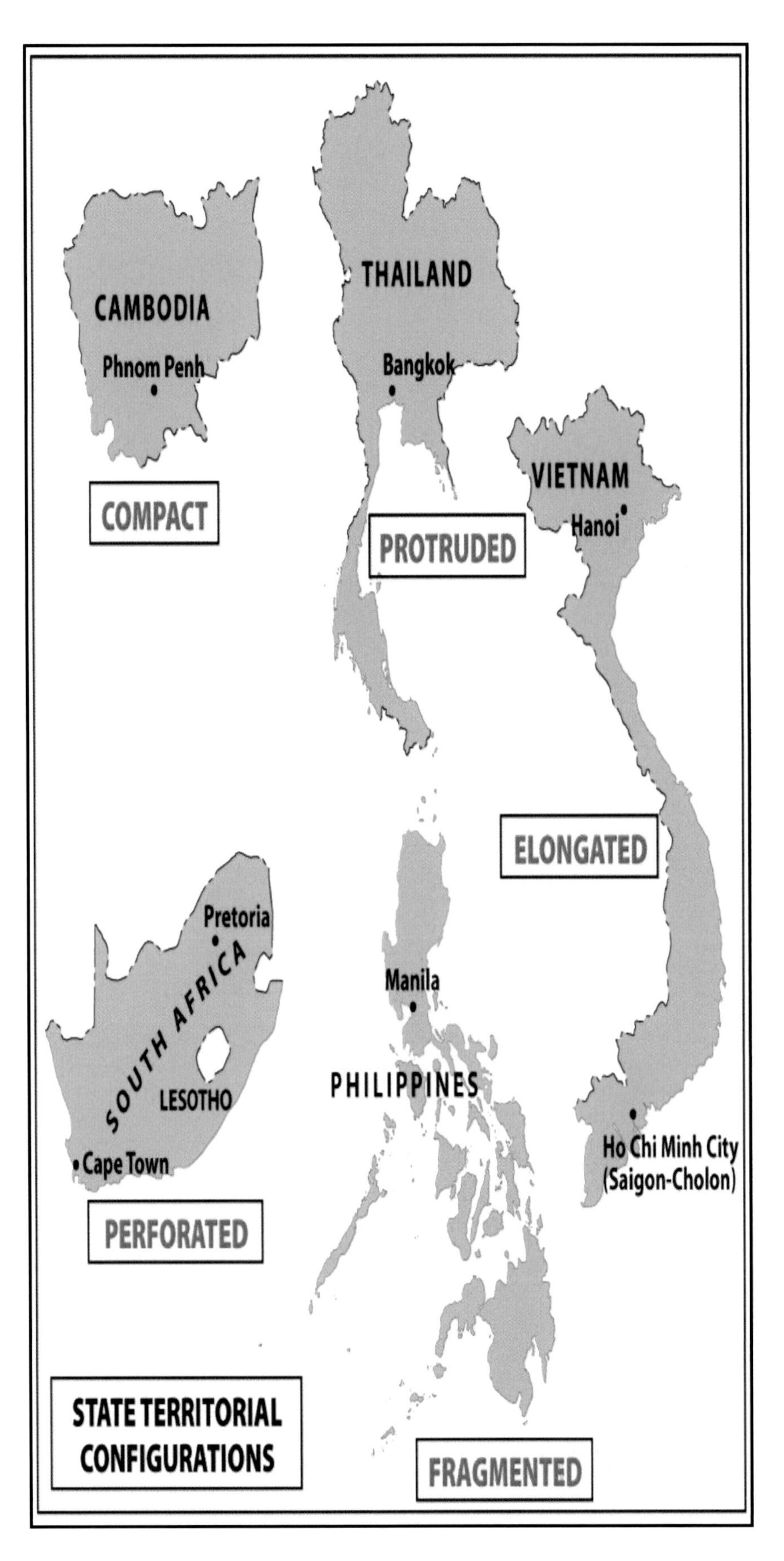
CAMBODIA
Phnom Penh
COMPACT
THAILAND
Bangkok
PROTRUDED
VIETNAM
Hanoi
ELONGATED
Ho Chi Minh City
(Saigon-Cholon)
Pretoria
SOUTH AFRICA
LESOTHO
Cape Town
PERFORATED
Manila
PHILIPPINES
FRAGMENTED
STATE TERRITORIAL
CONFIGURATIONS

Compact State

CAMBODIA

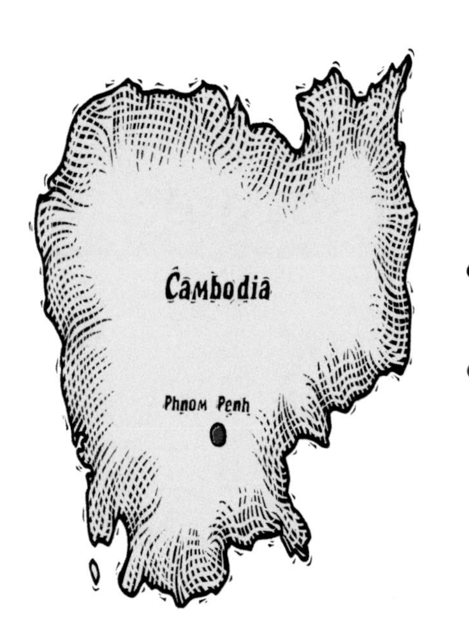
Cambodia
Phnom Penh

- A politico-geographic term to describe a state that possesses a **circular, oval, or rectangular** territory in which the distance from the center to any point on the boundary exhibits little variation
- Relatively easy to govern
- **Cambodia**, Uruguay, and Poland are examples

Elongated State

VIETNAM

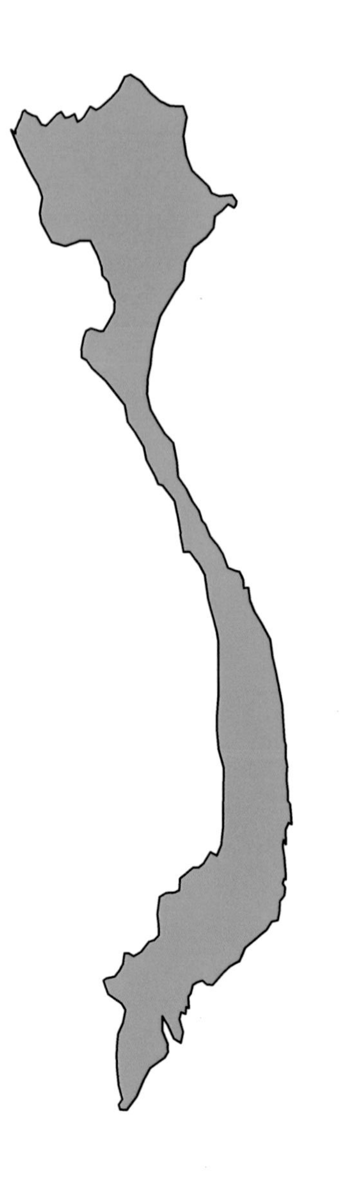

- A state whose territory is decidedly **long and narrow**; its length is at least six times greater than its average width
- Difficulties with transportation and communications; often high regionalism
- Chile, **Vietnam**, and **Laos** are classic examples.

Protruded State

THAILAND

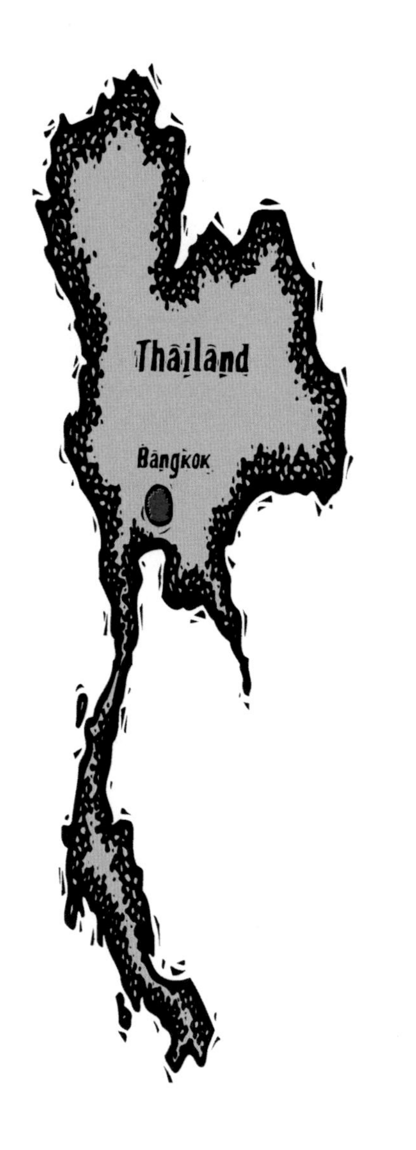
Thailand
Bangkok

- A type of territorial shape that exhibits a **narrow, elongated land extension** leading away from the main body of the territory
- 'protrusion' is often peripheral from the core with differing culture and economy
- **Thailand** and **Myanmar** are leading examples

Fragmented State

MALAYSIA

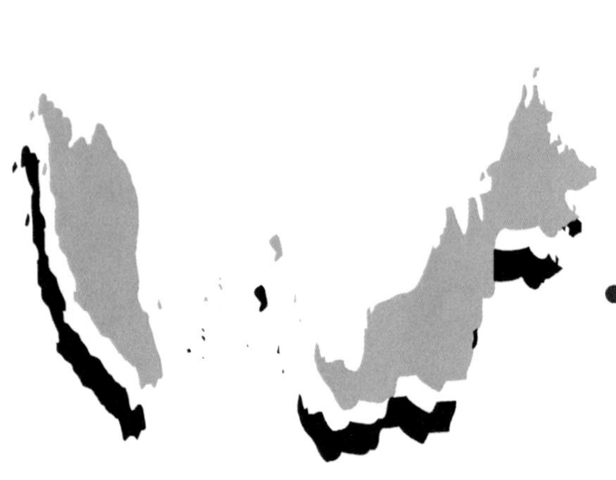

- A state whose territory consists of **several separated parts**, not a contiguous whole
- The individual parts may be isolated from each other by the land area of other states or by international waters
- Separation is a challenge to communications and transportation; high regionalism
- **Philippines** and **Indonesia** are also examples.

Perforated State

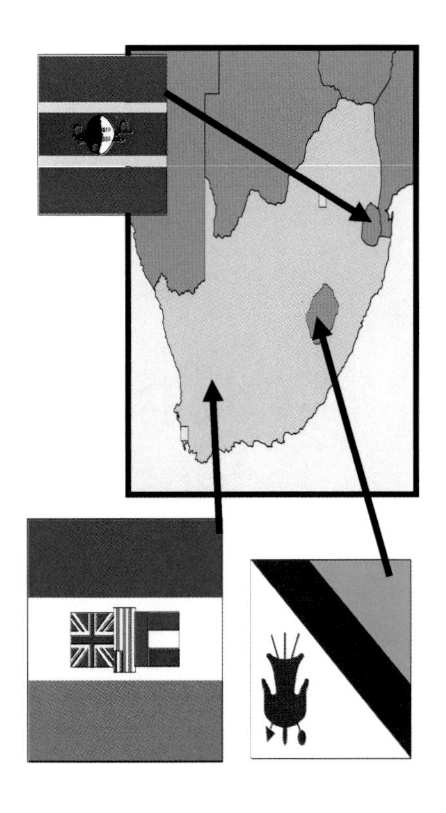

- Completely surrounded the territory of other states
- A **‘hole’ exists within** the state’s territorial extent
- Access to the outside world is difficult for the ‘hole’ state – needs to be on friendly terms with the ‘perforated’ state
- No SE Asian example
- South Africa is an excellent ‘out of this realm’ example (Lesotho and Swaziland are the ‘holes’)

Irredentism

A policy of cultural extension and political expansion aimed at a national group living in a neighboring country

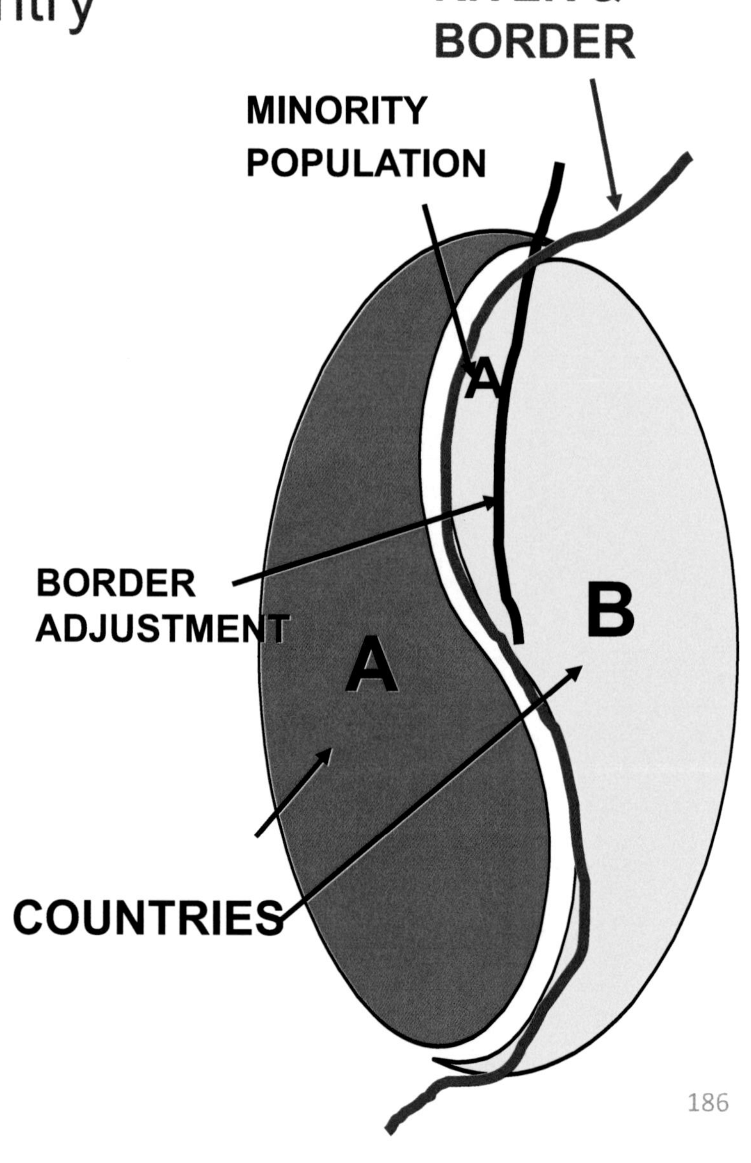
RIVER &
BORDER
MINORITY
POPULATION
A
BORDER
ADJUSTMENT
A
B
COUNTRIES

Ethnic Cleansing

Refers to the forcible ouster of entire populations from their homelands by stronger powers bent on taking their territories

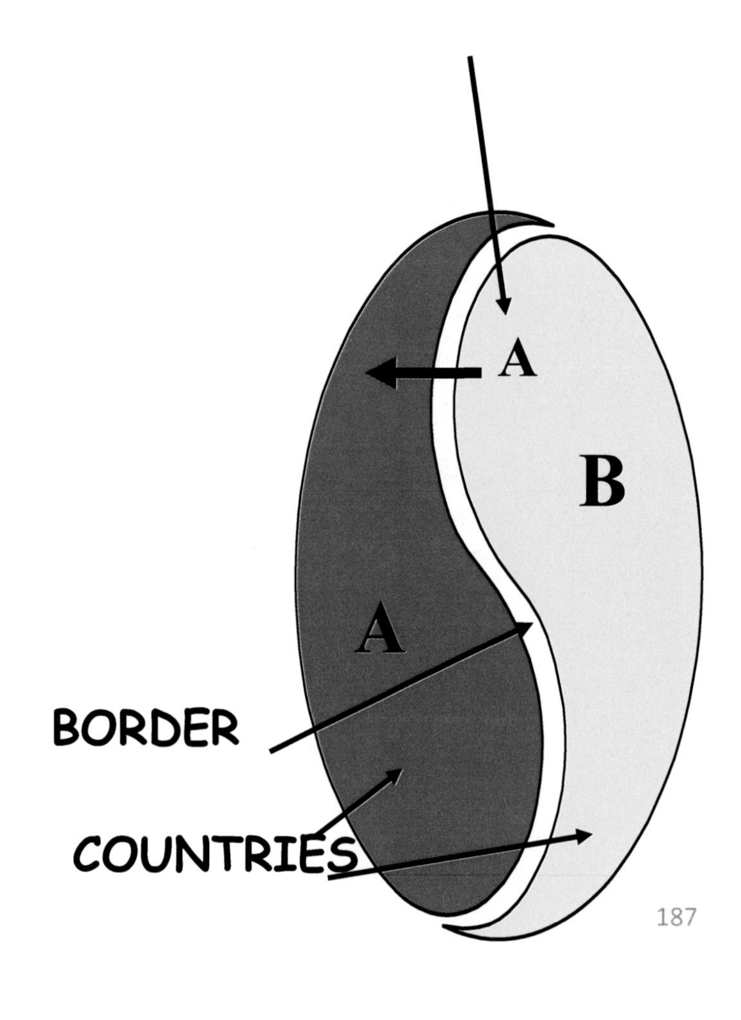
MINORITY
POPULATION
A
B
A
BORDER
COUNTRIES

Geopolitics

Geopolitics is based on geography and politics. Politics is built mainly on two foundations: military and economic. The two interact and support each other but are ultimately distinct. Though **demography** has an influence on politics.

For China, securing its buffer regions generally eliminates military problems, it is becoming more of a free-market economy and is encouraging a "One China" mentality.

中华人民共和国万岁
世界人民大团结万
Beijing, China – Tyrell Heaton

A portrait of Mao Zedong (Communist leader in the 1950s) hangs at Tiananmen Gate in Tiananmen Square. Zedong wanted an end to the free market. While China is still considered a Communist government, it is very much capitalistic. Though, almost all the large and successful Chinese companies are state owned and the few major genuinely private companies (like Huawei, Lenovo and Ali Baba) have close links with government.

Geopolitics of China

The People's Republic of China have publicly stated that they believe in One China. That includes, Taiwan, Hong Kong, Macau, Tibet, and Xinjiang. Though many citizens in these areas are pro-independent and want to be autonomous of Chinese rule.

Heilongjiang
Jilin
Liaoning
Xinjiang
Inner Mongolia
Beijing
Tianjin
Hebei
Ningxia
Shanxi
Shandong
Qinghai
Gansu
Shaanxi
Henan
Jiangsu
Tibet
Sichuan
Hubei
Anhui
Shanghai
Chongqing
Zhejiang
Jiangxi
Hunan
Diaoyu Islands
Guizhou
Fujian
Yunnan
Taiwan
Guangxi
Guangdong
Hong Kong
Macau
Dongsha Islands
Zhongsha Islands

Xinjiang Tibet Macau Hong Kong Taiwan

Underlying forces that affect geopolitical power

Centrifugal forces

- Refer to forces that tend to divide a country
  - Religious, linguistic, ethnic, or ideological ***differences***

Centripetal forces

- Forces that unite and bind a country together
  - A strong national culture, shared ideological objectives, and a common faith

Devolution

The process whereby regions within a state demand and gain political strength and growing autonomy at the expense of the central government

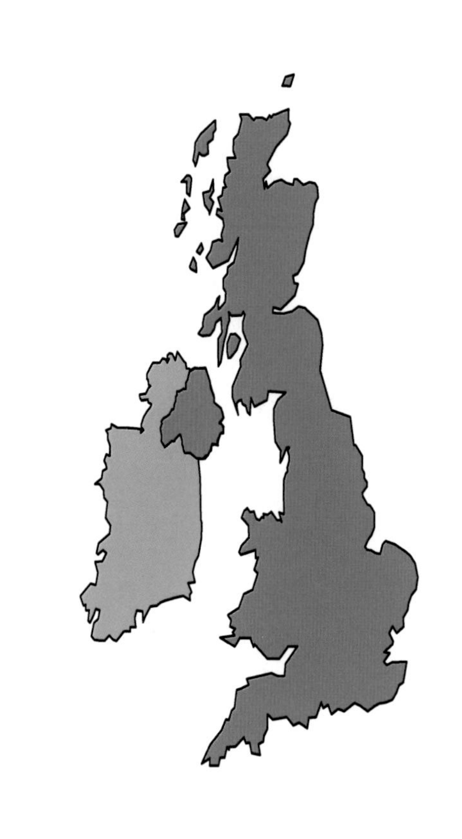

Examples:

- Scotland and Wales in the United Kingdom
- Linguistic and cultural differences in Belgium

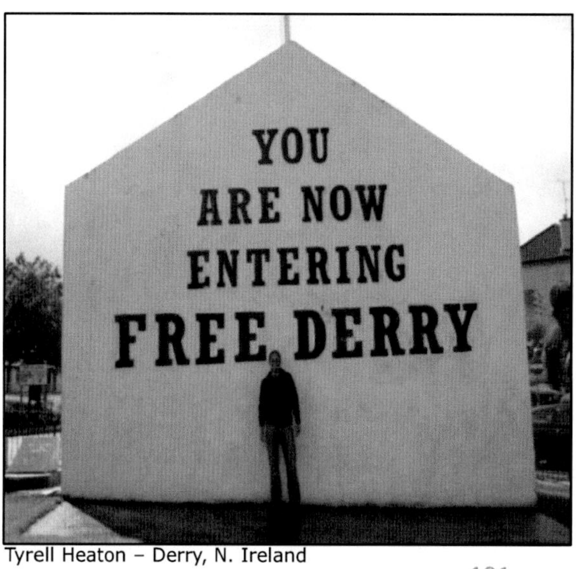
YOU
ARE NOW
ENTERING
FREE DERRY

Tyrell Heaton – Derry, N. Ireland

Cultural Differences & Devolution

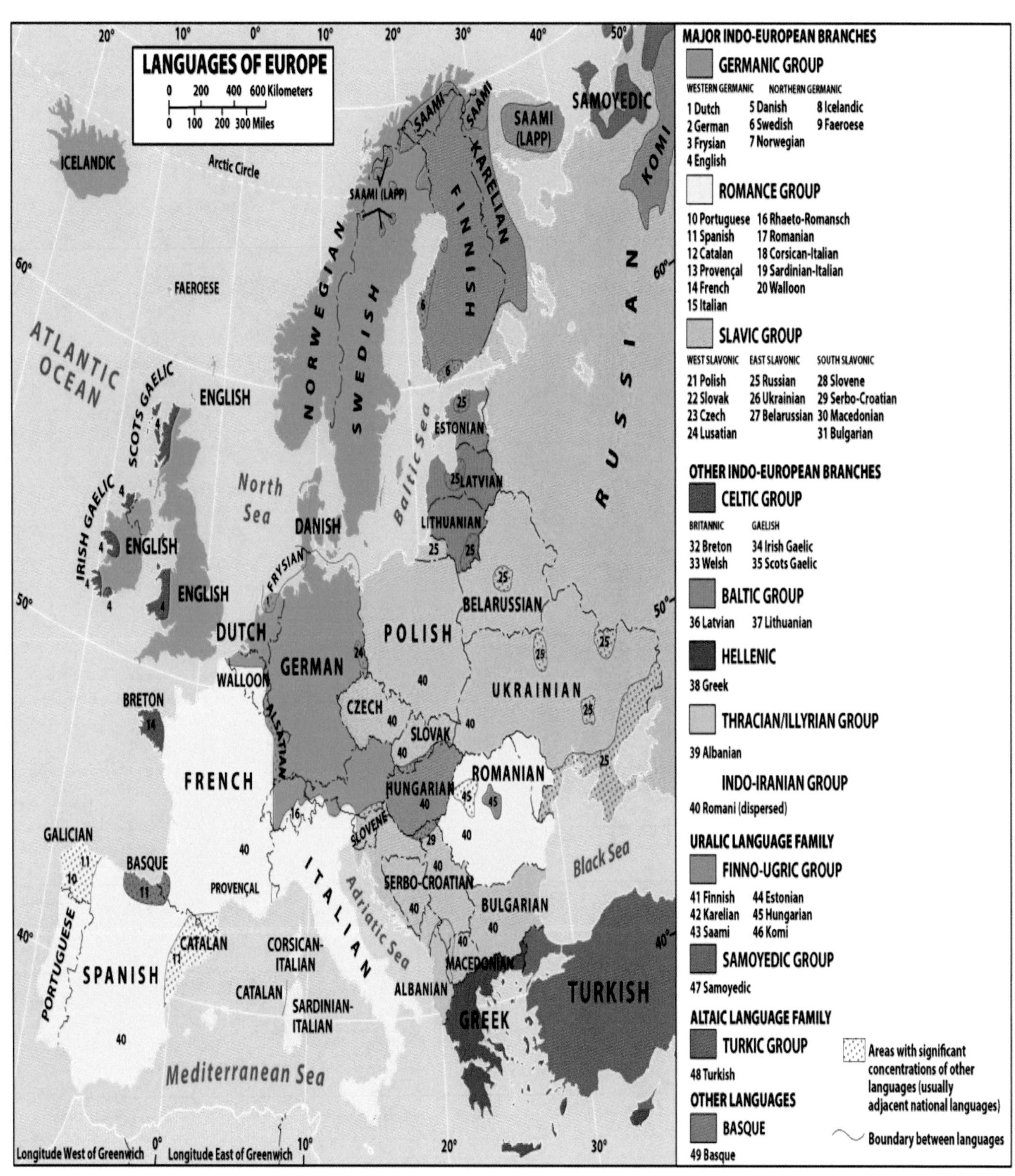

LANGUAGES OF EUROPE
0 200 400 600 Kilometers
0 100 200 300 Miles
20° 10° 0° 10° 20° 30° 40° 50°
60° 50° 40°
ICELANDIC
Arctic Circle
FAEROESE
ATLANTIC OCEAN
SAAMI
SAAMI (LAPP)
SAMOYEDIC
KOMI
KARELIAN
FINNISH
NORWEGIAN
SWEDISH
RUSSIAN
SCOTS GAELIC
ENGLISH
IRISH GAELIC
North Sea
Baltic Sea
ESTONIAN
LATVIAN
LITHUANIAN
DANISH
FRYSIAN
DUTCH
GERMAN
POLISH
BELARUSSIAN
UKRAINIAN
WALLOON
BRETON
CZECH
SLOVAK
ALSATIAN
FRENCH
HUNGARIAN
ROMANIAN
SLOVENE
GALICIAN
BASQUE
PROVENÇAL
ITALIAN
Adriatic Sea
SERBO-CROATIAN
BULGARIAN
Black Sea
PORTUGUESE
SPANISH
CATALAN
CORSICAN-ITALIAN
SARDINIAN-ITALIAN
ALBANIAN
MACEDONIAN
GREEK
TURKISH
Mediterranean Sea
Longitude West of Greenwich
Longitude East of Greenwich
MAJOR INDO-EUROPEAN BRANCHES
GERMANIC GROUP
WESTERN GERMANIC
NORTHERN GERMANIC
1 Dutch
2 German
3 Frysian
4 English
5 Danish
6 Swedish
7 Norwegian
8 Icelandic
9 Faeroese
ROMANCE GROUP
10 Portuguese
11 Spanish
12 Catalan
13 Provençal
14 French
15 Italian
16 Rhaeto-Romansch
17 Romanian
18 Corsican-Italian
19 Sardinian-Italian
20 Walloon
SLAVIC GROUP
WEST SLAVONIC
EAST SLAVONIC
SOUTH SLAVONIC
21 Polish
22 Slovak
23 Czech
24 Lusatian
25 Russian
26 Ukrainian
27 Belarussian
28 Slovene
29 Serbo-Croatian
30 Macedonian
31 Bulgarian
OTHER INDO-EUROPEAN BRANCHES
CELTIC GROUP
BRITANNIC
GAELISH
32 Breton
33 Welsh
34 Irish Gaelic
35 Scots Gaelic
BALTIC GROUP
36 Latvian
37 Lithuanian
HELLENIC
38 Greek
THRACIAN/ILLYRIAN GROUP
39 Albanian
INDO-IRANIAN GROUP
40 Romani (dispersed)
URALIC LANGUAGE FAMILY
FINNO-UGRIC GROUP
41 Finnish
42 Karelian
43 Saami
44 Estonian
45 Hungarian
46 Komi
SAMOYEDIC GROUP
47 Samoyedic
ALTAIC LANGUAGE FAMILY
TURKIC GROUP
48 Turkish
OTHER LANGUAGES
BASQUE
49 Basque
Areas with significant concentrations of other languages (usually adjacent national languages)
Boundary between languages

Cultural Differences & Devolution

Regions with active autonomous movement

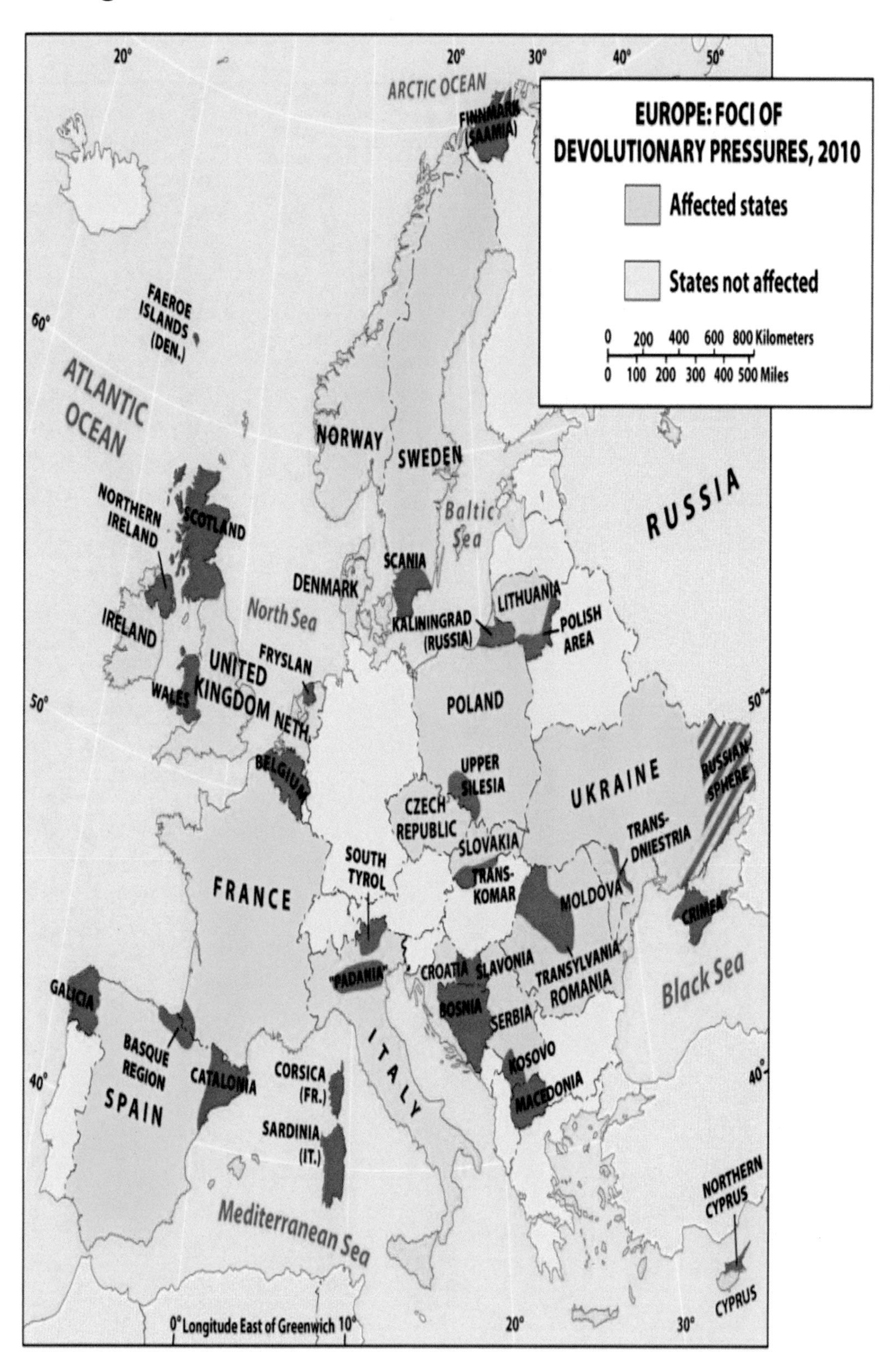
EUROPE: FOCI OF DEVOLUTIONARY PRESSURES, 2010
Affected states
States not affected
0 200 400 600 800 Kilometers
0 100 200 300 400 500 Miles
ARCTIC OCEAN
FINNMARK (SAAMIA)
FAEROE ISLANDS (DEN.)
ATLANTIC OCEAN
NORWAY
SWEDEN
Baltic Sea
RUSSIA
NORTHERN IRELAND
SCOTLAND
SCANIA
DENMARK
North Sea
IRELAND
KALININGRAD (RUSSIA)
LITHUANIA
POLISH AREA
FRYSLAN
UNITED KINGDOM
WALES
NETH.
POLAND
BELGIUM
UPPER SILESIA
UKRAINE
RUSSIAN SPHERE
CZECH REPUBLIC
SLOVAKIA
TRANS-DNIESTRIA
SOUTH TYROL
TRANS-KOMAR
MOLDOVA
FRANCE
CRIMEA
"PADANIA"
CROATIA
SLAVONIA
TRANSYLVANIA
ROMANIA
Black Sea
GALICIA
BOSNIA
SERBIA
BASQUE REGION
KOSOVO
CATALONIA
CORSICA (FR.)
ITALY
MACEDONIA
SPAIN
SARDINIA (IT.)
NORTHERN CYPRUS
Mediterranean Sea
CYPRUS
0° Longitude East of Greenwich 10°
20°
30°
40°
50°
60°

Shatter Belt

A term applied to Eastern Europe by geographers to describe a zone of chronic political splintering and fracturing

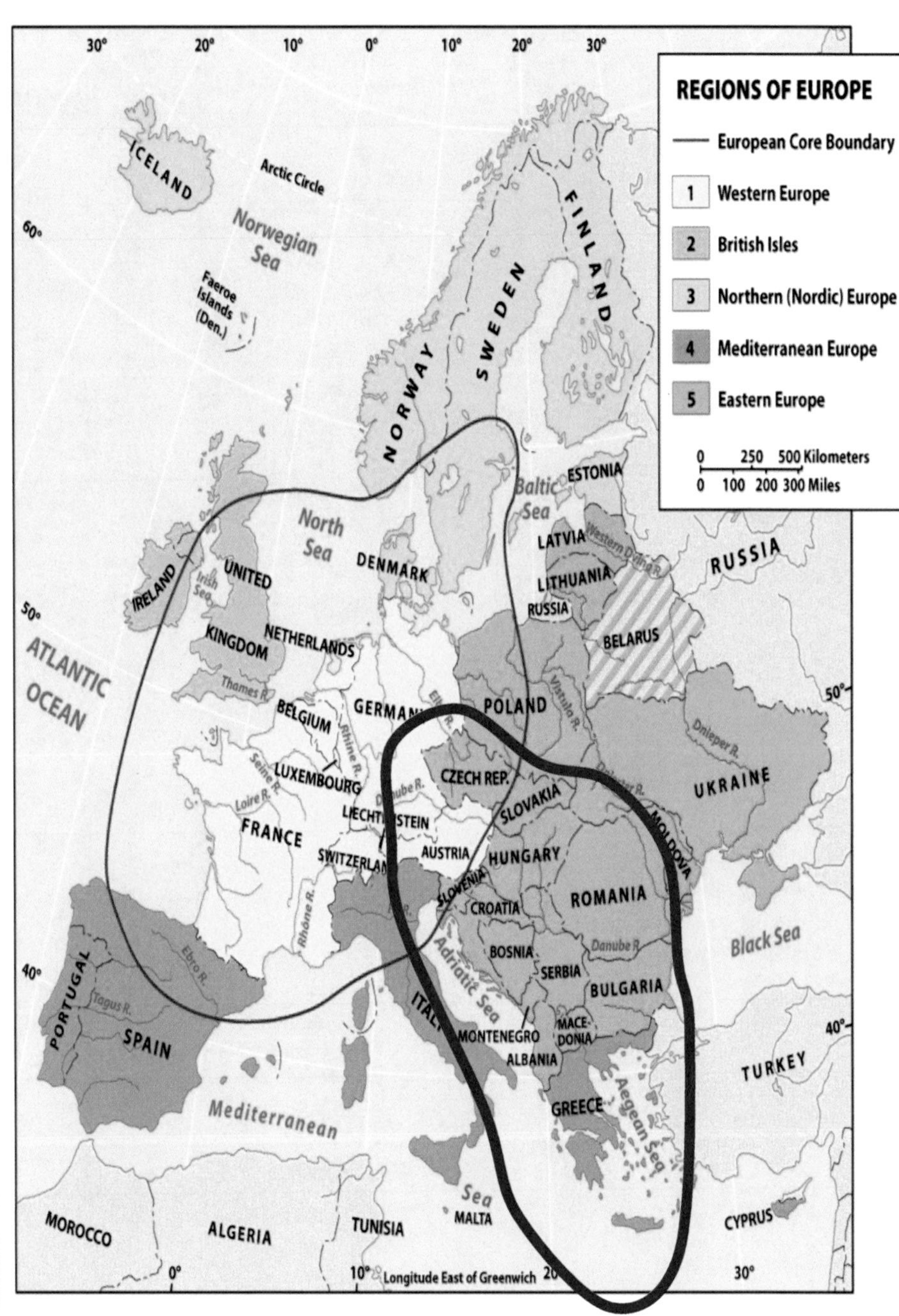
REGIONS OF EUROPE
European Core Boundary
1 Western Europe
2 British Isles
3 Northern (Nordic) Europe
4 Mediterranean Europe
5 Eastern Europe
0 250 500 Kilometers
0 100 200 300 Miles
ICELAND
Arctic Circle
Norwegian Sea
Faeroe Islands (Den.)
NORWAY
SWEDEN
FINLAND
ESTONIA
Baltic Sea
LATVIA
LITHUANIA
RUSSIA
BELARUS
North Sea
DENMARK
IRELAND
UNITED KINGDOM
NETHERLANDS
ATLANTIC OCEAN
BELGIUM
GERMANY
POLAND
CZECH REP.
SLOVAKIA
UKRAINE
MOLDOVA
LUXEMBOURG
LIECHTENSTEIN
FRANCE
SWITZERLAND
AUSTRIA
HUNGARY
SLOVENIA
CROATIA
ROMANIA
BOSNIA
SERBIA
BULGARIA
Black Sea
Adriatic Sea
ITALY
MONTENEGRO
MACEDONIA
ALBANIA
GREECE
Aegean Sea
TURKEY
PORTUGAL
SPAIN
Mediterranean Sea
MALTA
MOROCCO
ALGERIA
TUNISIA
CYPRUS
Longitude East of Greenwich

Tyrell Heaton - Sofia, Bulgaria

Balkanization

- From the verb ***Balkanize,*** which means to break up (as in a region) into smaller and often hostile units
- Originates from a mountain range in Bulgaria
- Applied to the southern half of eastern Europe, i.e., The ***Balkan countries*** of the **Balkan Peninsula**

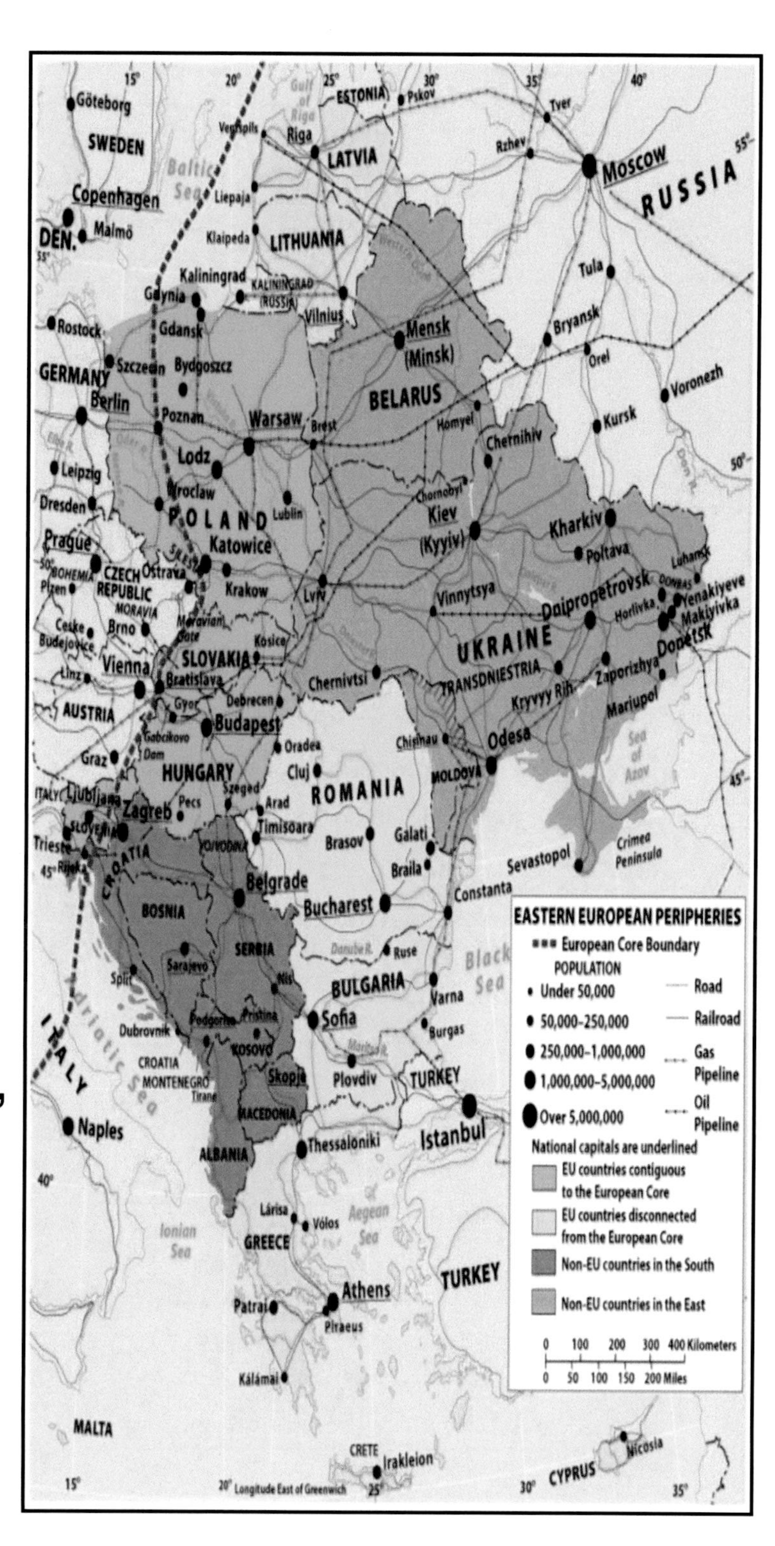

EASTERN EUROPEAN PERIPHERIES
European Core Boundary
POPULATION
Under 50,000
50,000-250,000
250,000-1,000,000
1,000,000-5,000,000
Over 5,000,000
Road
Railroad
Gas Pipeline
Oil Pipeline
National capitals are underlined
EU countries contiguous to the European Core
EU countries disconnected from the European Core
Non-EU countries in the South
Non-EU countries in the East
0 100 200 300 400 Kilometers
0 50 100 150 200 Miles
SWEDEN
DEN.
Copenhagen
Malmö
Göteborg
ESTONIA
LATVIA
Riga
LITHUANIA
Vilnius
Kaliningrad
RUSSIA
MOSCOW
BELARUS
Mensk (Minsk)
POLAND
Warsaw
Gdansk
Poznan
Lodz
Wroclaw
Krakow
Katowice
GERMANY
Berlin
Leipzig
Dresden
Prague
CZECH REPUBLIC
SLOVAKIA
Bratislava
Vienna
AUSTRIA
HUNGARY
Budapest
UKRAINE
Kiev (Kyyiv)
Kharkiv
Dnipropetrovsk
Donetsk
Odesa
MOLDOVA
TRANSDNIESTRIA
ROMANIA
Bucharest
SLOVENIA
Ljubljana
Zagreb
CROATIA
BOSNIA
Sarajevo
SERBIA
Belgrade
KOSOVO
MONTENEGRO
MACEDONIA
Skopje
ALBANIA
BULGARIA
Sofia
GREECE
Athens
Thessaloniki
TURKEY
Istanbul
ITALY
Naples
MALTA
CRETE
CYPRUS
Nicosia
Black Sea
Adriatic Sea
Aegean Sea
Ionian Sea
Sea of Azov
Crimea Peninsula
Sevastopol
20° Longitude East of Greenwich

Francophone Quebec

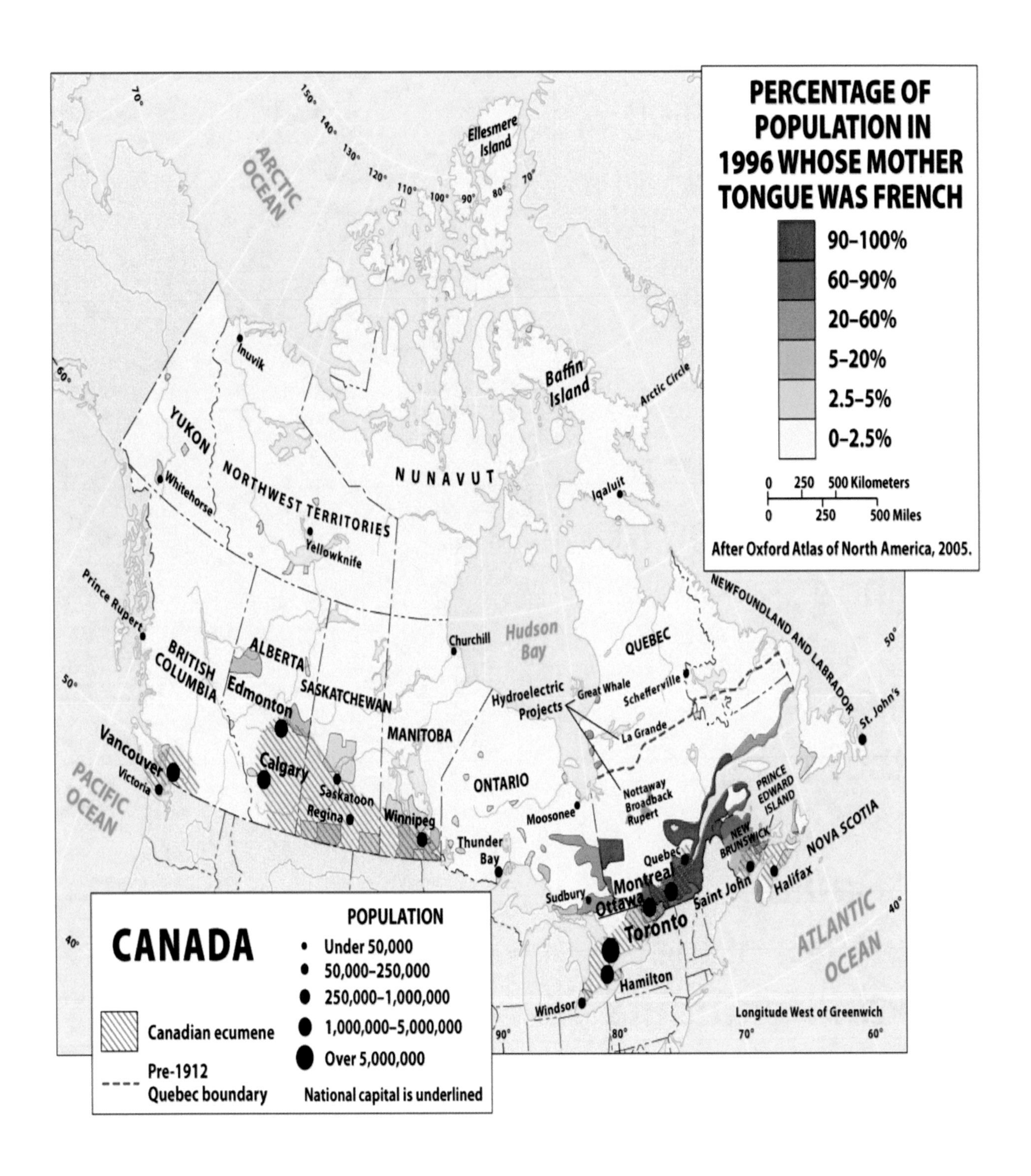

PERCENTAGE OF POPULATION IN 1996 WHOSE MOTHER TONGUE WAS FRENCH
90-100%
60-90%
20-60%
5-20%
2.5-5%
0-2.5%
0 250 500 Kilometers
0 250 500 Miles
After Oxford Atlas of North America, 2005.
ARCTIC OCEAN
Ellesmere Island
Baffin Island
Arctic Circle
Inuvik
YUKON
NORTHWEST TERRITORIES
NUNAVUT
Whitehorse
Yellowknife
Iqaluit
Hudson Bay
Churchill
Prince Rupert
BRITISH COLUMBIA
ALBERTA
Edmonton
SASKATCHEWAN
MANITOBA
ONTARIO
QUEBEC
NEWFOUNDLAND AND LABRADOR
St. John's
Hydroelectric Projects
Great Whale
Schefferville
La Grande
Nottaway Broadback Rupert
Moosonee
Vancouver
Victoria
Calgary
Saskatoon
Regina
Winnipeg
Thunder Bay
Sudbury
Ottawa
Montreal
Quebec
Toronto
Hamilton
Windsor
Saint John
Halifax
PRINCE EDWARD ISLAND
NEW BRUNSWICK
NOVA SCOTIA
PACIFIC OCEAN
ATLANTIC OCEAN
Longitude West of Greenwich
CANADA
POPULATION
Under 50,000
50,000-250,000
250,000-1,000,000
1,000,000-5,000,000
Over 5,000,000
National capital is underlined
Canadian ecumene
Pre-1912 Quebec boundary

The Quebec Question

- Culturally different from the rest
  - French is a significant part of Quebec's cultural landscape
  - Primarily French-speaking
- Province with secessionist tendency
  - 1995 referendum
    No 50.58%
    Yes 49.42%
- Increase in acknowledgement of difference
  - Nation within the Canadian federation
  - High degree of autonomy

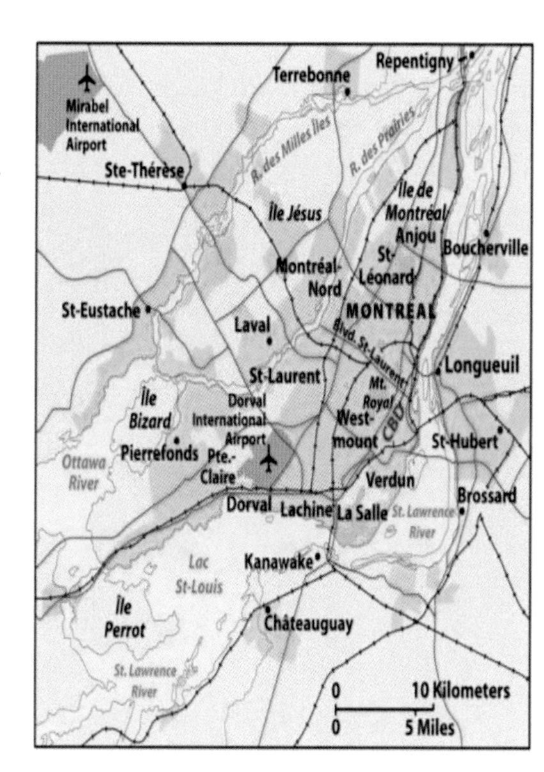
Mirabel International Airport
Terrebonne
Repentigny
Ste-Thérèse
R. des Milles Îles
R. des Prairies
Île Jésus
Île de Montréal
Anjou
Boucherville
Montréal-Nord
St-Léonard
St-Eustache
Laval
MONTREAL
Blvd. St-Laurent
St-Laurent
Longueuil
Île Bizard
Dorval International Airport
Mt. Royal
Westmount
CBD
St-Hubert
Ottawa River
Pierrefonds
Pte.-Claire
Verdun
Brossard
Dorval
Lachine
La Salle
St. Lawrence River
Lac St-Louis
Kanawake
Île Perrot
Châteauguay
St. Lawrence River
0
10 Kilometers
0
5 Miles

Québec
G05 AVG
Je me souviens
Montreal, Quebec – Tyrell Heaton

North American Free Trade Agreement
United States, Mexico, Canada Agreement

NAFTA / USMCA

- NAFTA went into effect January 1, **1994**
- USMCA went into effect Dec. 2, 2018
- Established a **trade agreement** between **Mexico, Canada and the US**, which:
  - Reduced and regulated trade tariffs, barriers, and quotas between members
  - Standardized finance & service exchanges

Mexico and NAFTA / USMCA

- Positive:
  - It promised a higher standard of living
  - NAFTA created jobs for Mexicans as US companies began to invest more heavily in the Mexican market
  - Mexican exporters increased their sales to the US and Canada

- Negative:
  - Not all people in Mexico have benefited, NAFTA has increased income inequality
  - (Maize) farmers have suffered greatly due to US subsidy of its own farmers
  - More migratns

Mexico – country of contrasts

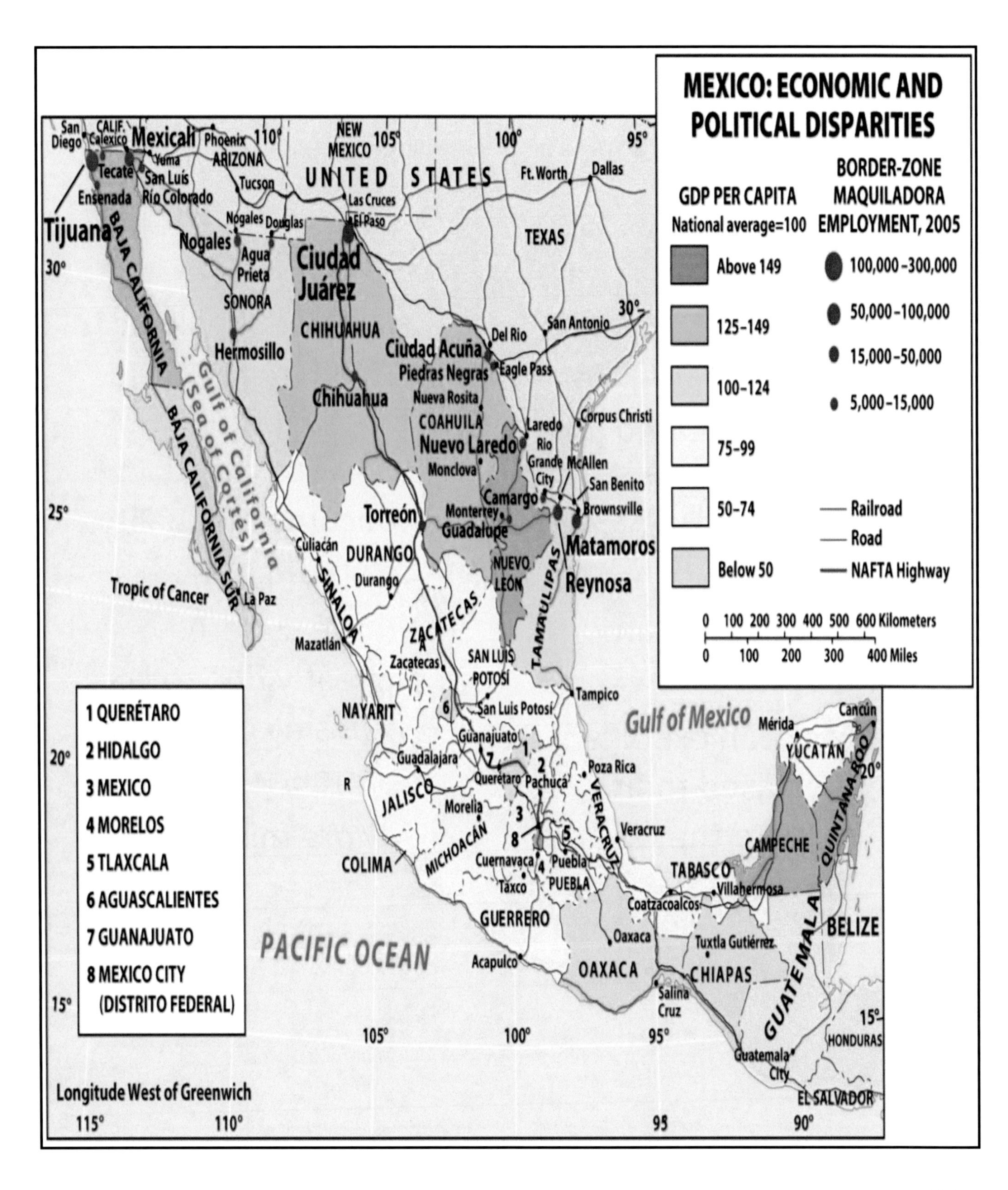

MEXICO: ECONOMIC AND POLITICAL DISPARITIES
GDP PER CAPITA
National average=100
Above 149
125-149
100-124
75-99
50-74
Below 50
BORDER-ZONE MAQUILADORA EMPLOYMENT, 2005
100,000-300,000
50,000-100,000
15,000-50,000
5,000-15,000
Railroad
Road
NAFTA Highway
0 100 200 300 400 500 600 Kilometers
0 100 200 300 400 Miles
1 QUERÉTARO
2 HIDALGO
3 MEXICO
4 MORELOS
5 TLAXCALA
6 AGUASCALIENTES
7 GUANAJUATO
8 MEXICO CITY (DISTRITO FEDERAL)
UNITED STATES
PACIFIC OCEAN
Gulf of Mexico
Gulf of California (Sea of Cortés)
Tropic of Cancer
Longitude West of Greenwich
Tijuana
Mexicali
Nogales
Ciudad Juárez
Ciudad Acuña
Piedras Negras
Nuevo Laredo
Matamoros
Reynosa
BAJA CALIFORNIA
BAJA CALIFORNIA SUR
SONORA
CHIHUAHUA
COAHUILA
NUEVO LEÓN
TAMAULIPAS
SINALOA
DURANGO
ZACATECAS
SAN LUIS POTOSÍ
NAYARIT
JALISCO
COLIMA
MICHOACÁN
GUERRERO
PUEBLA
VERACRUZ
OAXACA
CHIAPAS
TABASCO
CAMPECHE
YUCATÁN
QUINTANA ROO
GUATEMALA
BELIZE
HONDURAS
EL SALVADOR
TEXAS
ARIZONA
NEW MEXICO
CALIF.

Brussels, Belgium European Union Headquarters

What does the future hold for Europe?

Unification?
Instability?

Supranationalism

- A venture involving **three or more** states
- Political, economic, and/or cultural **cooperation** to promote shared objectives
- European **supranationalism** started with the 1944 Benelux Agreement, an economic union between **Belgium, the Netherlands, and Luxembourg**

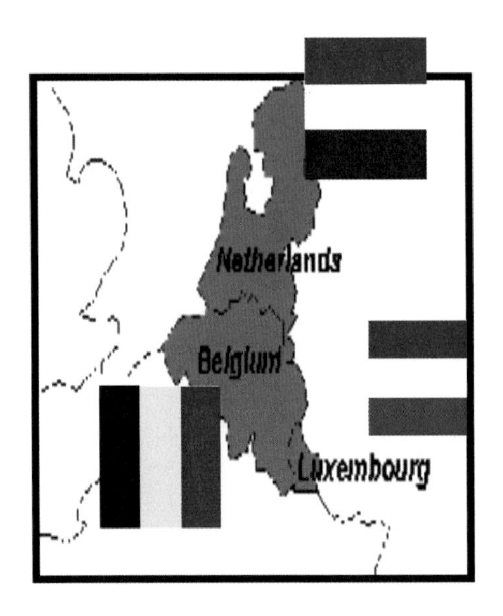
Netherlands
Belgium
Luxembourg

Benelux Countries

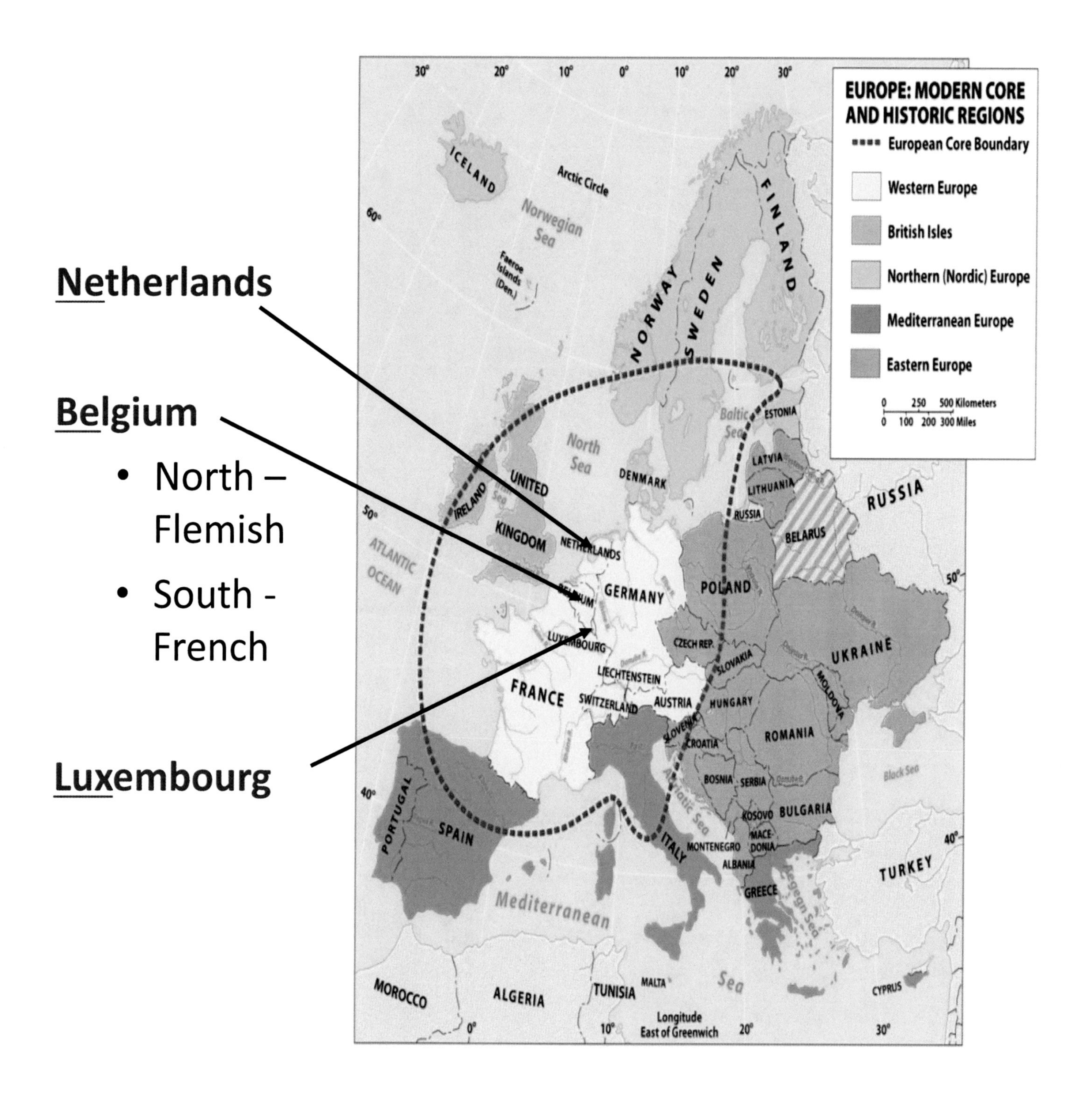
Netherlands
Belgium
• North – Flemish
• South - French
Luxembourg
EUROPE: MODERN CORE AND HISTORIC REGIONS
European Core Boundary
Western Europe
British Isles
Northern (Nordic) Europe
Mediterranean Europe
Eastern Europe
0 250 500 Kilometers
0 100 200 300 Miles
ICELAND
Arctic Circle
Norwegian Sea
Faeroe Islands (Den.)
NORWAY
SWEDEN
FINLAND
ESTONIA
Baltic Sea
North Sea
DENMARK
LATVIA
LITHUANIA
RUSSIA
BELARUS
UNITED KINGDOM
IRELAND
ATLANTIC OCEAN
NETHERLANDS
GERMANY
POLAND
LUXEMBOURG
CZECH REP.
SLOVAKIA
UKRAINE
LIECHTENSTEIN
MOLDOVA
FRANCE
SWITZERLAND
AUSTRIA
HUNGARY
SLOVENIA
CROATIA
ROMANIA
BOSNIA
SERBIA
Black Sea
PORTUGAL
SPAIN
ITALY
KOSOVO
BULGARIA
MONTENEGRO
MACEDONIA
ALBANIA
TURKEY
GREECE
Mediterranean Sea
MOROCCO
ALGERIA
TUNISIA
MALTA
CYPRUS
Longitude East of Greenwich

European Supranationalism

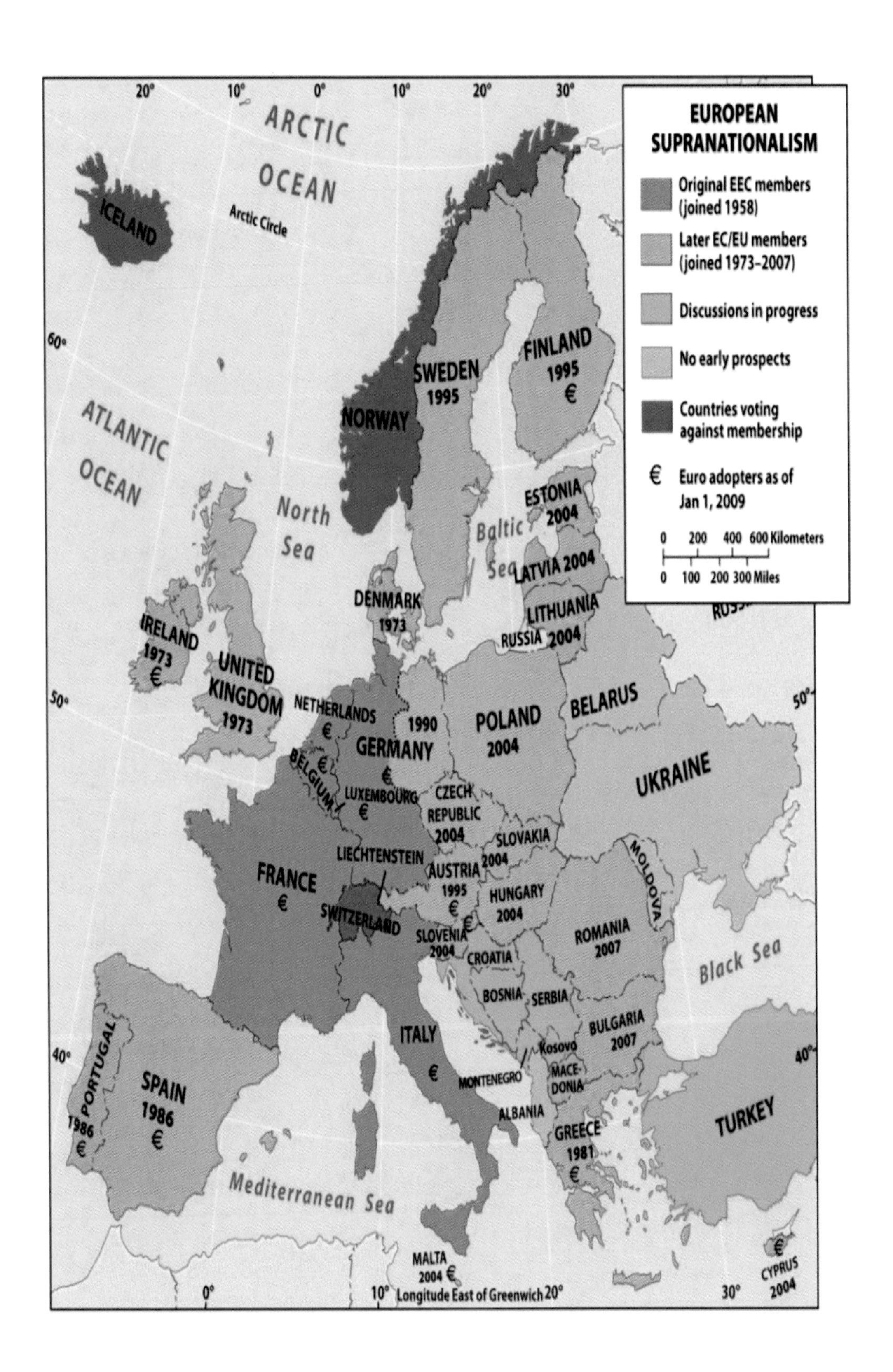
EUROPEAN SUPRANATIONALISM
Original EEC members (joined 1958)
Later EC/EU members (joined 1973–2007)
Discussions in progress
No early prospects
Countries voting against membership
€ Euro adopters as of Jan 1, 2009
0 200 400 600 Kilometers
0 100 200 300 Miles
ARCTIC OCEAN
Arctic Circle
ATLANTIC OCEAN
North Sea
Baltic Sea
Mediterranean Sea
Black Sea
ICELAND
NORWAY
SWEDEN 1995
FINLAND 1995 €
ESTONIA 2004
LATVIA 2004
LITHUANIA 2004
RUSSIA
DENMARK 1973
IRELAND 1973 €
UNITED KINGDOM 1973
NETHERLANDS €
BELGIUM €
LUXEMBOURG €
GERMANY €
1990
POLAND 2004
BELARUS
UKRAINE
CZECH REPUBLIC 2004
SLOVAKIA 2004
AUSTRIA 1995 €
LIECHTENSTEIN
HUNGARY 2004
MOLDOVA
ROMANIA 2007
FRANCE €
SWITZERLAND
SLOVENIA 2004
CROATIA
BOSNIA
SERBIA
BULGARIA 2007
Kosovo
MACEDONIA
MONTENEGRO
ALBANIA
ITALY €
GREECE 1981 €
TURKEY
PORTUGAL 1986 €
SPAIN 1986 €
MALTA 2004 €
CYPRUS 2004 €
Longitude East of Greenwich
20° 10° 0° 10° 20° 30°
60° 50° 40°

Supranationalism: Problems

- Disparities in levels of economic development
- Loss of autonomy
- Bureaucracy
- Technical barriers
- Cultural barriers
- **Devolution**

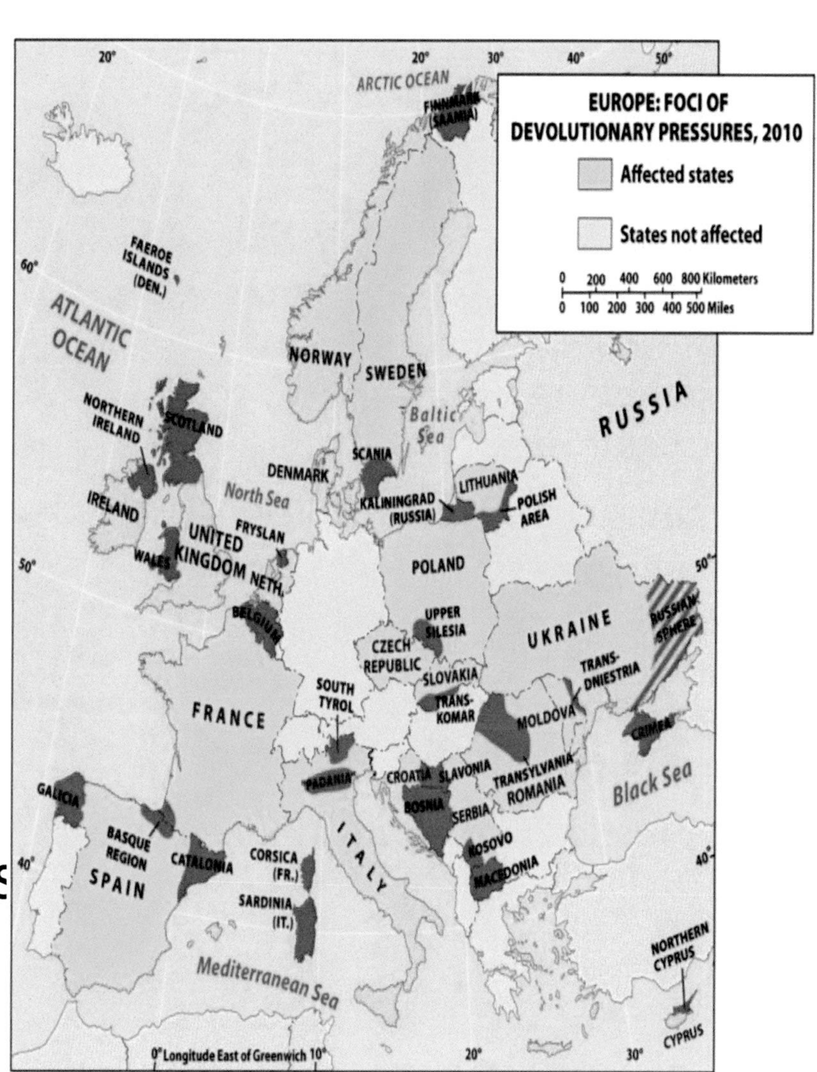

EUROPE: FOCI OF DEVOLUTIONARY PRESSURES, 2010
Affected states
States not affected
0 200 400 600 800 Kilometers
0 100 200 300 400 500 Miles
ARCTIC OCEAN
ATLANTIC OCEAN
FAEROE ISLANDS (DEN.)
NORWAY
SWEDEN
RUSSIA
Baltic Sea
North Sea
NORTHERN IRELAND
SCOTLAND
IRELAND
WALES
UNITED KINGDOM
DENMARK
SCANIA
FRYSLAN
NETH.
BELGIUM
KALININGRAD (RUSSIA)
LITHUANIA
POLISH AREA
POLAND
UPPER SILESIA
CZECH REPUBLIC
SLOVAKIA
TRANS-KOMAR
UKRAINE
TRANS-DNIESTRIA
MOLDOVA
CRIMEA
FRANCE
SOUTH TYROL
PADANIA
CROATIA
SLAVONIA
TRANSYLVANIA
ROMANIA
BOSNIA
SERBIA
KOSOVO
MACEDONIA
Black Sea
GALICIA
BASQUE REGION
SPAIN
CATALONIA
CORSICA (FR.)
SARDINIA (IT.)
ITALY
Mediterranean Sea
NORTHERN CYPRUS
CYPRUS
0° Longitude East of Greenwich 10°

European Union (EU)

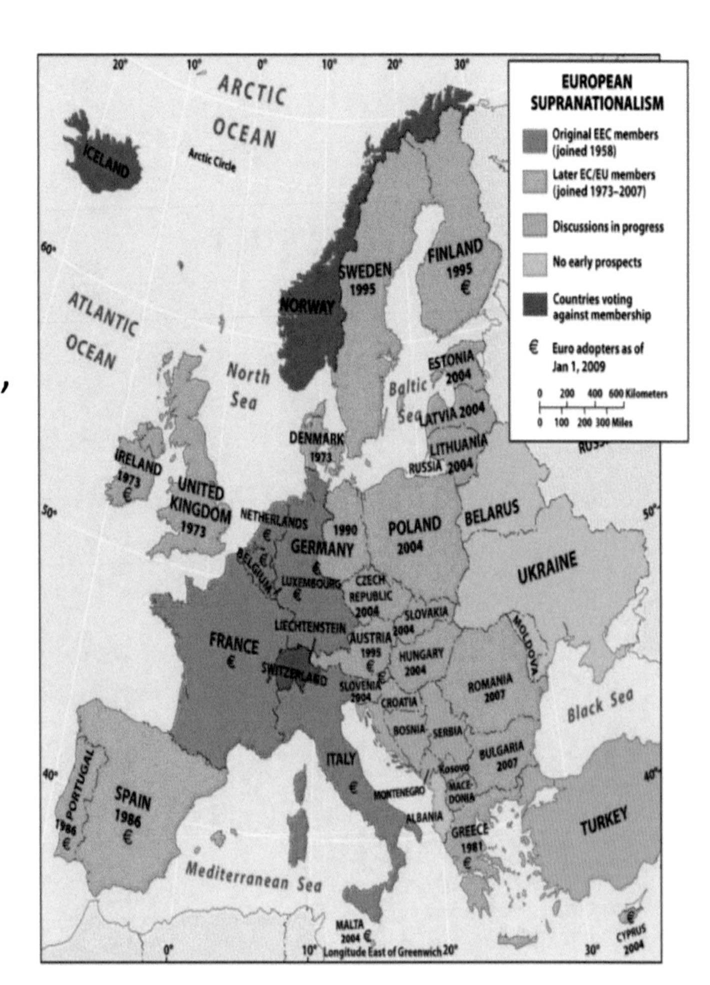
ARCTIC
OCEAN
Arctic Circle
ICELAND
EUROPEAN SUPRANATIONALISM
Original EEC members (joined 1958)
Later EC/EU members (joined 1973–2007)
Discussions in progress
No early prospects
Countries voting against membership
Euro adopters as of Jan 1, 2009
ATLANTIC OCEAN
North Sea
NORWAY
SWEDEN 1995
FINLAND 1995
ESTONIA 2004
LATVIA 2004
LITHUANIA 2004
Baltic Sea
DENMARK 1973
IRELAND 1973
UNITED KINGDOM 1973
NETHERLANDS
GERMANY
POLAND 2004
BELARUS
UKRAINE
FRANCE
SWITZERLAND
AUSTRIA 1995
HUNGARY 2004
ROMANIA 2007
MOLDOVA
Black Sea
PORTUGAL 1986
SPAIN 1986
ITALY
BULGARIA 2007
GREECE 1981
TURKEY
Mediterranean Sea
MALTA 2004
CYPRUS 2004

- Established: 7 February 1992
- Effective: 1 November 1993
- Original Members: (12) Belgium, Denmark, France, Germany, Greece, Ireland, Italy, Luxembourg, Netherlands, Portugal, Spain, UK
- Aimed to coordinate policy among the members in three areas:
  - **Economics**
  - **Defence**
  - **Justice and home affairs**

CURRENT MEMBERS OF THE EUROPEAN UNION

Belgium, Netherlands, Luxembourg, France, Italy, Germany, Britain, Ireland, Hungary, Latvia, Lithuania, Malta, Slovenia, Denmark, Greece, Spain, Portugal, Austria, Sweden, Finland, Cyprus, Czech Republic, Estonia, Poland, Slovakia, Romania, Croatia, Bulgaria

Euro Currency

- Each country used to have their own currency – high transaction costs
- Today 15 of the 27 EU members participate in the Euro currency
- Notable exceptions:
  - UK
  - Denmark
  - Sweden

EUROPEAN SUPRANATIONALISM
Original EEC members (joined 1958)
Later EC/EU members (joined 1973–2007)
Discussions in progress
No early prospects
Countries voting against membership
€ Euro adopters as of Jan 1, 2009
0 200 400 600 Kilometers
0 100 200 300 Miles
ARCTIC OCEAN
Arctic Circle
ICELAND
NORWAY
SWEDEN 1995
FINLAND 1995 €
ATLANTIC OCEAN
North Sea
Baltic Sea
ESTONIA 2004
LATVIA 2004
LITHUANIA 2004
RUSSIA
DENMARK 1973
IRELAND 1973 €
UNITED KINGDOM 1973
NETHERLANDS €
BELGIUM €
LUXEMBOURG €
GERMANY €
1990
POLAND 2004
BELARUS
UKRAINE
CZECH REPUBLIC 2004
SLOVAKIA 2004
LIECHTENSTEIN
AUSTRIA 1995 €
HUNGARY 2004
FRANCE €
SWITZERLAND
SLOVENIA 2004
CROATIA
ROMANIA 2007
MOLDOVA
Black Sea
BOSNIA
SERBIA
BULGARIA 2007
Kosovo
MACE-DONIA
ITALY €
MONTENEGRO
ALBANIA
GREECE 1981 €
TURKEY
PORTUGAL 1986 €
SPAIN 1986 €
Mediterranean Sea
MALTA 2004 €
CYPRUS 2004
Longitude East of Greenwich

Forward Capital

- A Capital city positioned in a contested or potentially contested territory
  - Usually near an international border
  - Confirms the state's determination to maintain its presence in the territory under contention
- Examples:
  - St Petersburg, Russia
  - Islamabad, Pakistan
  - Astana, Kazakhstan
  - Abuja, Nigeria
  - **Brasilia, Brazil**

Brasília, Brazil

Bogotá
Cayenne
FRENCH GUIANA
SURINAME
Manaus
Belém
São Luís
Fortaleza
Amazon R.
Teresina
Pôrto Velho
Recife
BRAZIL
São Francisco R.
Maceió
BOLIVIA
La Paz
Cuiabá
Goiânia
Brasília
Salvador
Santa Cruz
Campo Grande
Paraná R.
Belo Horizonte
Sucre
PARAGUAY
Campinas
Rio de Janeiro
São Paulo
Asunción
São José dos Campos
Santos
Tucumán
Curitiba
ARGENTINA
Pôrto Alegre
Mendoza
Córdoba
URUGUAY

Forward Capital

Capital city positioned in actually or potentially **contested territory**, usually near an international **border**, confirming the state's determination **to maintain** its presence in the region

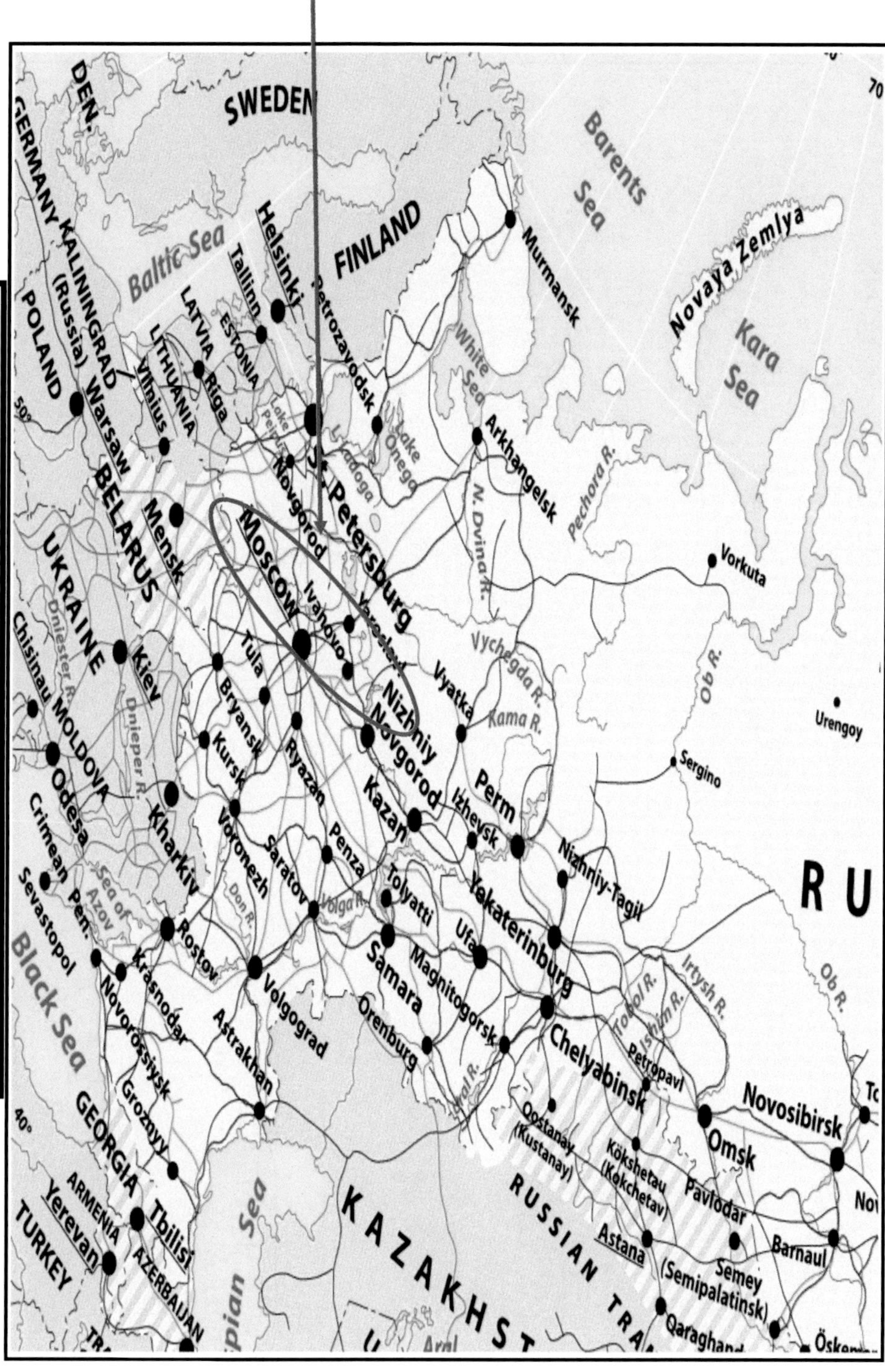

SWEDEN
FINLAND
DEN.
GERMANY
KALININGRAD (Russia)
POLAND
Baltic Sea
Helsinki
Tallinn
ESTONIA
LATVIA
Riga
LITHUANIA
Vilnius
Warsaw
BELARUS
Mensk
UKRAINE
Kiev
Chisinau
MOLDOVA
Odesa
Kharkiv
Crimean Pen.
Sevastopol
Black Sea
Sea of Azov
Dniester R.
Dnieper R.
Don R.
Volga R.
St. Petersburg
Petrozavodsk
Lake Ladoga
Lake Onega
Novgorod
Moscow
Ivanovo
Yaroslavl
Tula
Bryansk
Kursk
Voronezh
Ryazan
Nizhniy Novgorod
Kazan
Penza
Saratov
Rostov
Krasnodar
Novorossiysk
Volgograd
Astrakhan
Grozny
GEORGIA
Tbilisi
ARMENIA
Yerevan
AZERBAIJAN
TURKEY
Murmansk
Barents Sea
White Sea
Arkhangelsk
N. Dvina R.
Pechora R.
Novaya Zemlya
Kara Sea
Vorkuta
Vychegda R.
Kama R.
Vyatka
Perm
Izhevsk
Tolyatti
Samara
Ufa
Orenburg
Magnitogorsk
Yekaterinburg
Nizhniy-Tagil
Chelyabinsk
Ob R.
Sergino
Urengoy
Irtysh R.
Tobol R.
Ishim R.
Petropavl
Qostanay (Kustanay)
Kökshetau (Kokchetav)
Astana
Pavlodar
Omsk
Novosibirsk
Barnaul
Semey (Semipalatinsk)
KAZAKHST
RUSSIAN
RU
50°
40°
70

Gerrymandering - and the geography of politics

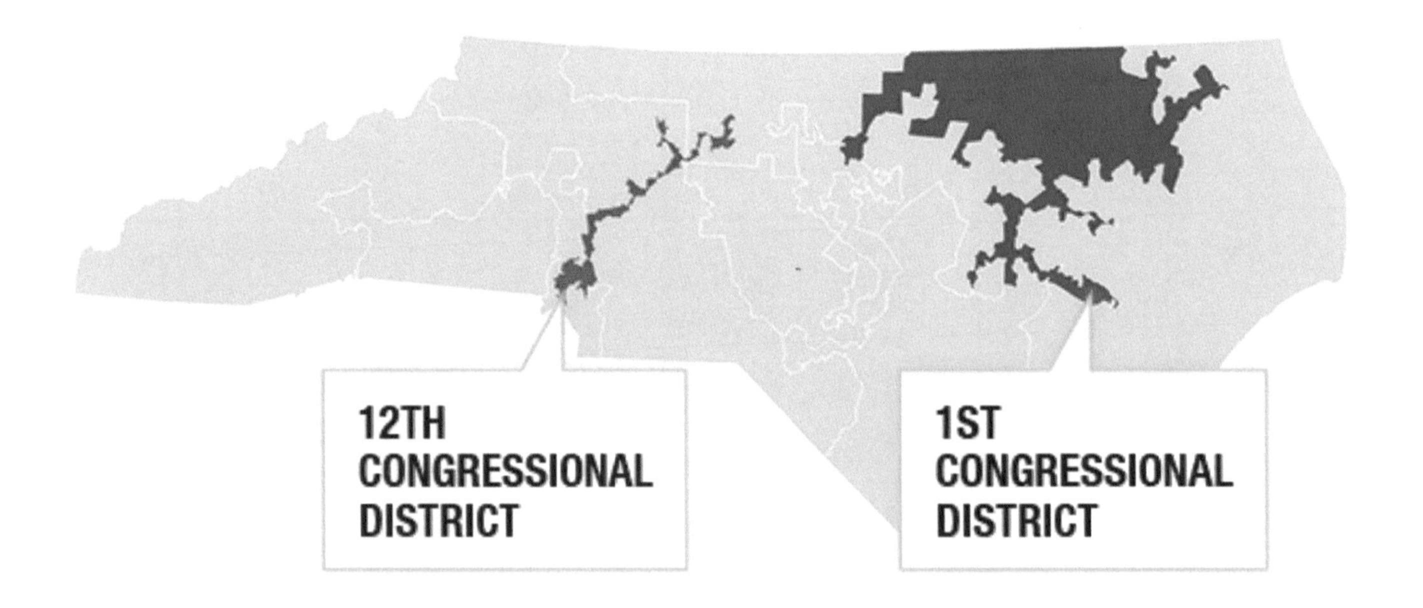
12TH
CONGRESSIONAL
DISTRICT
1ST
CONGRESSIONAL
DISTRICT

One of the first solutions to fixing politics = stop gerrymandering, the shaping of congressional districts to guarantee electoral outcomes. The worst offender is North Carolina, notice District 12 (the blue); this snake-like District 12 runs more than 100 miles southwest to Charlotte. Technically gerrymandering is against the law... but the 12th...well, look at its irregular blocks of land all slightly connected. Legislators get by with this calling it "point contiguity," you can bet something dicey is going on:

In Pennsylvania. In 2012, Democrats won 51 percent of the popular House vote. But the only won 5 out of 18 House seats -- fewer than one third. This was because when Pennsylvania Republicans redrew the state's Congressional districts, they made highly irregular districts that look like the one here, PA-7, one of the most geographically irregular districts in the nation.

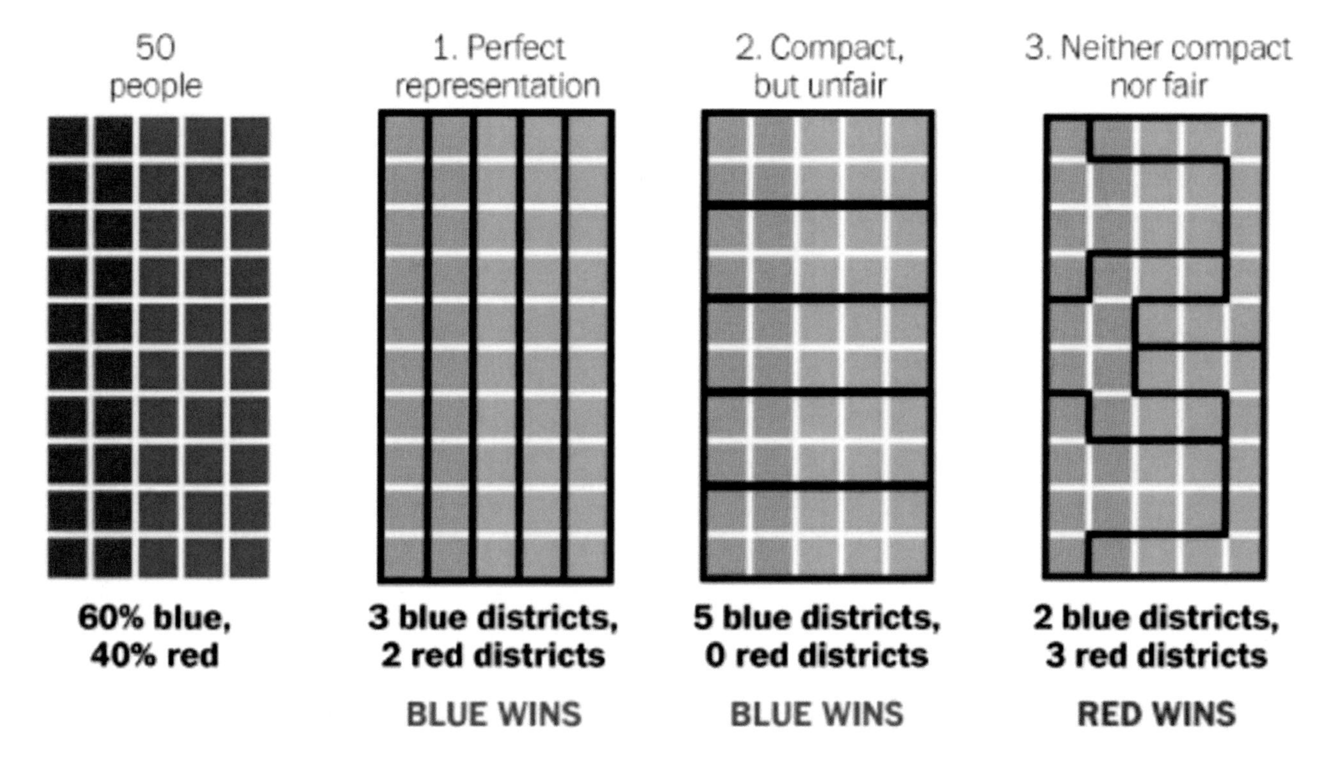
Gerrymandering, explained
Three different ways to divide 50 people into five districts
50 people
1. Perfect representation
2. Compact, but unfair
3. Neither compact nor fair
60% blue, 40% red
3 blue districts, 2 red districts
5 blue districts, 0 red districts
2 blue districts, 3 red districts
BLUE WINS
BLUE WINS
RED WINS

Suppose we have a very tiny state of fifty people. Thirty of them belong to the Blue Party, and 20 belong to the Red Party. And just our luck, they all live in a nice even grid with the Blues on one side of the state and the Reds on the other.

Now, let's say we need to divide this state into five districts. Each district will send one representative to the House to represent the people. Ideally, we want the representation to be proportional: if 60 percent of our residents are Blue and 40 percent are Red, those five seats should be divvied up the same way.

Fortunately, because our citizens live in a neatly ordered grid, it's easy to draw five lengthy districts -- two for the Reds , and three for the Blues. Voila! Perfectly proportional representation, just as the Founders intended. That's grid 1 above, "perfect representation."

Now, let's say instead that the Blue Party controls the state government, and they get to decide how the lines are drawn. Rather than draw districts vertically they draw them horizontally, so that in each district there are six Blues and four Reds. You can see that in grid 2 above, "compact but unfair."

With a comfortable Blue majority in this state, each district elects a blue candidate to the House. The Blues win 5 seats and the Reds don't get a single one. Oh well! All's fair in love and politics.

England vs Great Britain vs United Kingdom – explained:

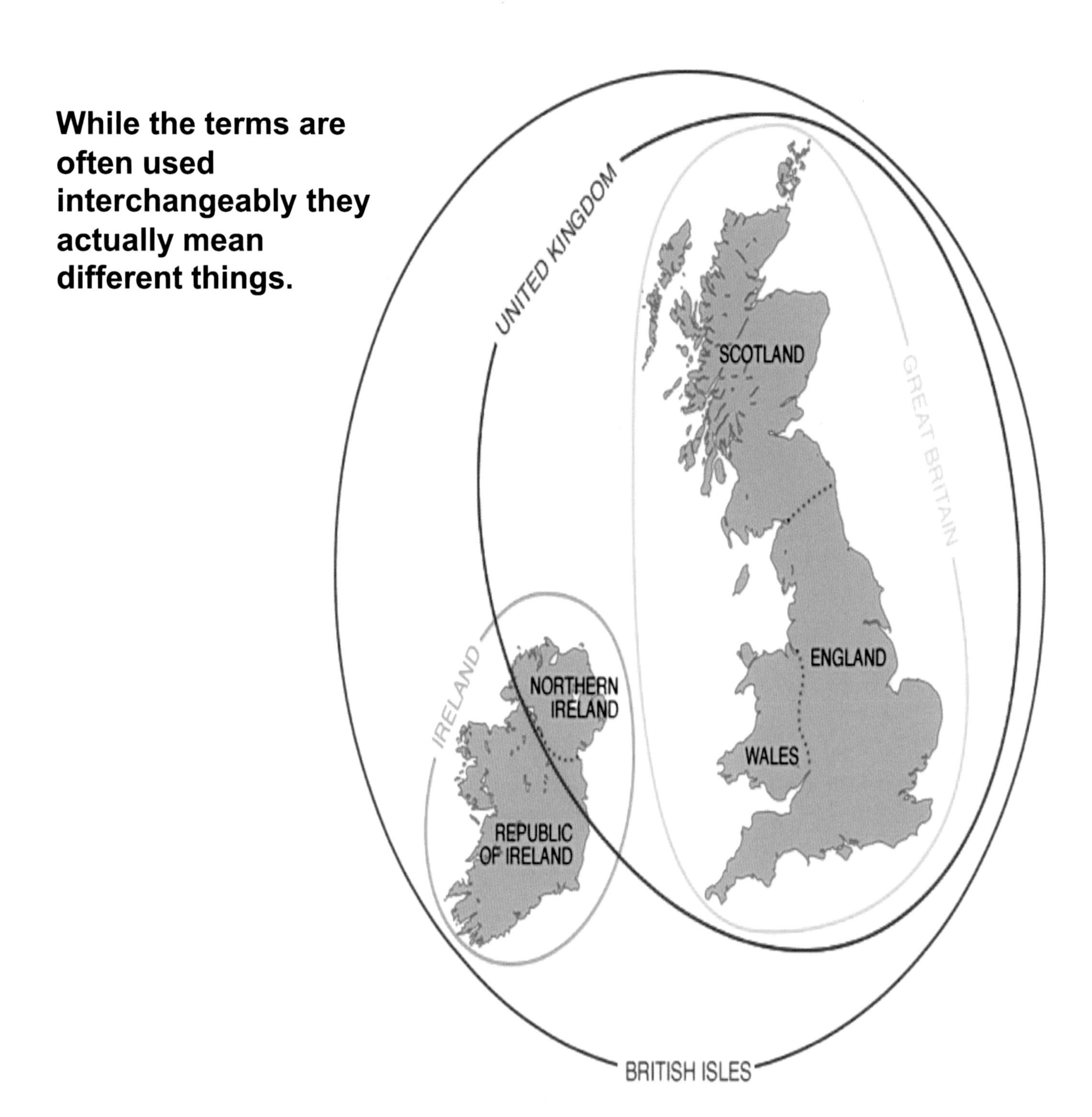
While the terms are often used interchangeably they actually mean different things.
UNITED KINGDOM
GREAT BRITAIN
SCOTLAND
ENGLAND
WALES
IRELAND
NORTHERN IRELAND
REPUBLIC OF IRELAND
BRITISH ISLES

Economic Geography

Hanwha
신한생명
WHISEN

Seoul, South Korea – Tyrell Heaton

Classification of Economic Activity

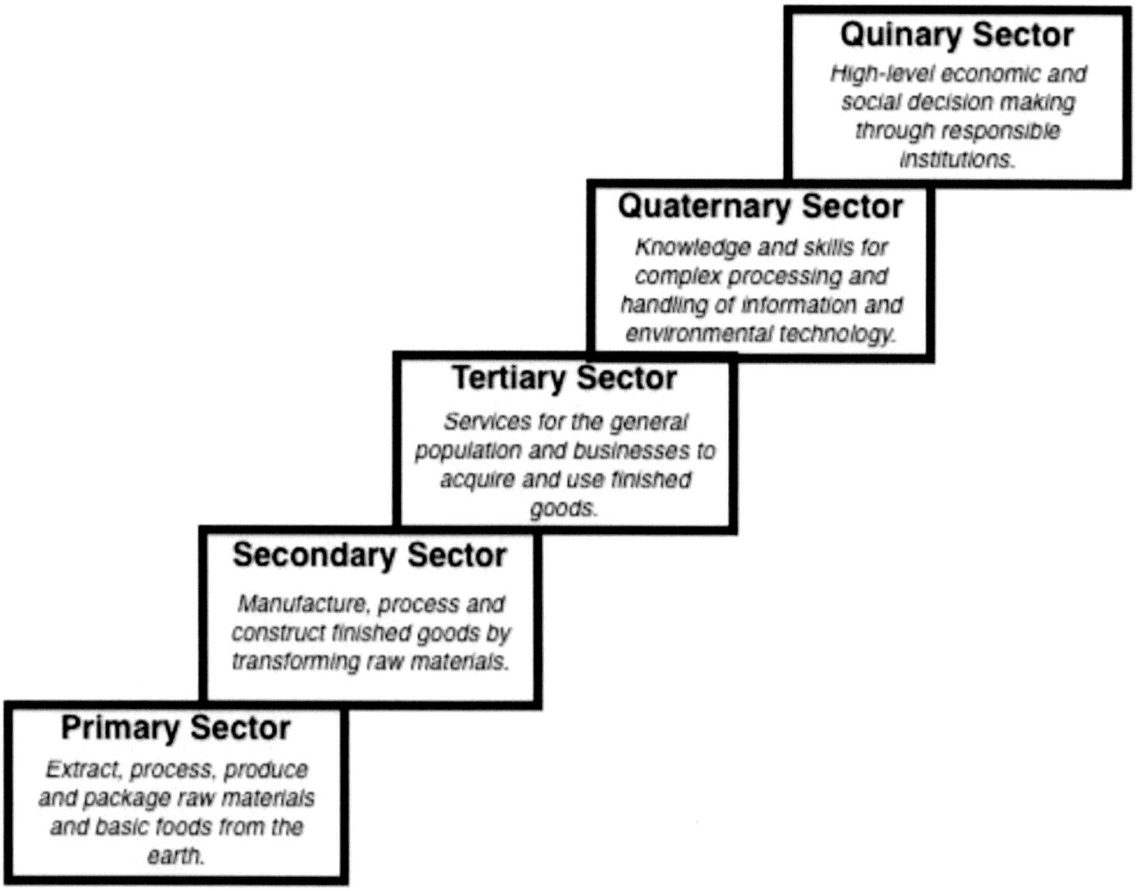

Quinary Sector
High-level economic and social decision making through responsible institutions.

Quaternary Sector
Knowledge and skills for complex processing and handling of information and environmental technology.

Tertiary Sector
Services for the general population and businesses to acquire and use finished goods.

Secondary Sector
Manufacture, process and construct finished goods by transforming raw materials.

Primary Sector
Extract, process, produce and package raw materials and basic foods from the earth.

The Primary Sector are activities such as agriculture, mining, extractive, and gathering industries

The Secondary Sector involves the transformation of the raw material into the finished or manufactured goods. This sector has developed because of the demand for more goods and services, and it also helps in the industrialization process. In the developed country like the U.S.A., nearly 20% of the workforce is involved in this sector, and they are known as the blue-collar workers. Secondary Sector are activities such as manufacturing, processing, construction, and power production.

The Tertiary Sector is the service sector, which involves the giving away direct services to its consumers, wholesale and retail trade, transportation, communication, consumer services (restaurants, tourism, etc.), education, fire, police, health care, and nonprofit organizations.

The Quaternary Sector involves the services related to the knowledge sector, services concerned with information or the exchange of money/goods, services tied to research or higher education.

The Quinary Sector focus on interpretation of existing or the new ideas, evaluation of new technologies, and the creation of services; oftentimes these are referred to as "gold collar" jobs. It is also one of the parts of the tertiary sector, but it involves highly paid professionals, research scientists, and government officials. The people are designated with high positions and powers, and those who make important decisions that are especially far-reaching in the world around them often belong to this category.

Types of Economic Systems

TRADITIONAL ECONOMY: A traditional economic system focuses exclusively on goods and services that are directly related to its beliefs and traditions.

PLANNED ECONOMY: A planned or command economic system is characterized by a dominant centralized power.

FREE-MARKET ECONOMY: A market economic system relies on free markets and does not allow any kind of government involvement.

MIXED ECONOMY: A mixed economic system is any kind of mixture of a market and a command economic system.

CHARACTERISTICS	TRADITIONAL ECONOMY	PLANNED ECONOMY	FREE-MARKET ECONOMY	MIXED ECONOMY
Role of government	No formal government other than a sovereign or feudal lord	Decides all economic activities	Little or no role of government	Government creates laws and regulates business activities
Freedom of choice	Freedom of choice in so far as resources available to produce	No freedom of choice	Consumers and producers have freedom of choice	Limited freedom of choice given government controls
Ownership of natural resources	Sovereign or feudal lord	State/public sector	Private sector	Both public and private sector
Price determination	Barter was the main form of trade	Government sets price	Price mechanism system determines price	Price Mechanism system but regulated by government
Which sector answers the basic economic questions?	Traditions and customs	State/public sector	Private sector	Both public and private sector

Von Thünen's Isolated State

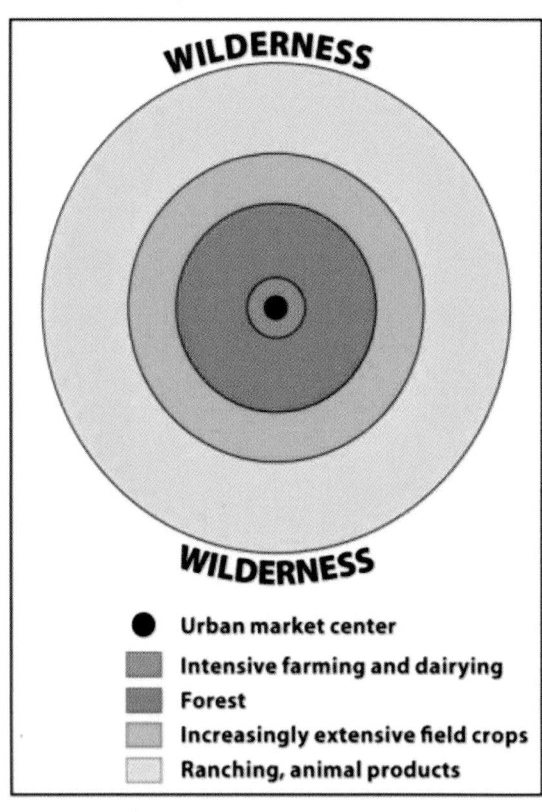
WILDERNESS
WILDERNESS
Urban market center
Intensive farming and dairying
Forest
Increasingly extensive field crops
Ranching, animal products

- A **classic model** in geography
- Fashioned in 1826 to explain the economic patterns developing around **European cities**
- Based on four **concentric land-use rings** surrounding a marketplace
- Land use was a function of **transportation costs**
- ***The isolated state*** became the foundation for modern ***location theory***

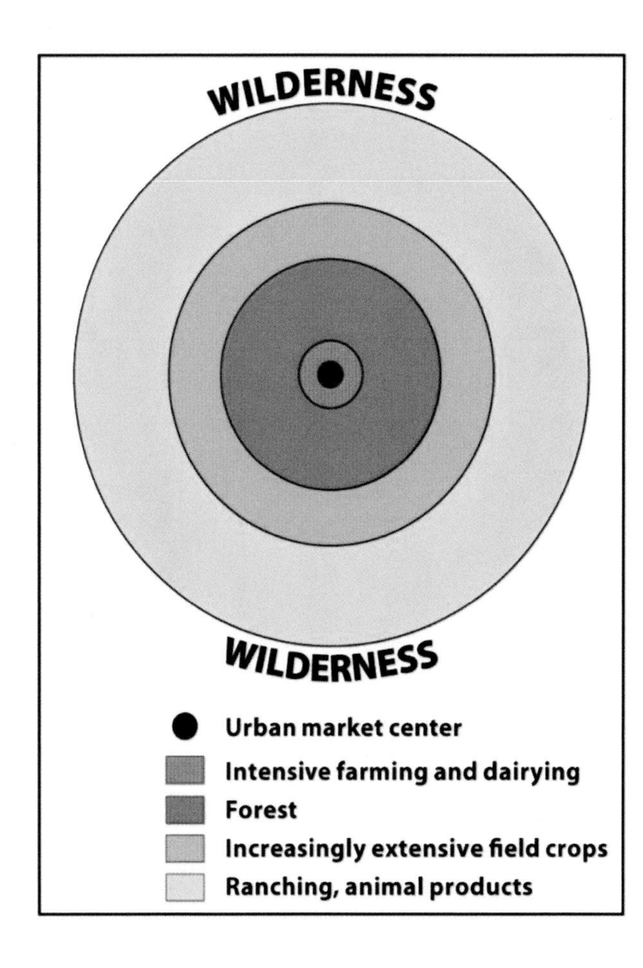
WILDERNESS
WILDERNESS
Urban market center
Intensive farming and dairying
Forest
Increasingly extensive field crops
Ranching, animal products

Von Thünen's Isolated State Model

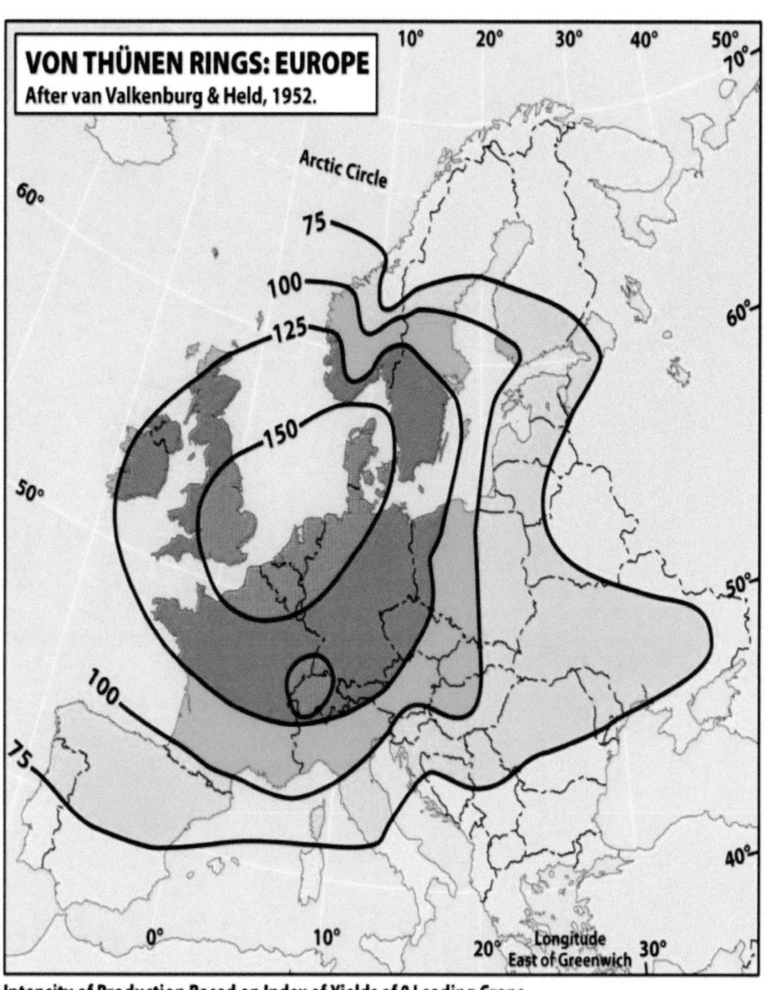
VON THÜNEN RINGS: EUROPE
After van Valkenburg & Held, 1952.
Arctic Circle
75
100
125
150
100
75
10°
20°
30°
40°
50°
70°
60°
60°
50°
50°
40°
0°
10°
20°
30°
Longitude
East of Greenwich
Intensity of Production Based on Index of Yields of 8 Leading Crops.

20th century application to the European realm

Agrarian Revolution

Agriculture by hand - Germany Tyrell Heaton

- Began in Europe in the 1750s
- Based on new agricultural innovations
- Enabled increased food production
- Enabled sustained population increase

Altitudinal Zonation

- Found in mountainous Middle and South America
- Temperature decreases with altitude
- Has a great impact of which crops can be grown

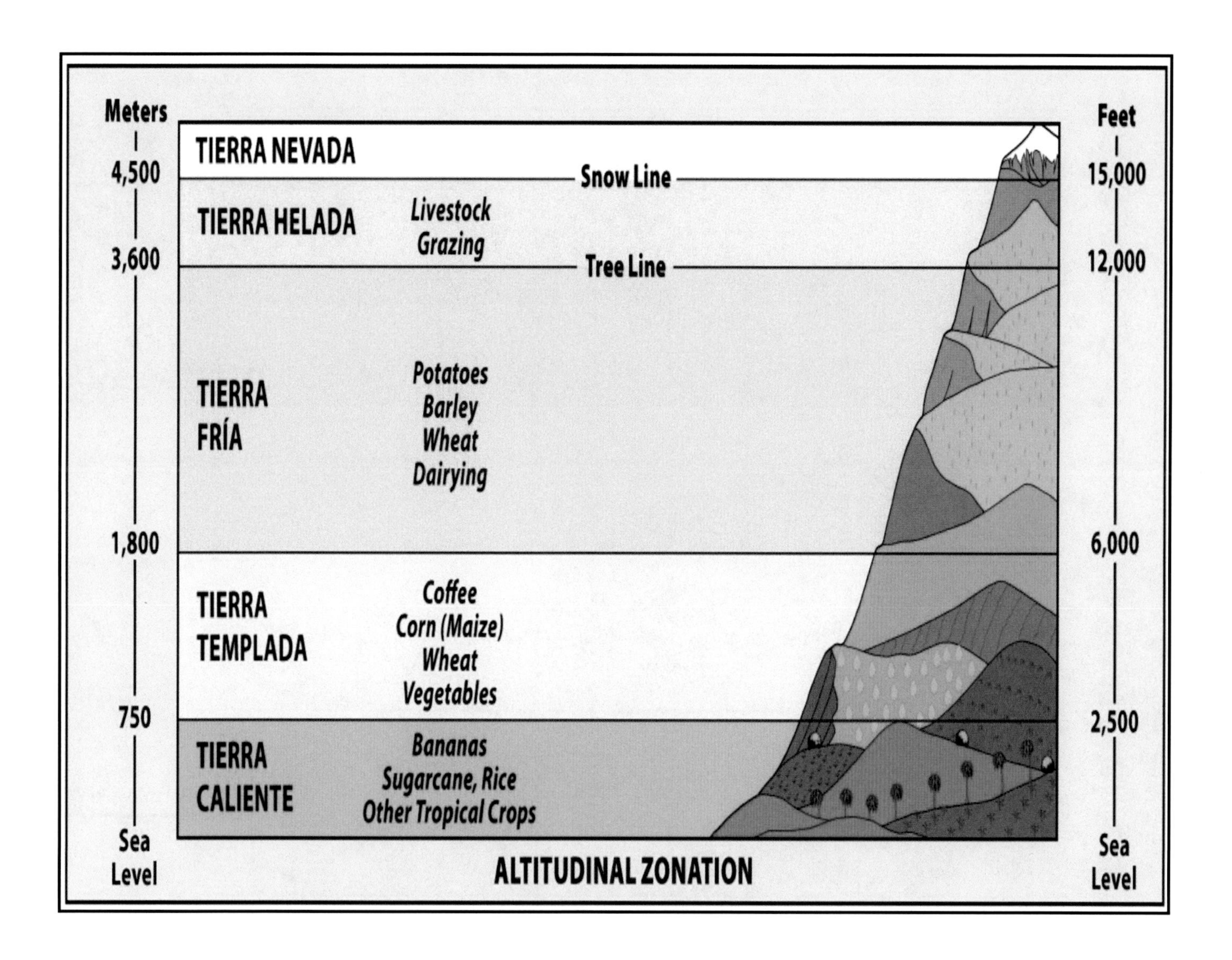

Meters
4,500
3,600
1,800
750
Sea Level
Feet
15,000
12,000
6,000
2,500
Sea Level
TIERRA NEVADA
Snow Line
TIERRA HELADA
Livestock Grazing
Tree Line
TIERRA FRÍA
Potatoes
Barley
Wheat
Dairying
TIERRA TEMPLADA
Coffee
Corn (Maize)
Wheat
Vegetables
TIERRA CALIENTE
Bananas
Sugarcane, Rice
Other Tropical Crops
ALTITUDINAL ZONATION

Terrace Farming

Terrace farming prevents the washing away of soil nutrients by the rains. ... terraces trap rainwater allowing the people to engage in cultivation of water-intensive crops such as rice.

Terrace farming is an important agricultural method that has made farming in mountainous parts of the world possible.

Tyrell Heaton –in the Sacred Valley, near Pisac, Peru

Terrace Farming in Peru

Terrace Farming in China

Tyrell Heaton – north of Beijing, China

Tropical Deforestation

- **Clearing of rural lands** to accommodate cattle and export production of commodities
- **Logging** of tropical forests to meet global demands for new housing, paper, and furniture
- **Population expansion**: forests are cut to provide crop-raising space and firewood

Tyrell Heaton – mainland Belize: slash and burning the forest and other vegetation to make room for agriculture

This is what healthy forest looks like in that area

Tyrell Heaton

Developing the Amazon

Macapá
Marajó Bay
Marajó Island
Ananindeua
BELÉM
Negro
AMAZON
Porteira
Balbina Reservoir
Alenquer
La Pedrera
Japurá
Putumayo
MANAUS
Santarém
Tefé
Amazon
Itaituba
São Luís
Tocantins
Xingu
SELVAS
Madeira
Tapajós
Marabá
Imperatriz
Teresina
Araras
Cruzeiro do Sul
BASIN
Purus
Araguaína
Floriano
SERTÃO
Pucallpa
Pôrto Velho
Teles Pires
Petrolina
Rio Branco
Palmas
Sobradinho Reservoir
Riberalta
Ji-Paraná (Rondônia)
BRAZIL
Araguaia
Feira

- Application of the '**Growth Pole**' concept
- Using the **resources of the region** for the development of the country
- **Environmental concerns**
  - Deforestation, more than 15% of forest is gone

Agricultural Systems in South America

Wide Range of Systems

- Subsistence in the Andean highlands and in lowland Amazon
- Commercial commodity production in temperate and savanna environments
- Cattle important everywhere

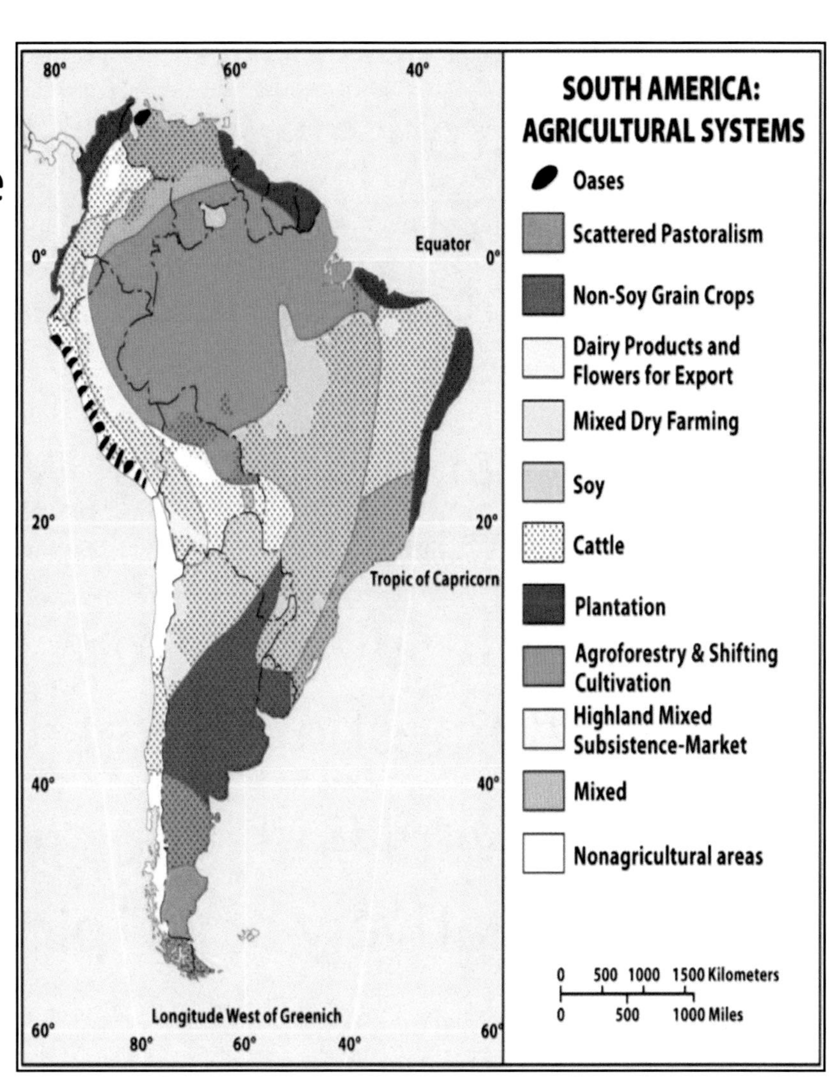

SOUTH AMERICA: AGRICULTURAL SYSTEMS
Oases
Scattered Pastoralism
Non-Soy Grain Crops
Dairy Products and Flowers for Export
Mixed Dry Farming
Soy
Cattle
Plantation
Agroforestry & Shifting Cultivation
Highland Mixed Subsistence-Market
Mixed
Nonagricultural areas
Equator
Tropic of Capricorn
Longitude West of Greenich
80°
60°
40°
0°
20°
40°
60°
0 500 1000 1500 Kilometers
0 500 1000 Miles

Hacienda vs. Plantation

- **Hacienda:**
  - Spanish cattle-holding institution
  - Purpose was land-holding not profit-generating
  - Not efficient but high social prestige
  - Year round jobs; workers lived on the land
  - Self-sufficient but surplus for domestic market
  - Diversified crops grown on relatively small plots of land

Hacienda vs. Plantation

- **Plantation:**
  - Production oriented for export
  - Efficiency is key
  - Typically a single cash crop (monocrop)
  - Seasonal employment
  - Purpose was commercial profit
  - Market vulnerability
  - Capital and technology imported

Maquiladoras

- Initiated after WWII to accommodate returning *Braceros* (contract laborers who had worked in the US during WWII)
- Came into its own after the initiation of **NAFTA**
  - Takes advantage of much lower wages in Mexico
- **Foreign owned assembly plants**
  - Assemble imported, duty-free components/raw materials
  - Export the finished products mostly to the US
    - Electronic components and appliances,
    - auto parts, clothing, furniture

- Today
  - >4,000 *Maquiladoras*
  - >1.2 million employees
  - Threatened by lower wages in China

Agriculture in the United States

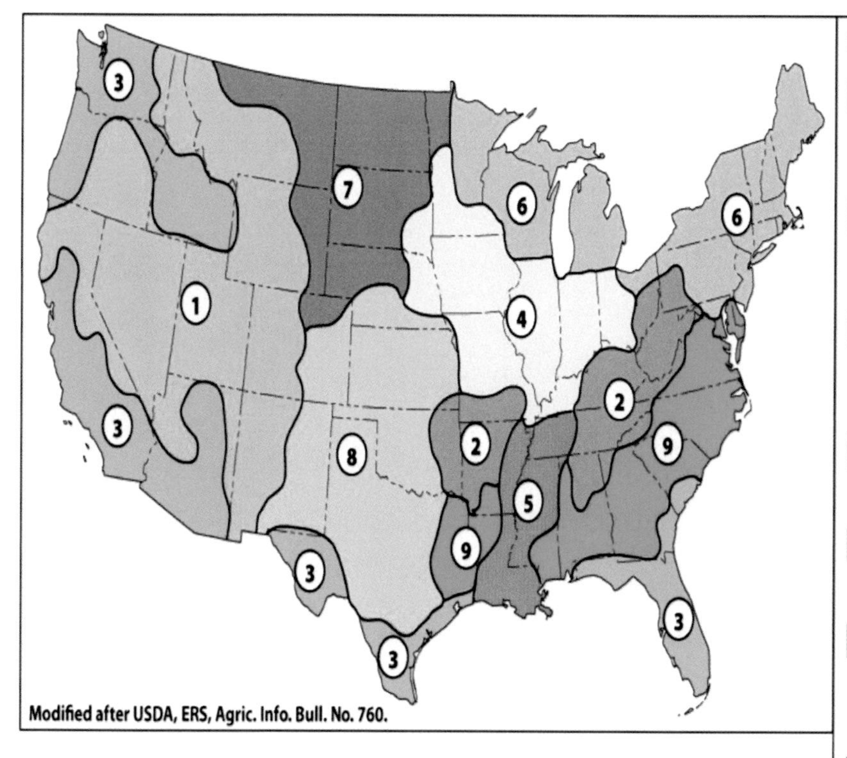
Modified after USDA, ERS, Agric. Info. Bull. No. 760.

U.S. FARM RESOURCE REGIONS

1 BASIN AND RANGE
Largest share of nonfamily farms, smallest share of U.S. cropland.
4 percent of farms, 4 percent of value of production, 4 percent of cropland.
Cattle, wheat, and sorghum farms.

2 EASTERN UPLANDS
Most small farms of any region.
15 percent of farms, 5 percent of production value, and 6 percent of cropland.
Part-time cattle, tobacco, and poultry farms.

3 FRUITFUL RIM
Largest share of large and very large family and nonfamily farms.
10 percent of farms, 22 percent of production value, 8 percent of cropland.
Fruit, vegetable, nursery, and cotton farms.

4 HEARTLAND
Most farms (22 percent), highest value of production (23 percent), and most cropland (27 percent).
Cash grain and cattle farms.

5 MISSISSIPPI PORTAL
Higher proportions of both small and larger farms than elsewhere.
5 percent of farms, 4 percent of value, 5 percent of cropland.
Cotton, rice, poultry, and hog farms.

6 NORTHERN CRESCENT
Most populous region.
15 percent of farms, 15 percent of value of production, 9 percent of cropland.
Dairy, general crop, and cash grain farms.

7 NORTHERN GREAT PLAINS
Largest farms and smallest population.
5 percent of farms, 6 percent of production value, 17 percent of cropland.
Wheat, cattle, and sheep farms.

8 PRAIRIE GATEWAY
Second in wheat, oat, barley, rice, and cotton production.
13 percent of farms, 12 percent of production value, 17 percent of cropland.
Cattle, wheat, sorghum, cotton, and rice farms.

9 SOUTHERN SEABOARD
Mix of small and larger farms.
11 percent of farms, 9 percent of production value, 6 percent of cropland.
Part-time cattle, general field crop, and poultry farms.

Rural South Dakota – Tyrell Heaton

Climate as a Limiting Element

Agriculture

- Short growing seasons
- Drought prone
- Erosion (accelerated via snow melt)

Settlement patterns & transportation

Industry

- High energy consumption
- Specialized equipment and facilities - $$$

Logistics

- Permafrost in far north; spring and fall mud

Village east of the Ural Mountains near Omsk, Russia.
Continentality causes hot summers and very cold winters.
Tyrell Heaton

The vast size of Siberia makes isolation and transportation an issue

Tyrell Heaton
Tyrell Heaton

Truck on road in Eastern Siberia

On the train across Siberia there are trees for days on end

Spatial Interaction

- Involves contact of people in two or more places for the purposes of **exchanging** goods or ideas
- **Movement** across geographic space
- Principles:
  - **Complementarity**
  - **Transferability**
  - **Intervening Opportunity**

APL

Tyrell Heaton – Container ship going up the Savannah River, Georgia

Complementarity

- Two places, through an **exchange** of goods, can specifically satisfy each other's demands
- One area has a **surplus** of an item demanded by a second area

Germany
Italy

Transferability

- The **ease** with which a commodity may be transported or the capacity to move a good at a bearable **cost**
- Rivers, mountain passes, road networks serve as routes
- Advances in transportation technology increase transferability

Tyrell Heaton - Ambassador Bridge connecting Windsor Canada to Detroit, USA

Intervening Opportunity

The presence of a nearer source of supply or opportunity that acts to diminish the attractiveness of more distant sources and sites

Notice the difference between traffic patterns with an intervening opportunity

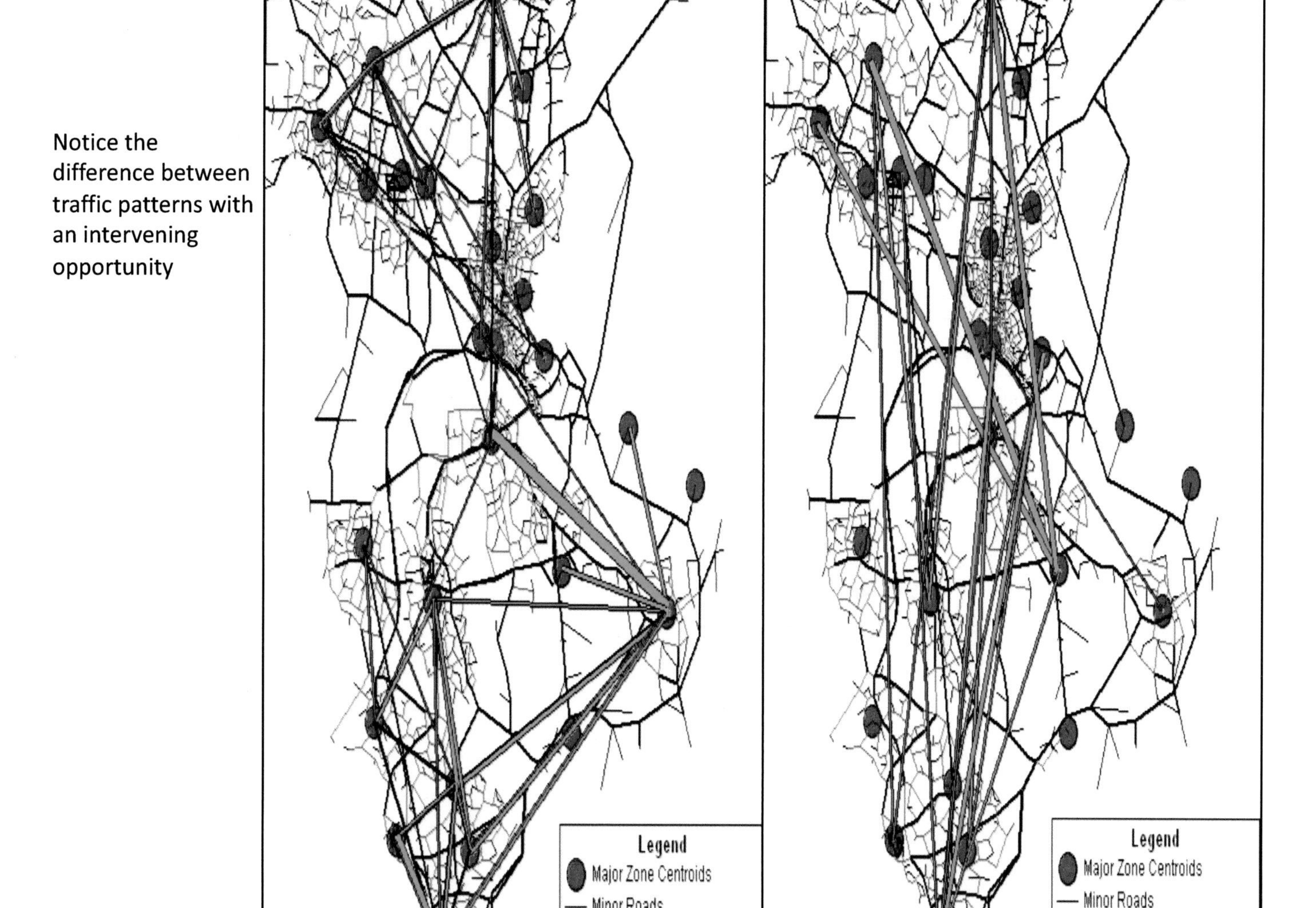

Legend
Major Zone Centroids
Minor Roads
Main Roads
Positive Residuals > 100 Trips
750
375
187.5
Legend
Major Zone Centroids
Minor Roads
Main Roads
Negative Residuals > 100 Trips
750
375
187.5

Industrial Revolution

- Developed in the **UK** between 1750-1850
- Evolved from **technical innovations** that occurred in British industry
- Proved to be a major catalyst towards **increased urbanization**
- Produced a **distinct spatial pattern** in Europe

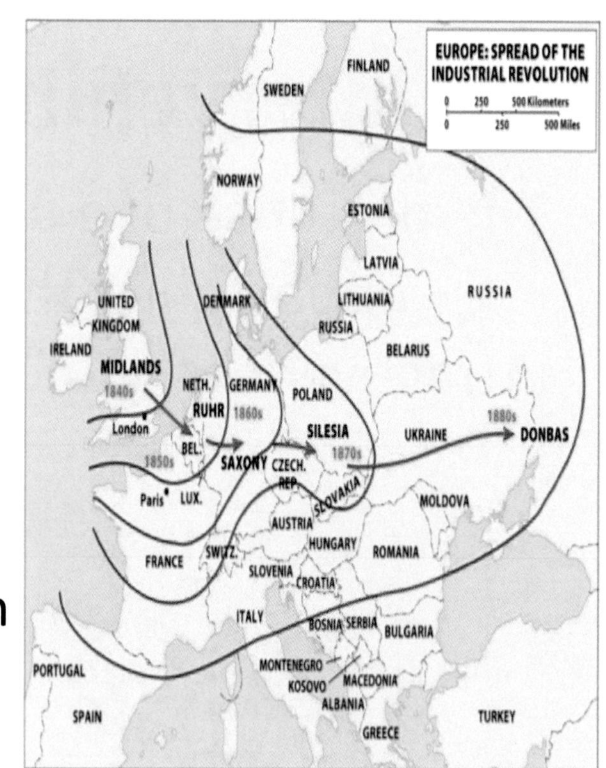

EUROPE: SPREAD OF THE INDUSTRIAL REVOLUTION
FINLAND
SWEDEN
NORWAY
ESTONIA
LATVIA
UNITED KINGDOM
DENMARK
LITHUANIA
RUSSIA
RUSSIA
IRELAND
BELARUS
MIDLANDS
1840s
NETH.
GERMANY
POLAND
RUHR
1860s
London
BEL.
SILESIA
1870s
UKRAINE
1880s
DONBAS
1850s
SAXONY
CZECH. REP.
SLOVAKIA
Paris
LUX.
MOLDOVA
AUSTRIA
FRANCE
SWITZ.
HUNGARY
ROMANIA
SLOVENIA
CROATIA
ITALY
BOSNIA
SERBIA
BULGARIA
PORTUGAL
MONTENEGRO
KOSOVO
MACEDONIA
ALBANIA
SPAIN
GREECE
TURKEY

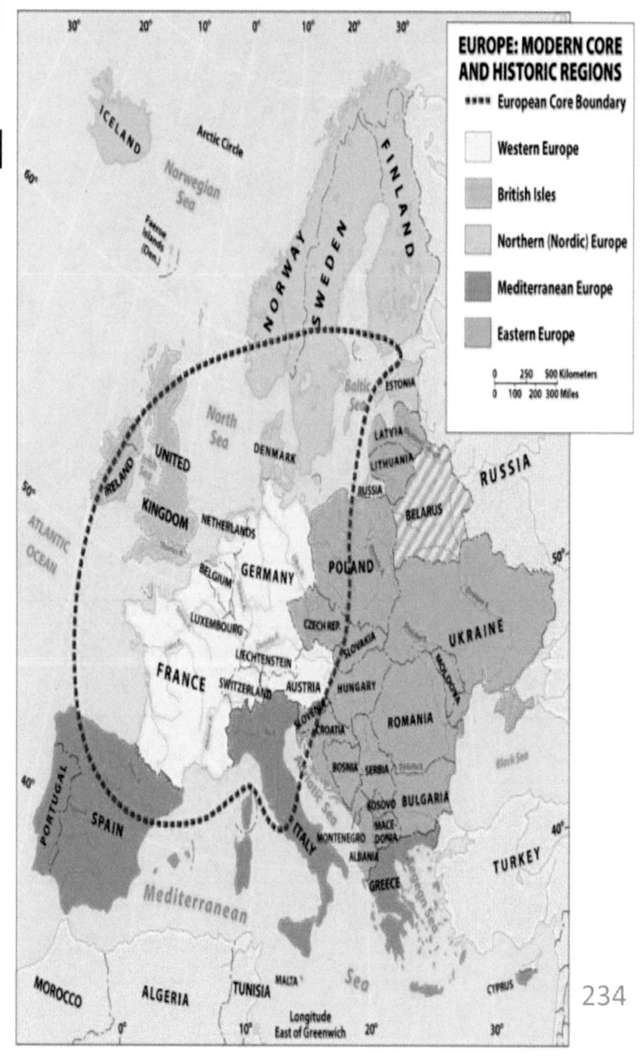

EUROPE: MODERN CORE AND HISTORIC REGIONS
European Core Boundary
Western Europe
British Isles
Northern (Nordic) Europe
Mediterranean Europe
Eastern Europe
ICELAND
Arctic Circle
Norwegian Sea
NORWAY
SWEDEN
FINLAND
ESTONIA
North Sea
Baltic Sea
LATVIA
LITHUANIA
DENMARK
RUSSIA
IRELAND
UNITED KINGDOM
RUSSIA
BELARUS
ATLANTIC OCEAN
NETHERLANDS
GERMANY
POLAND
BELGIUM
LUXEMBOURG
CZECH REP.
SLOVAKIA
UKRAINE
LIECHTENSTEIN
MOLDOVA
FRANCE
SWITZERLAND
AUSTRIA
HUNGARY
SLOVENIA
CROATIA
ROMANIA
BOSNIA
SERBIA
PORTUGAL
SPAIN
KOSOVO
BULGARIA
MONTENEGRO
MACEDONIA
ITALY
ALBANIA
GREECE
TURKEY
Mediterranean
Sea
MOROCCO
ALGERIA
TUNISIA
MALTA
CYPRUS
Longitude East of Greenwich

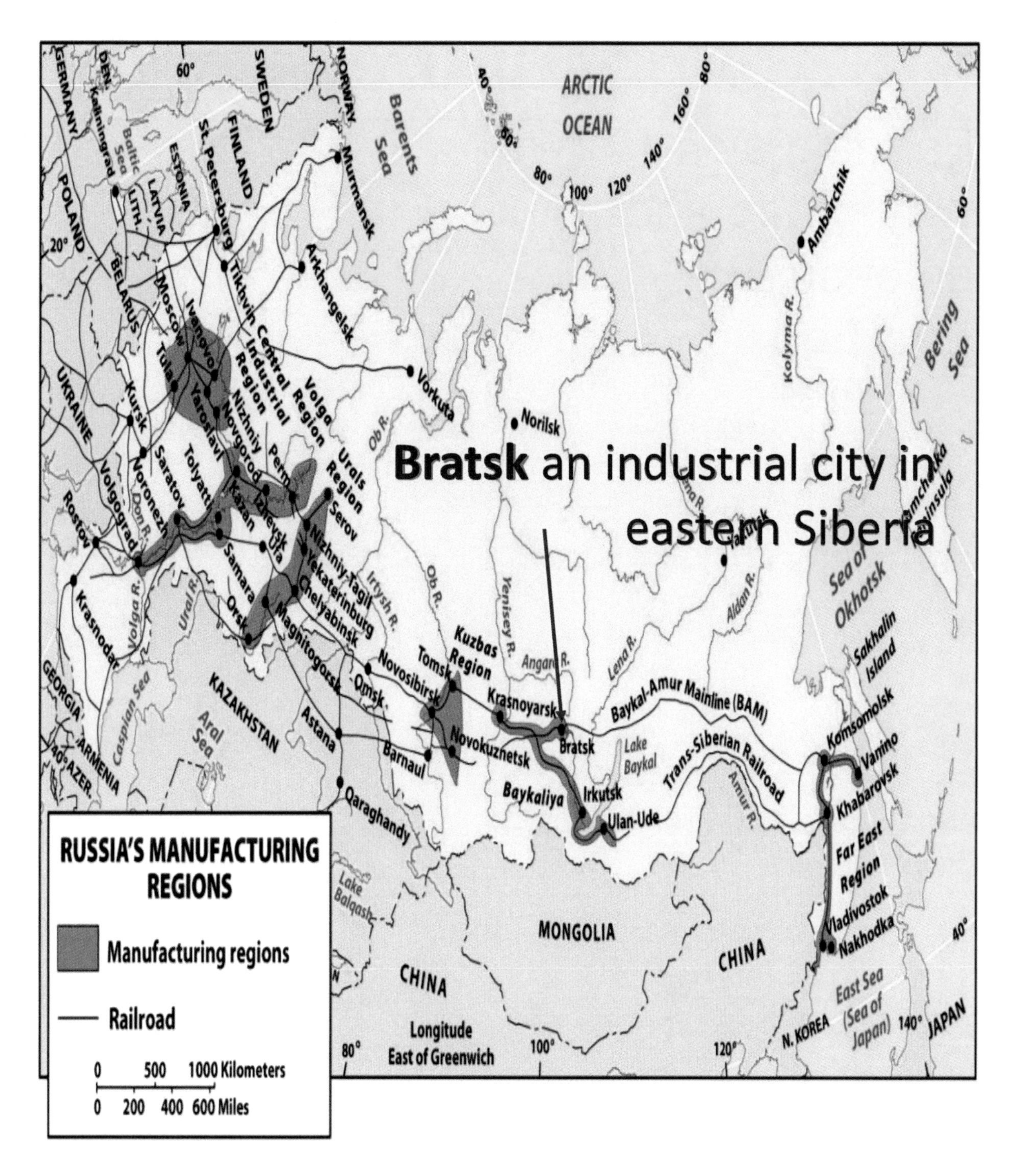

Bratsk an industrial city in eastern Siberia
RUSSIA'S MANUFACTURING REGIONS
Manufacturing regions
Railroad
0 500 1000 Kilometers
0 200 400 600 Miles
ARCTIC OCEAN
Barents Sea
Bering Sea
Sea of Okhotsk
Caspian Sea
Aral Sea
Baltic Sea
Lake Baykal
Lake Balqash
East Sea (Sea of Japan)
Longitude East of Greenwich
GERMANY
POLAND
DEN.
SWEDEN
NORWAY
FINLAND
ESTONIA
LATVIA
LITH.
BELARUS
UKRAINE
GEORGIA
ARMENIA
AZER.
KAZAKHSTAN
MONGOLIA
CHINA
N. KOREA
JAPAN
Kaliningrad
St. Petersburg
Murmansk
Arkhangelsk
Tikhvin
Moscow
Ivanovo
Tula
Yaroslavl
Kursk
Voronezh
Saratov
Tolyatti
Kazan
Nizhniy Novgorod
Perm
Izhevsk
Ufa
Samara
Volgograd
Rostov
Krasnodar
Orsk
Magnitogorsk
Chelyabinsk
Yekaterinburg
Nizhniy Tagil
Serov
Vorkuta
Norilsk
Omsk
Novosibirsk
Tomsk
Barnaul
Novokuznetsk
Krasnoyarsk
Bratsk
Irkutsk
Ulan-Ude
Baykaliya
Astana
Qaraghandy
Komsomolsk
Vanino
Khabarovsk
Vladivostok
Nakhodka
Ambarchik
Central Industrial Region
Volga Region
Urals Region
Kuzbas Region
Far East Region
Sakhalin Island
Baykal-Amur Mainline (BAM)
Trans-Siberian Railroad
Volga R.
Don R.
Ural R.
Ob R.
Irtysh R.
Yenisey R.
Angara R.
Lena R.
Aldan R.
Amur R.
Kolyma R.

Long-term **costs of industrialization**: widely dispersed production, distant markets, and pollution resulting from burning coal and other fuels without considering environmental impacts

Agriculture in India

Farming as a **way of life** and an enduring **tradition**

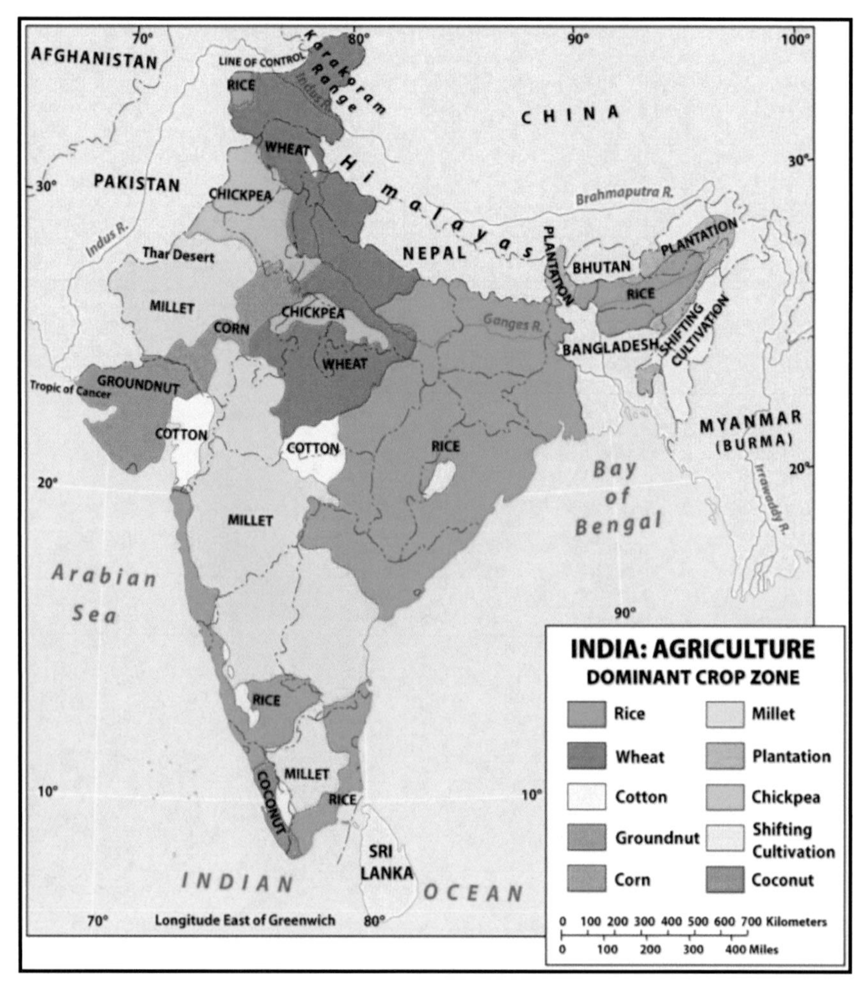

AFGHANISTAN
PAKISTAN
CHINA
NEPAL
BHUTAN
BANGLADESH
MYANMAR (BURMA)
SRI LANKA
Karakoram Range
Himalayas
LINE OF CONTROL
Indus R.
Brahmaputra R.
Ganges R.
Irrawaddy R.
Thar Desert
Tropic of Cancer
Arabian Sea
Bay of Bengal
INDIAN OCEAN
RICE
WHEAT
CHICKPEA
MILLET
CORN
GROUNDNUT
COTTON
PLANTATION
SHIFTING CULTIVATION
COCONUT
Longitude East of Greenwich
INDIA: AGRICULTURE
DOMINANT CROP ZONE
Rice
Millet
Wheat
Plantation
Cotton
Chickpea
Groundnut
Shifting Cultivation
Corn
Coconut
0 100 200 300 400 500 600 700 Kilometers
0 100 200 300 400 Miles

India - This is Lalu's garden; this is his wife in their 'kitchen' cooking up some fresh chapatti and greens

A Two Class System?

- •Per capita GNI- $8,230
- •Largest income gap in the realm (world)
    - •Wealthiest 10% of the population...
        - own 2/3 of the land
        - control more than 50% of the country's wealth
    - •Poverty has increased by 50% since 1980

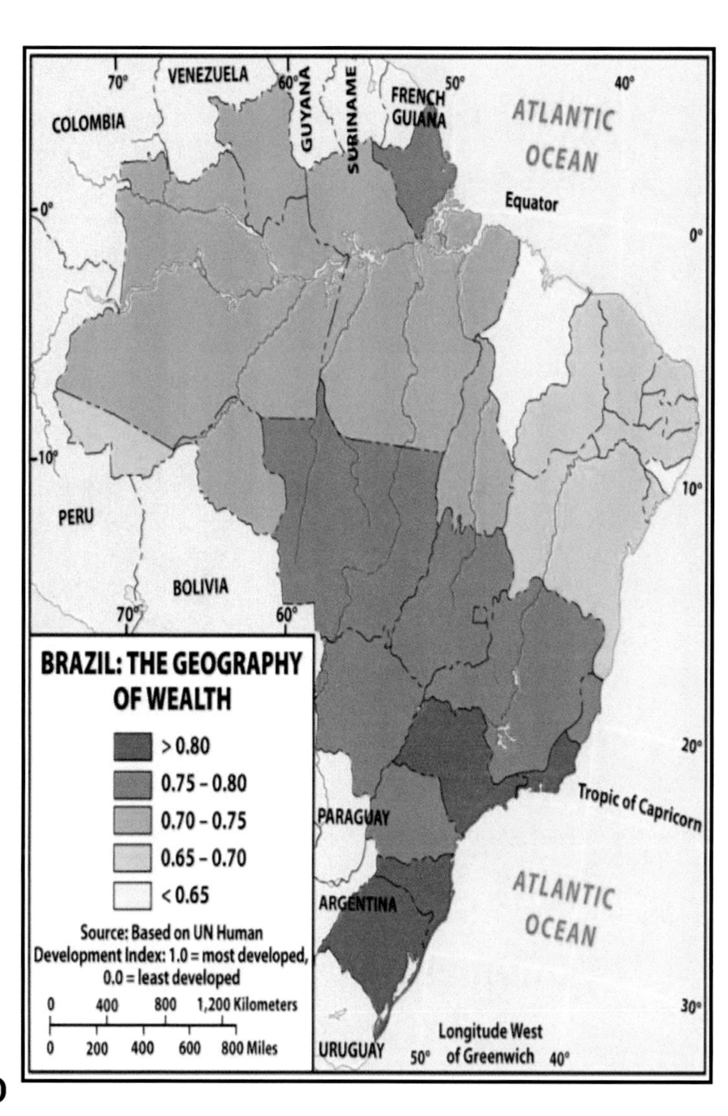

BRAZIL: THE GEOGRAPHY OF WEALTH
> 0.80
0.75 - 0.80
0.70 - 0.75
0.65 - 0.70
< 0.65
Source: Based on UN Human Development Index: 1.0 = most developed, 0.0 = least developed
0 400 800 1,200 Kilometers
0 200 400 600 800 Miles
VENEZUELA
COLOMBIA
GUYANA
SURINAME
FRENCH GUIANA
ATLANTIC OCEAN
Equator
PERU
BOLIVIA
PARAGUAY
ARGENTINA
URUGUAY
Tropic of Capricorn
ATLANTIC OCEAN
Longitude West of Greenwich

India's Rise as Center of Technology

- **Why has India done so well developing in the Information Technology sector?**
  - Cultural high **value of education**
  - Has excellent centers of **higher education,** especially in the sciences
  - Legacy of **colonialism:** **English** as the lingua franca of all educated Indians

Traditional manufacturing

Growth Pole Theory

- Aims to promote **growth in the peripheral parts** of countries
- Hope is that it will set off '**ripples**' of development
- **Subsidized investment** in an attempt to spread economic activities and benefits
  - Create jobs in depressed areas
  - Reduce uneven concentrations of wealth
  - Decentralize industry

The Rise of Modern Asia

Today, it is clear that the Asian century has begun. There are many factors that caused this enormous change, including globalization.

Hanwha

Tyrell Heaton, Seoul, South Korea

Asian self-confidence is growing … from the Korean and Vietnam wars to centuries of European colonial rule, this had progressively reduced Asian self-confidence. For instance in South Asia, future generations of Indian citizens will be wondering how 300 million Indians allowed themselves to be passively ruled by fewer than 100,000 Britons. Today East Asia is known as one of the most technologically advanced regions in the world and Japan's success after WWII helped bring a rise to the four Asian tigers (South Korea, Hong Kong, Taiwan, and Singapore).

The Four Asian Tigers

The term Four Asian Tigers (also known as the Four Dragons) was created to reference the newly highly free and developed economies of Hong Kong, Singapore, South Korea, and Taiwan.

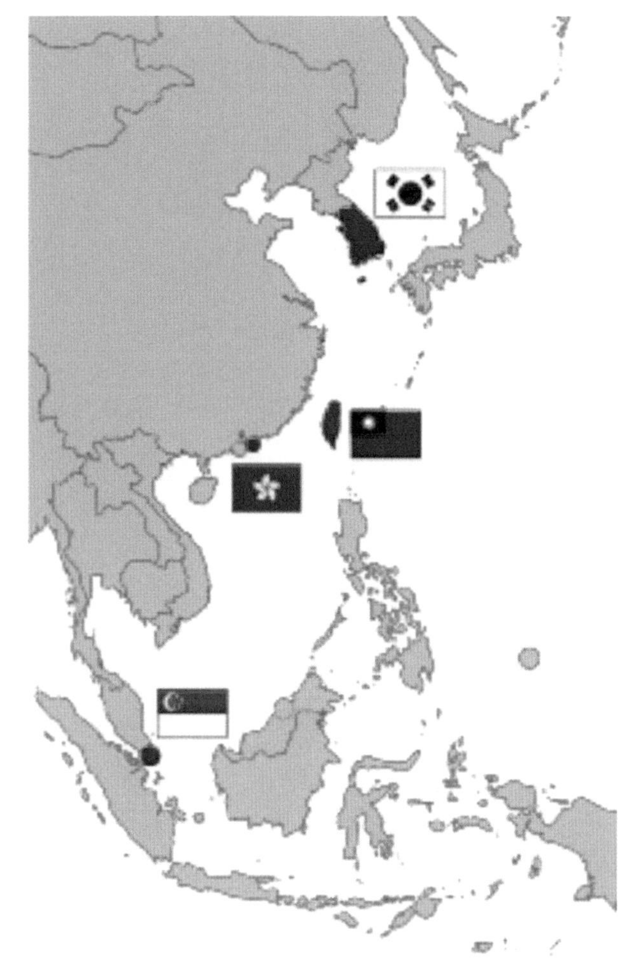

Each of the Asian Tigers has specific characteristics and pillars of their economies:

South Korea: Located at the north of Southeast Asia is considered one of the world's wealthiest nations. South Korea has a developed market economy, with high income and one of world's fastest growing economies since the second half of the twentieth century. South Korean highly educated population is largely responsible of the high tech explosion and rapid economic development, which its major economic trade is the exports.

Taiwan: It has a developed capitalist economy with a professional economic planning focused in industrialization and services. Taiwan is one of the major contributors to the Global Value Chain of the Electronics Industry. Electronic components, semiconductors and personal computers are three of the high international strength of Taiwan's Technology Industry.

Hong Kong: Considered one of the major international financial centers in the world, its service oriented economy is empowered by its low taxes, low export rates and financial market.

Singapore: Is a highly developed market economy with global strength in trade. Government linked companies play a substantial role in the country economy fueled by high rates of foreign direct investment. Its economy has a highly attractive climate for investors. Its major economic engines are the electronic, chemicals and financial services.

Australia's Economy

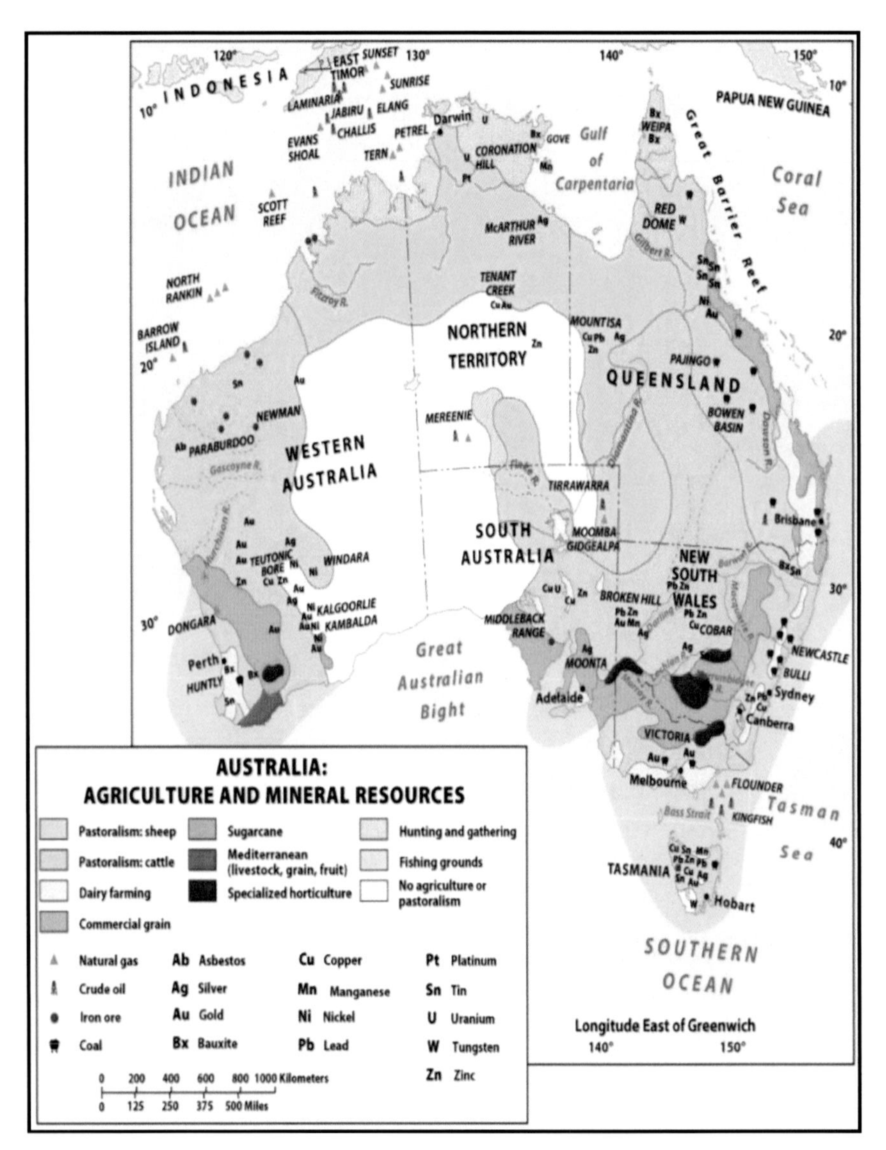

AUSTRALIA:
AGRICULTURE AND MINERAL RESOURCES
Pastoralism: sheep
Pastoralism: cattle
Dairy farming
Commercial grain
Sugarcane
Mediterranean (livestock, grain, fruit)
Specialized horticulture
Hunting and gathering
Fishing grounds
No agriculture or pastoralism
Natural gas
Crude oil
Iron ore
Coal
Ab Asbestos
Ag Silver
Au Gold
Bx Bauxite
Cu Copper
Mn Manganese
Ni Nickel
Pb Lead
Pt Platinum
Sn Tin
U Uranium
W Tungsten
Zn Zinc
0 200 400 600 800 1000 Kilometers
0 125 250 375 500 Miles
INDONESIA
PAPUA NEW GUINEA
INDIAN OCEAN
Coral Sea
Gulf of Carpentaria
Great Barrier Reef
NORTHERN TERRITORY
QUEENSLAND
WESTERN AUSTRALIA
SOUTH AUSTRALIA
NEW SOUTH WALES
VICTORIA
TASMANIA
Great Australian Bight
Tasman Sea
SOUTHERN OCEAN
Darwin
Brisbane
Sydney
Canberra
Melbourne
Adelaide
Perth
Hobart
Longitude East of Greenwich

- **Principal patterns**:
  - Exports raw materials
  - Has been based heavily on the primary sector activities
  - Dependent on world markets
- **Import-substitution industries**
- Small **domestic market**
- **Trade links** with *Asian tigers*
- Increasingly a **service** economy
- **Tourism** rising

Agglomeration

Agglomeration is a geographic concentration of related economic activities. The agglomeration of related economic activity is a central feature of economic geography.

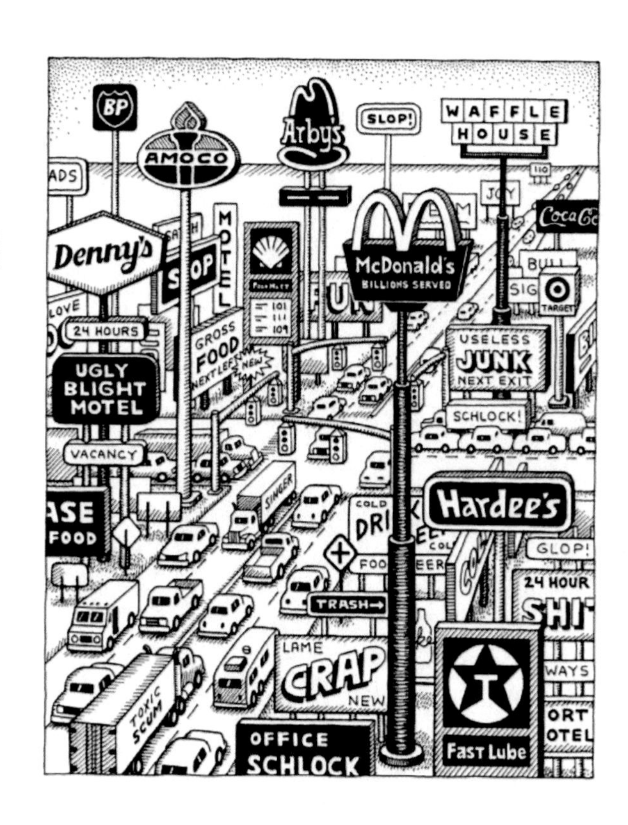
BP
AMOCO
Arby's
SLOP!
WAFFLE HOUSE
Denny's
MOTEL
McDonald's
BILLIONS SERVED
24 HOURS
UGLY BLIGHT MOTEL
GROSS FOOD
USELESS JUNK NEXT EXIT
SCHLOCK!
VACANCY
Hardee's
GLOP!
24 HOUR
TRASH
LAME CRAP NEW
TOXIC SCUM
OFFICE SCHLOCK
Fast Lube

Agglomeration arises from interdependencies across complementary economic activities that give rise to increasing returns.

Trade-offs:
Either enjoying agglomeration economies of scale, or avoiding transportation costs with regards to spatially immobile resources.

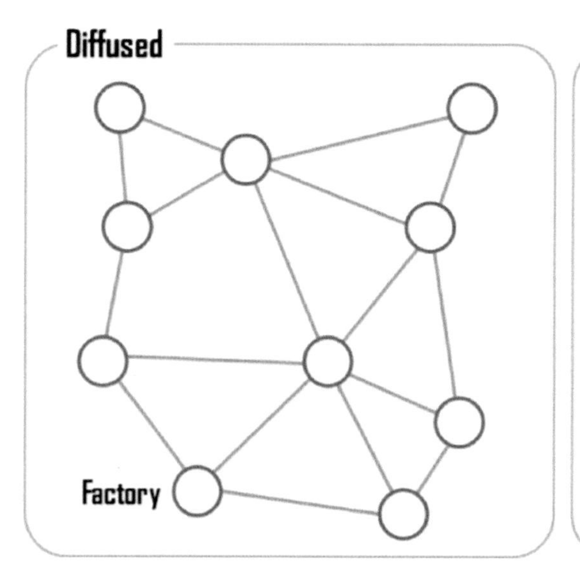
Diffused
Factory

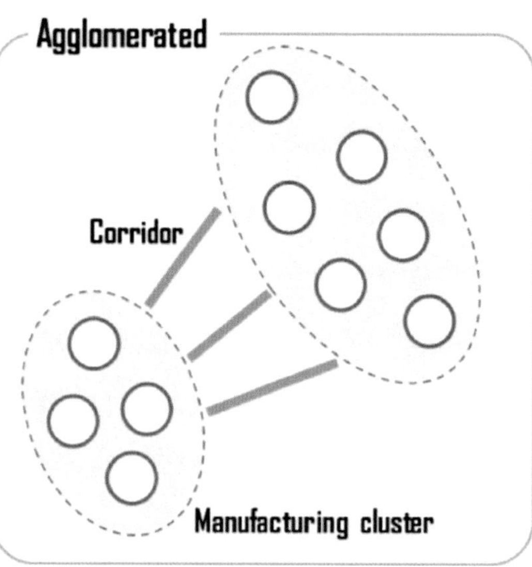
Agglomerated
Corridor
Manufacturing cluster

An Urbanizing World

Dubai, UAE – Tyrell Heaton

City

- The term is a **political designation**
- Refers to a **municipal entity** that is **governed** by some kind of administrative organization
- Cities (especially capitals) are often
  - the **foci of the state**
  - **microcosms** of their national cultures

Tyrell Heaton – Genoa, Italy

Urbanization

- Urbanization
  - The movement to and clustering of people in towns and cities
  - The percentage of a country's population living in cities
    - 80% - continent-wide in South America

Urbanization

1900	2 out of every 10 people lived in an urban area
1990	4 out of every 10 people lived in an urban area
2010	5 out of every 10 people lived in an urban area
2030	6 out of every 10 people will live in an urban area
2050	7 out of every 10 people will live in an urban area

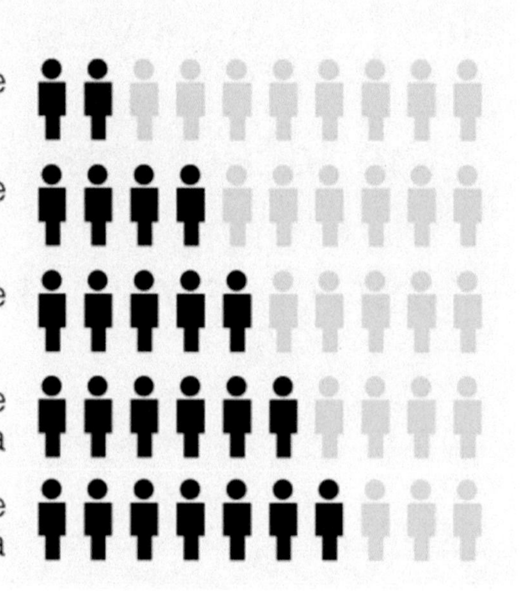

Defined by UN HABITAT as a city with a population of more than 10 million

Tyrell Heaton – Lima, Peru

An Urbanizing World

Cities today are growing at a phenomenal rate.

•Cities with more than 1 million people

In 1900 only 13 cities had a population of more than 1 million people; in 2010 there were 449 cities with more than 1 million people. By 2025 it is projected that there will be 609 cities with populations exceeding 1 million people.

In 1900, no cities had a population of more than 10 million, in 1975 there were just 5 and currently there are 37 metropolises with more than 10 million people, these are commonly referred to as megacities.

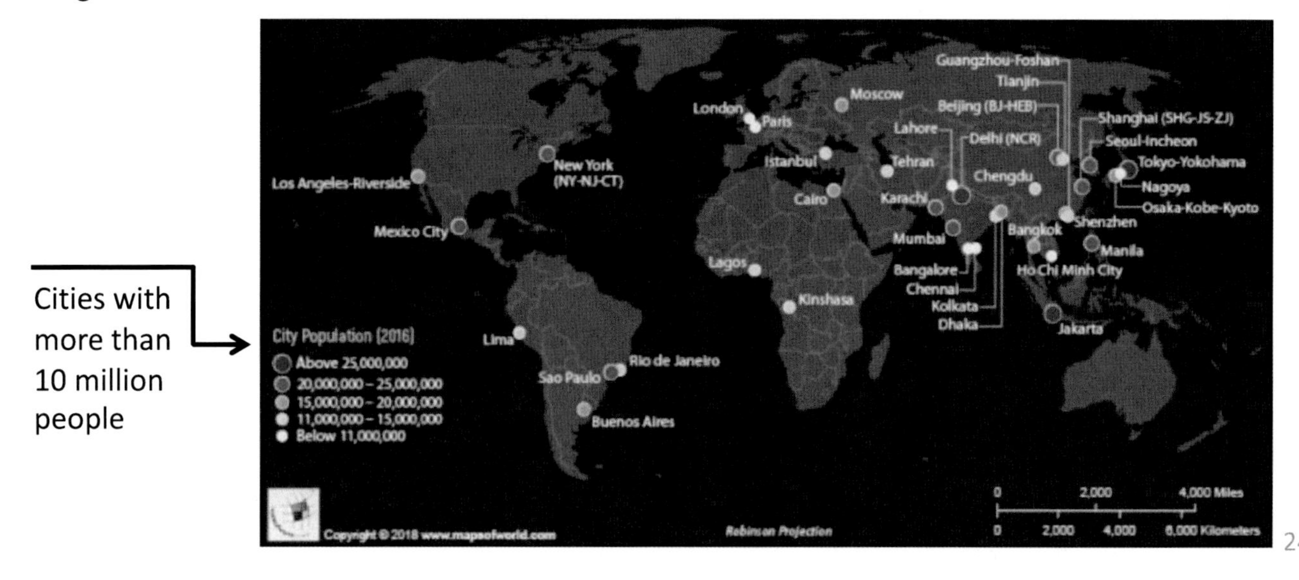

Cities with more than 10 million people
Guangzhou-Foshan
Tianjin
Moscow
Beijing (BJ-HEB)
London
Paris
Shanghai (SHG-JS-ZJ)
Lahore
Delhi (NCR)
Seoul-Incheon
New York (NY-NJ-CT)
Istanbul
Tehran
Tokyo-Yokohama
Los Angeles-Riverside
Chengdu
Nagoya
Cairo
Karachi
Osaka-Kobe-Kyoto
Shenzhen
Mexico City
Mumbai
Bangkok
Manila
Lagos
Bangalore
Ho Chi Minh City
Chennai
Kinshasa
Kolkata
Dhaka
Jakarta
City Population (2016)
Above 25,000,000
20,000,000 – 25,000,000
15,000,000 – 20,000,000
11,000,000 – 15,000,000
Below 11,000,000
Lima
Rio de Janeiro
Sao Paulo
Buenos Aires
0 2,000 4,000 Miles
0 2,000 4,000 6,000 Kilometers
Copyright © 2018 www.mapsofworld.com
Robinson Projection

The New Urban World

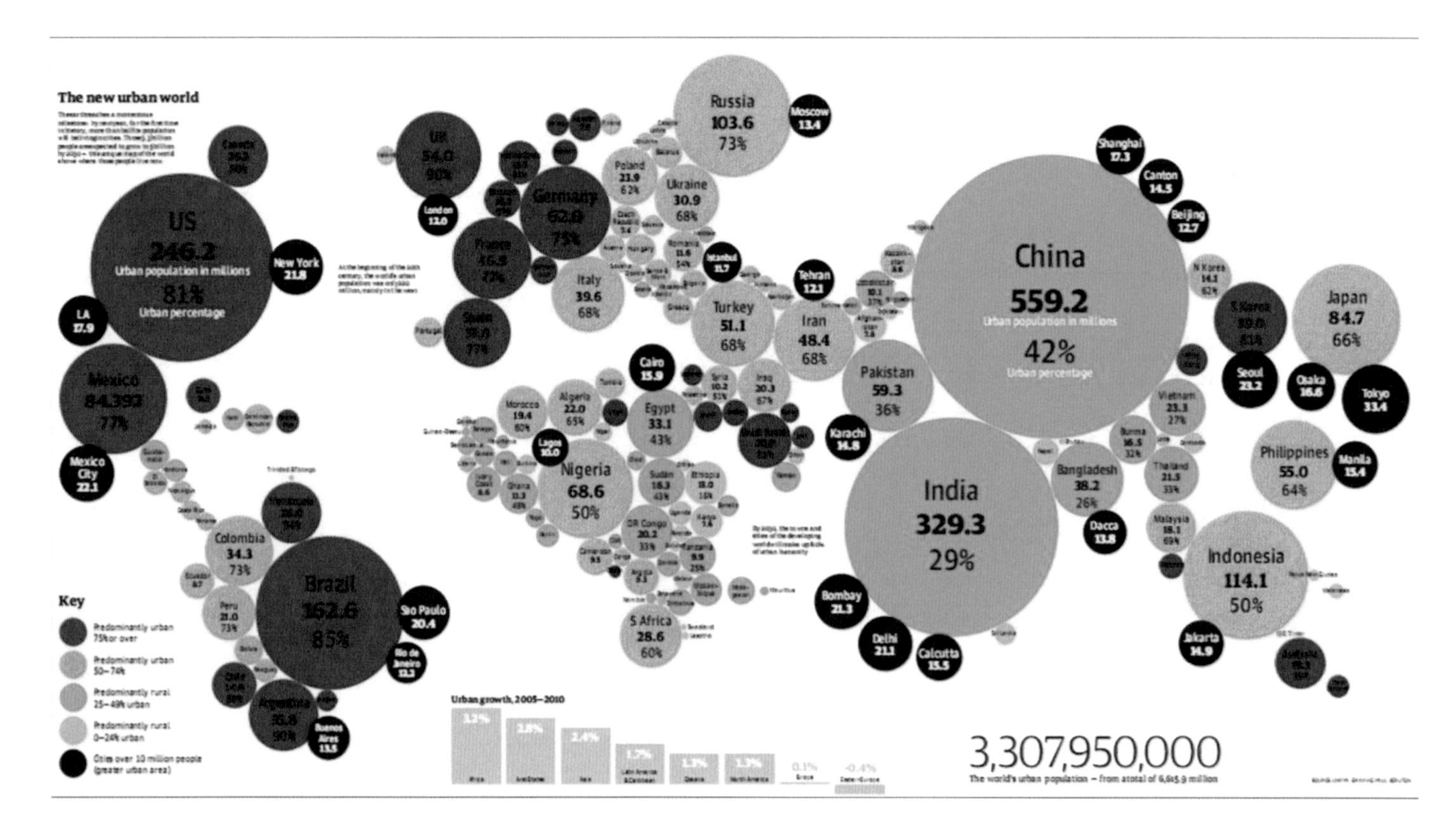

The new urban world
Russia
103.6
73%
Moscow
13.4
China
559.2
Urban population in millions
42%
Urban percentage
India
329.3
29%
US
246.2
Urban population in millions
81%
Urban percentage
New York
21.8
LA
17.9
Mexico City
22.1
Brazil
162.6
85%
Sao Paulo
20.4
Colombia
34.3
73%
UK
London
12.0
Germany
Italy
39.6
68%
Poland
23.9
62%
Ukraine
30.9
68%
Turkey
51.1
68%
Istanbul
11.7
Tehran
12.1
Iran
48.4
68%
Pakistan
59.3
36%
Karachi
14.8
Bombay
21.3
Delhi
21.1
Calcutta
15.5
Bangladesh
38.2
26%
Dacca
13.8
Shanghai
17.3
Canton
14.5
Beijing
12.7
Japan
84.7
66%
Seoul
23.2
Osaka
16.6
Tokyo
33.4
Vietnam
23.3
27%
Philippines
55.0
64%
Manila
15.4
Indonesia
114.1
50%
Jakarta
14.9
Cairo
15.9
Egypt
33.1
43%
Morocco
19.4
Algeria
22.0
65%
Lagos
10.0
Nigeria
68.6
50%
S Africa
28.6
60%
Key
Urban growth, 2005–2010
3,307,950,000

Worldwide more than the half of the world population live in cities; a city, an urban area, a metropolitan or a mega region. There are perhaps more than one million cities around the world, perhaps even more. And all of this cities have some similarities, but also a lot of differences that marks every single city to have their own specific and local identity.

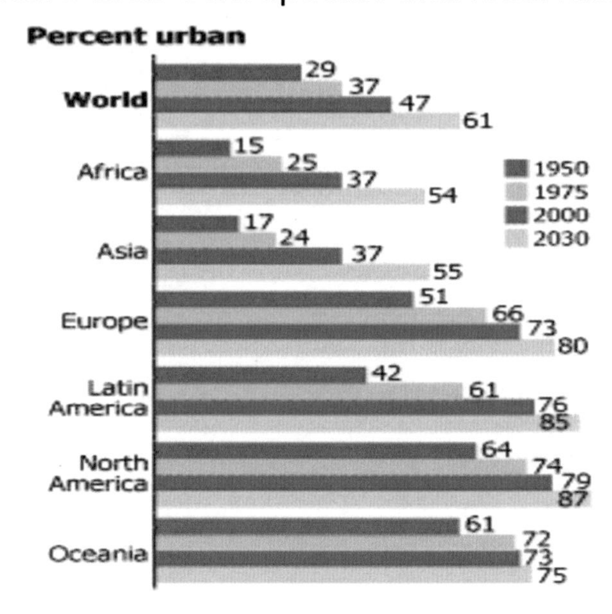

Percent urban
World
29
37
47
61
Africa
15
25
37
54
Asia
17
24
37
55
Europe
51
66
73
80
Latin America
42
61
76
85
North America
64
74
79
87
Oceania
61
72
73
75
1950
1975
2000
2030

Counter-Urbanization / Suburbanization

COUNTER-URBANIZATION is the movement out of cities to surrounding areas

SUBURBINIZATION is where the rural areas on the outskirts of towns (also known as Commuter/Dormitory towns) increasingly develop the characteristics of Urban areas. Also, outward growth of urban areas, groups of people moving to surrounding villages)

REASONS FOR COUNTER-URBANIZATION

1. Growth in transport and communication means people no longer need to live close to where they work. Increase in commuting. IT means people can work from home.
2. Government policies can encourage movement out of cities by setting up fast transport links in 'satellite towns'.
3. New business parks on out of town 'Greenfield Sites' mean people don't need to travel to the city centre – so they live close to work on outskirts.
4. Pollution and traffic congestion in cities encourage people to rural areas.
5. More people move when they retire.
6. Cities are so popular that house prices have become too high.

Suburbanization

Suburbanization is a population shift from central urban areas into suburbs, resulting in the formation of suburban sprawl. Suburbanization is inversely related to urbanization, which denotes a population shift from rural areas into urban centers.

Brisbane, Australia - The United States isn't the only country where suburbanization has occurred at a rapid rate.

In the USA there were several causes of suburbanization in the 1950s. One of them was the availability of land in the suburbs. The land was less expensive to buy in suburban areas than in urban areas. As a result people left the cities for the suburbs

Another factor in the growth of suburbs was the building of highways. In 1956, the Federal Highway Act was passed, this led to the building of highways throughout the country. As more highways were built, it made commuting from the suburbs to the cities much quicker and easier.

A third factor leading to suburban growth was the fear people had of increasing crime in the cities. People believed suburbs were safer areas than cities. The suburbs also offered a more spacious are in which to live.

Americans were more prosperous in the 1950s. Incomes were rising, and more people owned their homes. Additionally many veterans were able to get low interest loans from the GI Bill.

Rural Decline

Urbanization can have a negative effect on the rural environment

RURAL DECLINE is brought about for a number of reasons; Urbanization (inc. Push/Pull factors), Counter-Urbanization and building on 'Greenfield Sites'

Urbanization- people moving out of the countryside results in:

- little rural investment
- ageing population as young move out
- fewer extended families – changing social trends
- continued poverty
- continued reliance on agriculture
- economic stagnation

In LEDCs these factors are increased with natural disasters (drought etc),
not enough jobs etc...

Tyrell Heaton - Old Schoolhouse - White Owl, SD

Greenfield Sites are rural locations that not have been built on before.
These sites are popular with developers as they are cheaper and easier to build on. Building on 'Greenfield Sites' can lead to URBAN SPRAWL. Such housing developments can encourage further building – business parks, retail parks and leisure facilities.

Greenfield Site in Frankfurt, Indiana ⟶

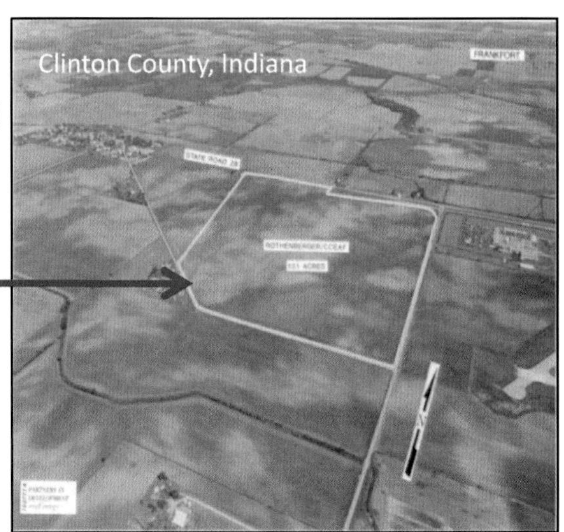
Clinton County, Indiana

Urban Tradition

- **Urbanization**
- Related concepts
  - **Primate city**
  - **Metropolis**
  - **CBD (Central Business District)**

Dubai 1990 - Dubai 2013 | Sheikh Zayed Road

Tyrell Heaton – Abu Dhabi, UAE

Primate Cities

- A country's **largest** city
- Always disproportionately larger than the second largest urban center -- more than twice the size
- Especially expressive of the national culture
- Usually (but not always) the capital

Tyrell Heaton – Kuala Lumpur, Malaysia

Examples:

Paris
London
Athens
Dublin
Lima
Buenos Aires
Bangkok
Seoul
Kuala Lumpur
Jakarta
Mexico City
Cairo
Tehran

CBD – Central Business District

Urban Development like the North American and European city model; also located on a great harbor.

0 20 Kilometers
0 10 Miles
Dharug National Park
Brisbane Water National Park
Gosford
Maroota
Hawkesbury River
Nepean River
Palm Beach
Richmond
Ku-Ring-Gai Chase National Park
Blue Mountains
South Creek
Blacktown
Parramatta
Sydney Harbor
Opera House
Fairfield
Cabramatta
SYDNEY
CBD
Canterbury
Sydney International Airport
Botany Bay
Tasman Sea
Narellan
Georges River
Sunderland
Kurnell
Heathcote National Park
Royal National Park

CBD

Sydney, Australia

CBD – Central Business District

concentric-ring theory

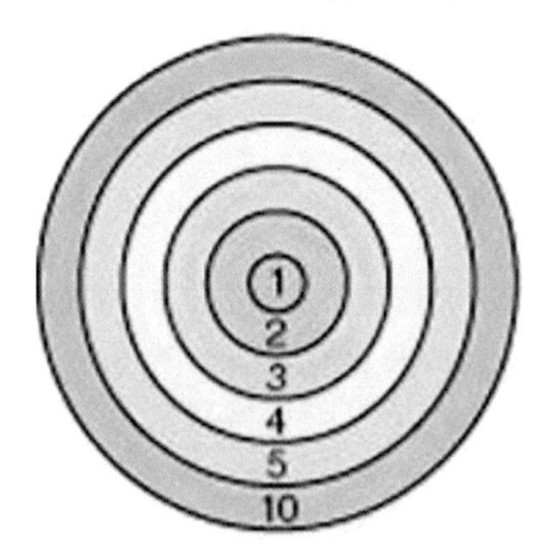
1
2
3
4
5
10

sector theory

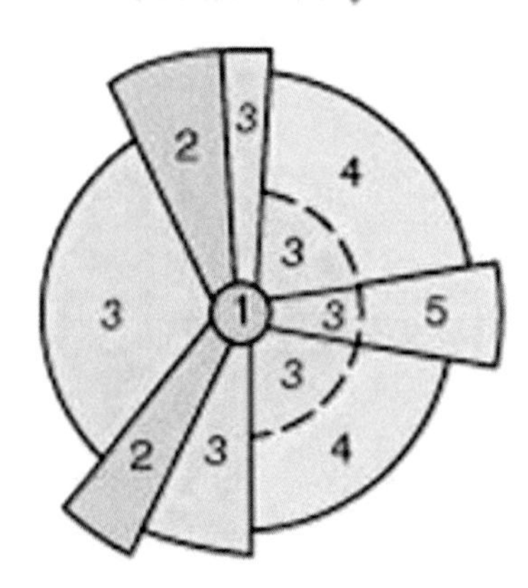
1
2
3
4
5

multiple-nuclei theory

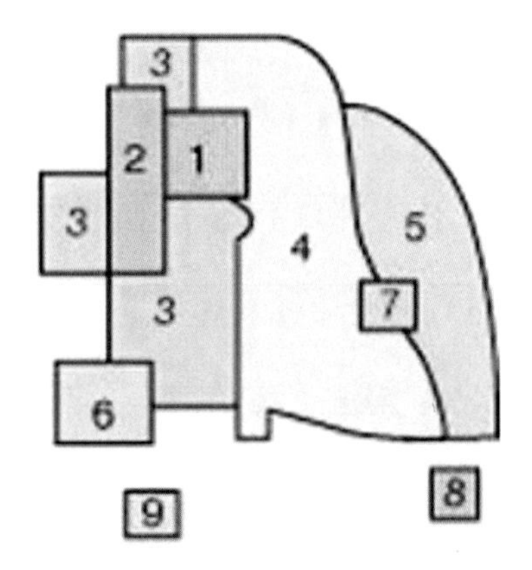
1
2
3
4
5
6
7
8
9

1 central business district (CBD)
2 wholesale light manufacturing
3 low-cost housing
4 medium-cost housing
5 high-cost housing
6 heavy manufacturing
7 outlying business district
8 residential suburb
9 industrial suburb
10 commuter zone

Urban Land Use Models

Burgess Zone Model

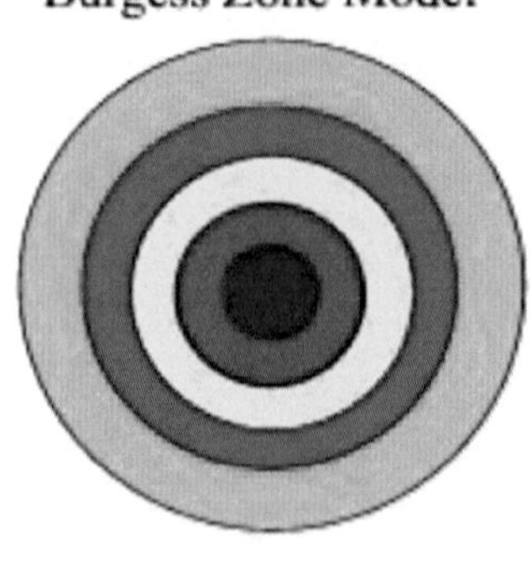

Hoyt Sector Model

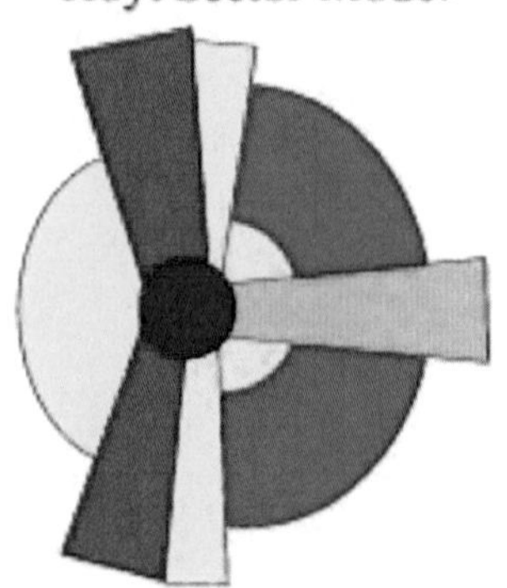

- Central Business District (CBD)
- Inner City - Wholesale Light Manufacturing
- Inner City - Low-class residential
- Inner Suburbs - Medium-Class Housing
- Outer Suburbs - High-class residential

Geographically, the CBD often coincides with the "city center" or "downtown”

The two concepts are separate: many cities have a central business district located away from its commercial or cultural city center or downtown.

Spanish Colonial Town

-**Layout** was mandated by Spanish colonial law

-Result is **regularity** in city layout throughout Spanish Middle and South America

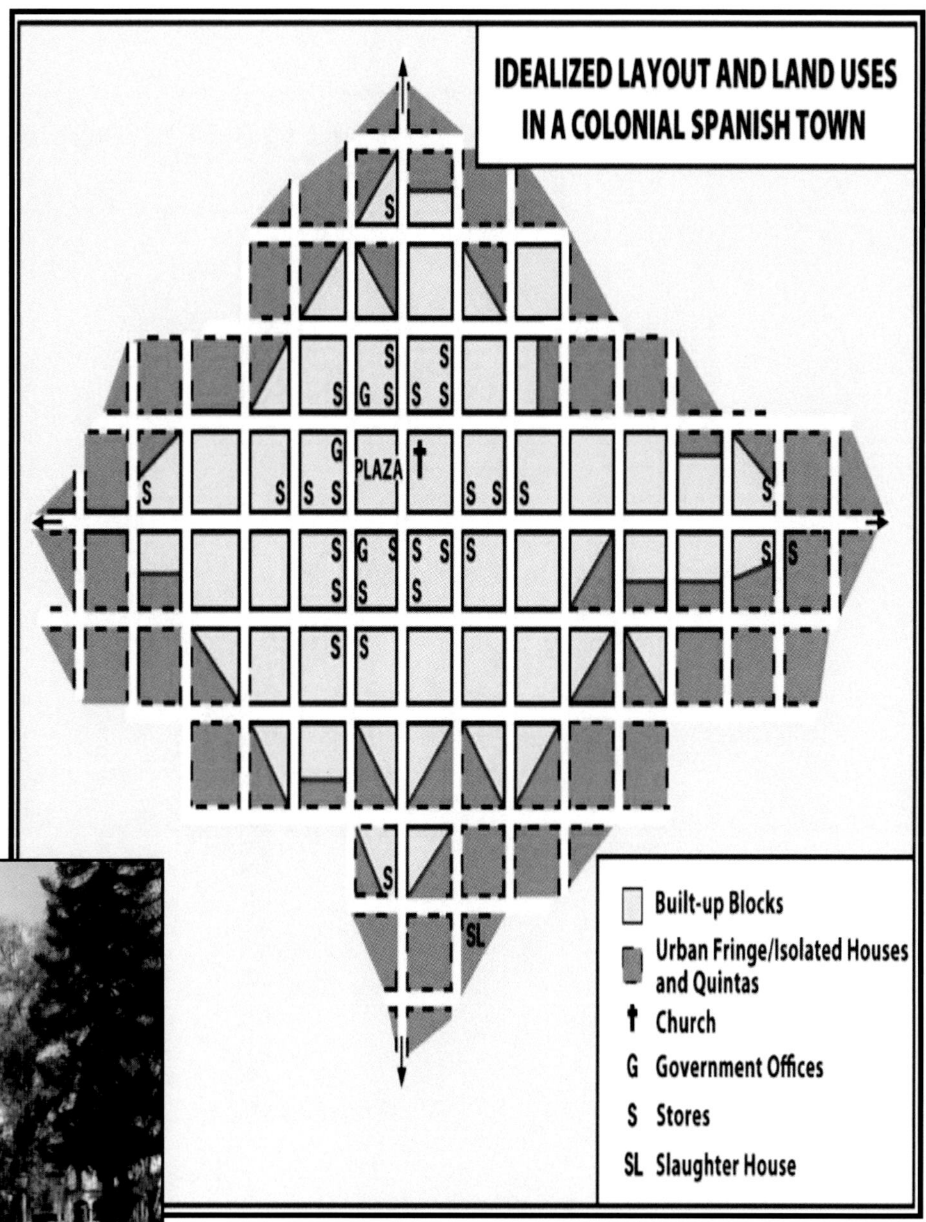

IDEALIZED LAYOUT AND LAND USES IN A COLONIAL SPANISH TOWN
PLAZA
SL
Built-up Blocks
Urban Fringe/Isolated Houses and Quintas
Church
G Government Offices
S Stores
SL Slaughter House

Central square, Patzcuaro, Mexico

Generalized Model of The Latin American City

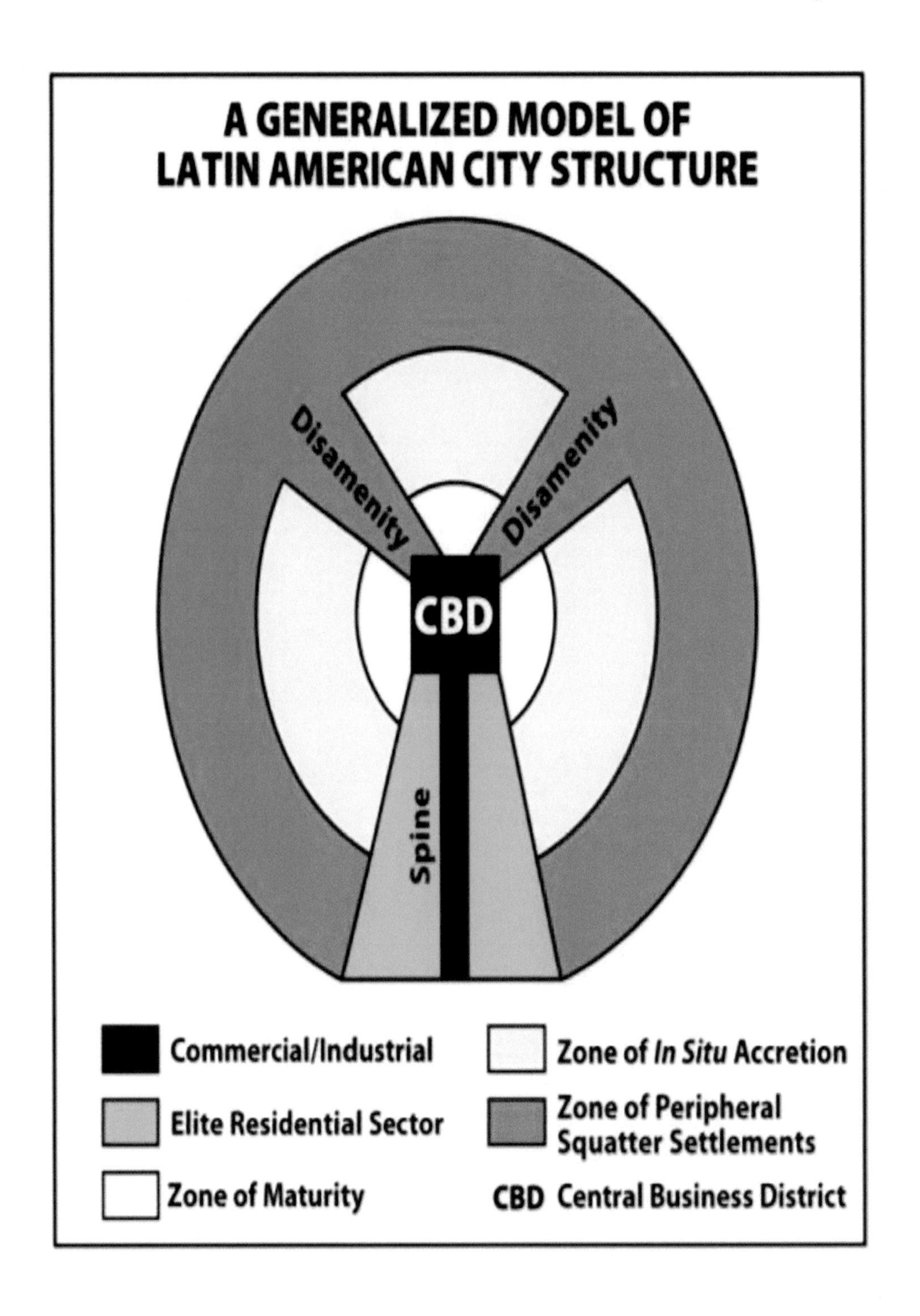

A GENERALIZED MODEL OF
LATIN AMERICAN CITY STRUCTURE
Disamenity
Disamenity
CBD
Spine
Commercial/Industrial
Zone of In Situ Accretion
Elite Residential Sector
Zone of Peripheral Squatter Settlements
Zone of Maturity
CBD Central Business District

Belém, Pará, Brazil

Rio de Janeiro's **shantytowns or *favelas***

Rio's '*zona sul*' or **upper class area**

Lima's shantytowns or *favelas*

Lima, Peru – Tyrell Heaton

North American Urban Expansion

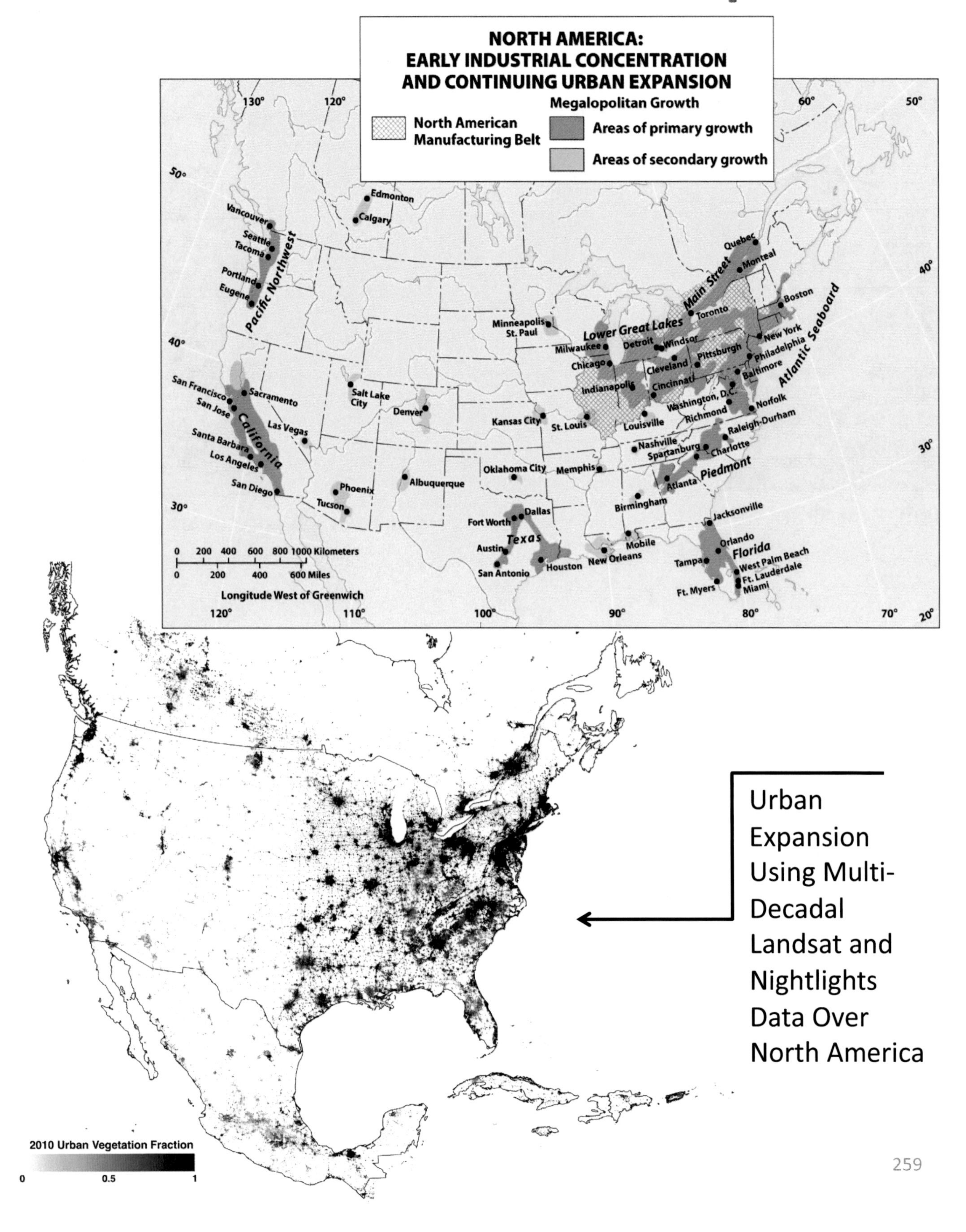

NORTH AMERICA:
EARLY INDUSTRIAL CONCENTRATION
AND CONTINUING URBAN EXPANSION
Megalopolitan Growth
North American Manufacturing Belt
Areas of primary growth
Areas of secondary growth
Pacific Northwest
California
Texas
Florida
Piedmont
Atlantic Seaboard
Lower Great Lakes
Main Street
0 200 400 600 800 1000 Kilometers
0 200 400 600 Miles
Longitude West of Greenwich
2010 Urban Vegetation Fraction
0
0.5
1

Urban Expansion Using Multi-Decadal Landsat and Nightlights Data Over North America

Central Place Theory

Walter Christaller developed his "Central Place Theory" in the 1930s. This theory is based on his idea that settlements only existed to function as "central places" to provide services for the surrounding area. This theory is part of the study of urbanization, taking into account the importance of supply and demand.

DISTINCT RULES

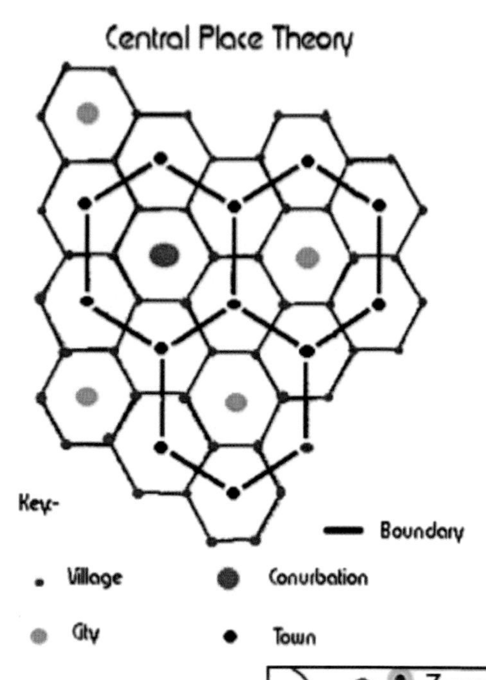

Central Place Theory
Key-
Boundary
Village
Conurbation
City
Town

- The larger the settlement, the less number of settlements and farther apart they are.
- The less there are of a settlement, the larger the hinterland, or sphere of influence, of its goods and services
- Places of the same size will be spaced the same distance apart

Over the years, geographers have completed a number of studies in which they have found reasonable spatial evidence that Central-Place Theory has practical application. Notice the somewhat hexagonal arrangement of central places in Central Mexico depicted

Zamora
Jacona
Tangamandapio
Purépero
Carapán
Villa Jiménez
Caurio
N
Tangancícuaro
Tarécuato
Patambán
Chilchota
Ocumicho
Zacapu
Naranja
Tanaco
Santiago Azajo
Tinguindín
Pamatácuaro
Cocucho
Nurío
Ahuirán
Cherán
Santa Clara
San Felipe
Purenchecuaro
Los Reyes
Corupo
Paracho
Quinceo
Sevina
Erongarícuaro
San Lorenzo
Capácuaro
Pátzcuaro
Angahuan
Tingambato
Huiramangaro
Peribán
URUAPAN
Ziracuaretiro
Zirahuen
Opopeo
Nuevo San Juan
Zirimícuaro
Villa Escalante
Pareo
Tancítaro
Taretán
Ario de Rosales
Parácuaro
Lombardía
Apatzingán
Buenos Aires
Presa del Rosario
Antunez
Nueva Italia
0
km
25

- Central places: population 20,000+
- Other towns: population 10,001–20,000
- "Urban" localities: population 2,501–10,000

Central Place Theory

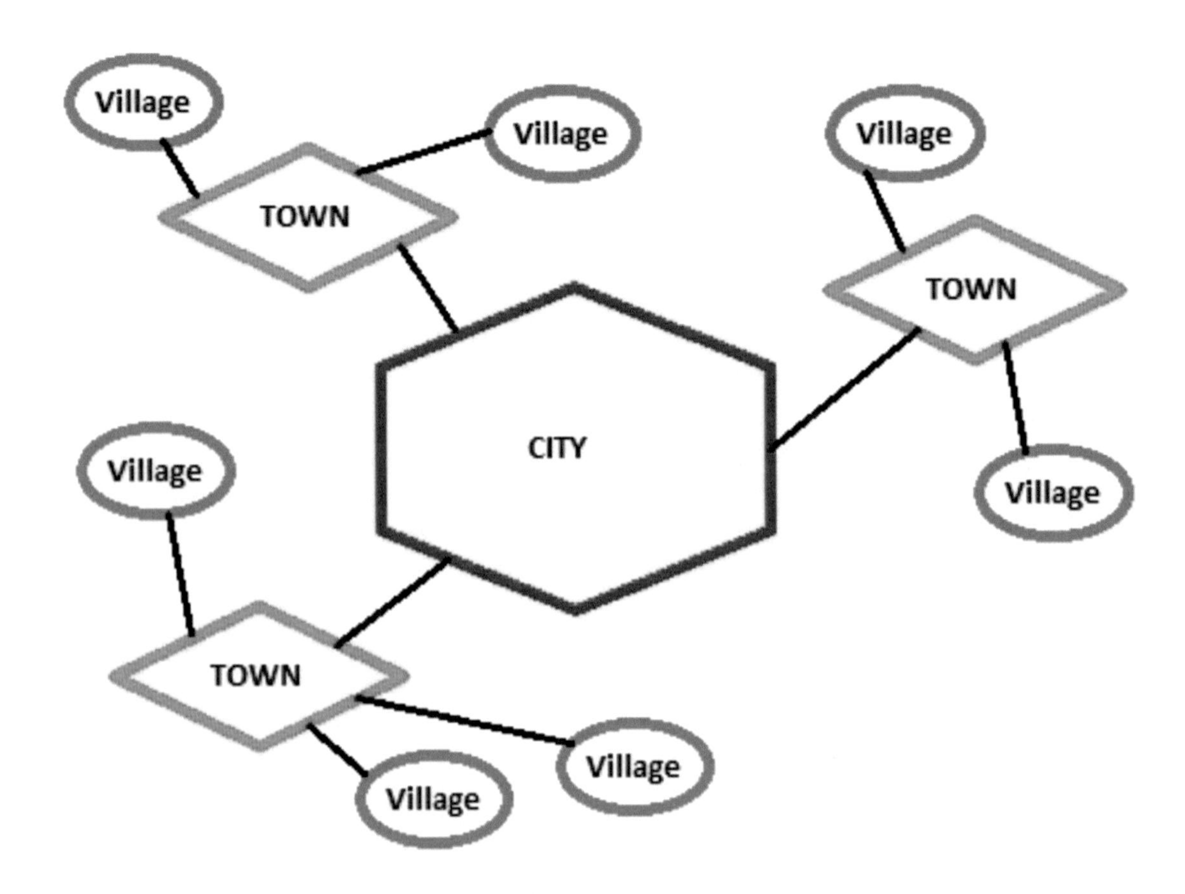
Village
Village
Village
TOWN
TOWN
CITY
Village
Village
TOWN
Village
Village

This night image of Central Europe is a good example of the regular pattern of urban development.

Urban Hierarchy

Urban areas exhibit a large range of population sizes—from hamlets to global cities—each having a corresponding economic role within the urban system. Settlements with larger populations that provide more and diverse services are higher up the urban hierarchy. Settlements with smaller populations and a limited number and type of services are further down the urban hierarchy.

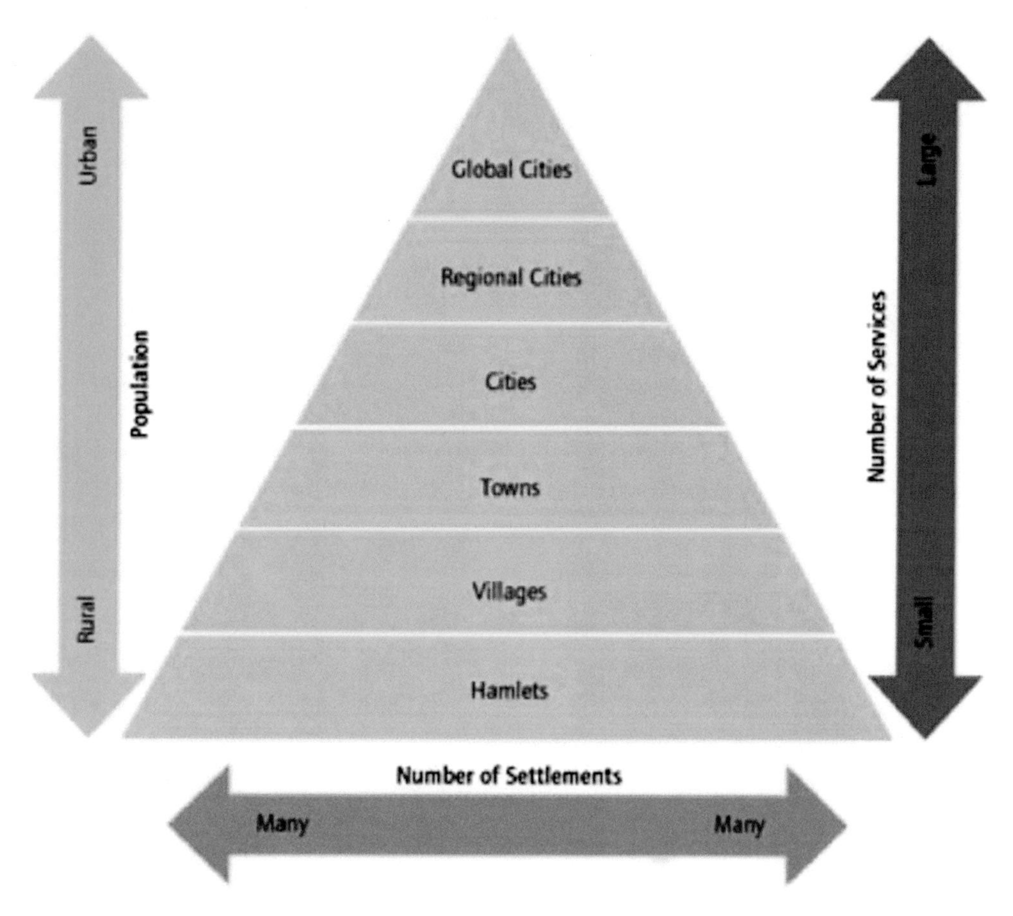
Urban
Rural
Population
Global Cities
Regional Cities
Cities
Towns
Villages
Hamlets
Large
Small
Number of Services
Number of Settlements
Many
Many

The urban hierarchy is illustrated by a pyramid where the smallest settlements (hamlets) are at the bottom of the pyramid and global cities are at the top.

Settlements at the bottom of the pyramid have small, rural populations and contain a small number and limited variety of economic services within

Residential Segregation

Residential segregation is the physical separation of two or more groups into different neighborhoods, or a form of segregation that sorts population groups into various neighborhood contexts and shapes the living environment at the neighborhood level. Currently in the United States this is mostly done by choice; however, circumstances such as socio-economic factors may play a role.

South Woodward Avenue
8 Mile Road
Woodward Avenue
Van Dyke Ave
Van Dyke St
E Davison St
Mount Olivet Cemetery

Detroit, amongst the most segregated cities in America, 8 Mile Road serves as a sharp racial dividing line.
1 Dot = 1 Person

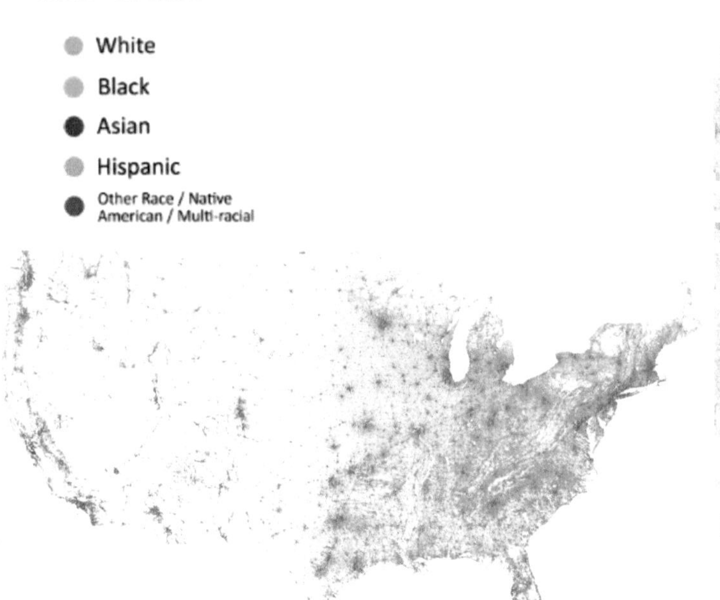
White
Black
Asian
Hispanic
Other Race / Native American / Multi-racial

Minneapolis (left); St. Paul (right) in Minnesota

Site and Situation

SITE & SITUATION OF SETTLEMENTS

Two key factors are important for where a Settlement will be located:

SITE is the physical landscape a settlement is built on

SITUATION is the settlement location relative to the surrounding area

Dunluce Castle, Northern Ireland – Tyrell Heaton

Site

WET POINT SITES - water supply is a key factor; many settlements grew near a river or spring. Early villages were often located at springs, at base of escarpments, or where simple wells could be constructed.
DRY POINT SITES are found on areas of higher land away from marshy areas or areas prone to flooding.
DEFENSE – sites were often chosen for the higher land which gave a good view in case of attack. These sites are also found on meanders in rivers (the "S" bend in the river) – which form a natural barrier.
BUILDING MATERIALS / FUEL SUPPLY were heavy and bulky to transport so villages grew where wood or stone were available.
GOOD FARMING LAND was essential to produce food (an ideal location would be suitable for growing food and rearing animals). Many villages grew on fertile lowlands.
ACCESSIBILITY & COMMUNICATION were essential – villages grew at bridging points, crossroads/route centers (and gaps between hills).
SHELTER & ASPECT is an important aspect in site. For example, in Great Britain a south-facing slope is protected from cold northerly winds and gains maximum benefit from sun's warmth.

These site factors are no longer as important as they used to be (POLITICAL and ECONOMIC factors are more important today). Most factors can be prevailed over with the aid of modern technology (Example = LAS VEGAS – built in middle of desert and everything has to be transported in for people.

Situation

A settlement with good access to natural resources and near other settlements will grow in size.
Settlements with the best situations grow into cities.

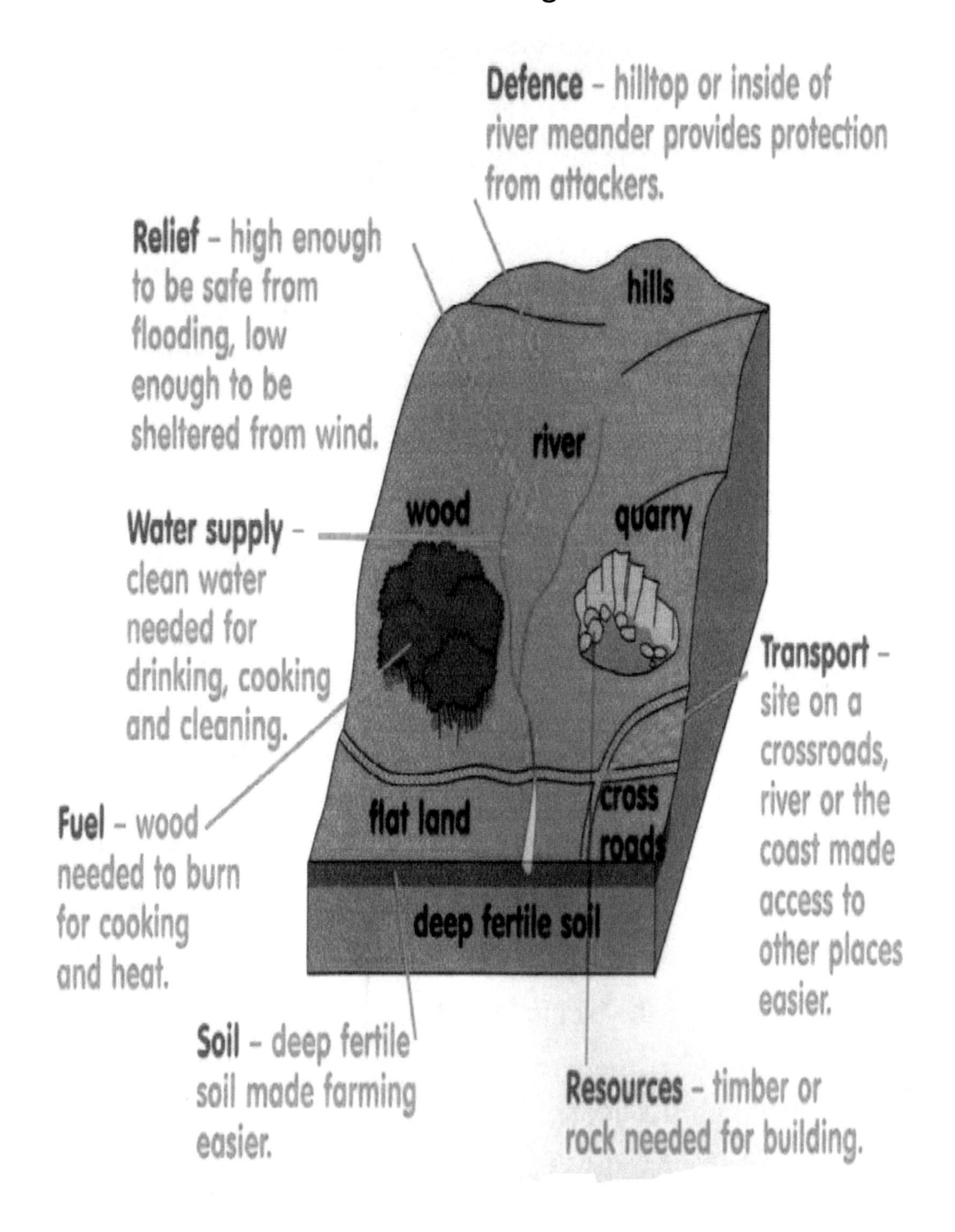
Defence – hilltop or inside of river meander provides protection from attackers.
Relief – high enough to be safe from flooding, low enough to be sheltered from wind.
hills
river
wood
quarry
Water supply – clean water needed for drinking, cooking and cleaning.
Transport – site on a crossroads, river or the coast made access to other places easier.
Fuel – wood needed to burn for cooking and heat.
flat land
cross roads
deep fertile soil
Soil – deep fertile soil made farming easier.
Resources – timber or rock needed for building.

Settlement Patterns

As Settlements grow they develop distinctive shapes and patterns. Settlements may contain a mixture of these patterns.

Linear buildings along a communicatio line; river, or road

Nucleated buildings grouped together, initially for defense, later for social anc economic reasons

Dispersed buildings are spread apart fı communication link and each other

Planned settlements on newly reclaim or developed land

Linear - settlement built in a line ⇨ along a road or in a valley ⇨ sometimes called ribbon development.

Dispersed - Isolated houses or farms ⇨ also found in areas of steep relief.

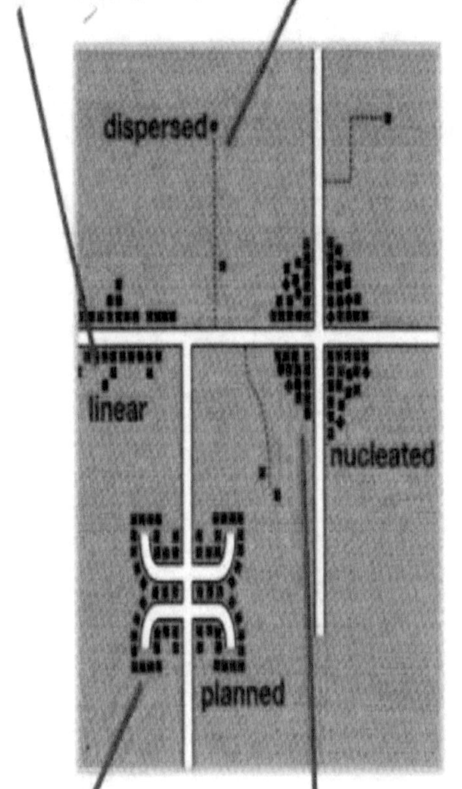
dispersed
linear
nucleated
planned

Planned - today many settlements are planned different shapes exist ⇨ square, crescent and even aeroplane (Brasilia).

Nucleated - houses clustered together around a central point ⇨ a crossroads, water supply or market place.

Example - **PARIS**

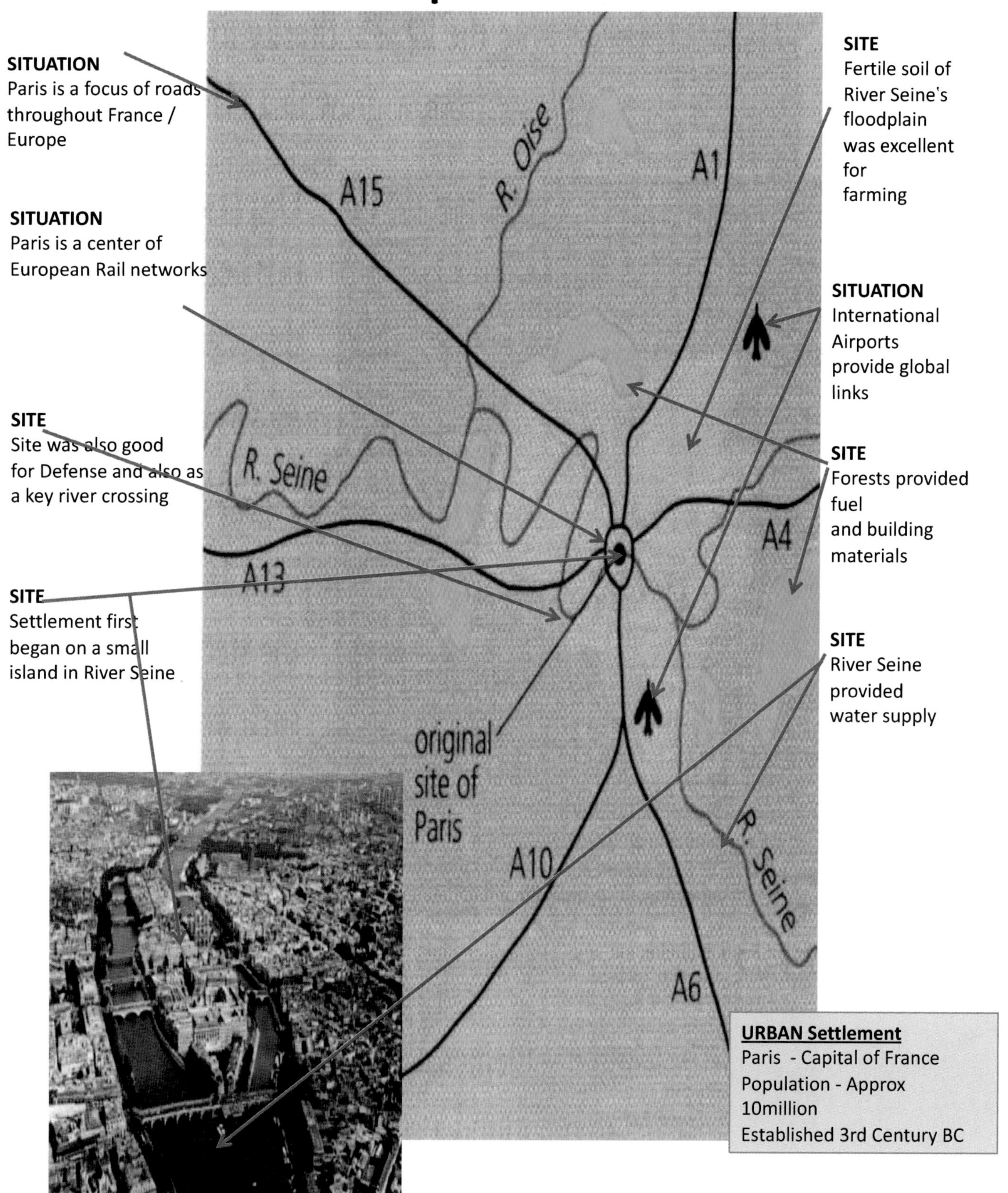
SITUATION
Paris is a focus of roads throughout France / Europe
SITUATION
Paris is a center of European Rail networks
SITE
Site was also good for Defense and also as a key river crossing
SITE
Settlement first began on a small island in River Seine
SITE
Fertile soil of River Seine's floodplain was excellent for farming
SITUATION
International Airports provide global links
SITE
Forests provided fuel and building materials
SITE
River Seine provided water supply
A15
R. Oise
A1
R. Seine
A4
A13
original site of Paris
A10
A6
R. Seine
URBAN Settlement
Paris - Capital of France
Population - Approx 10million
Established 3rd Century BC

Example – **Warkworth (UK)**

Warkworth never grew into a city despite many site advantages

SITE

River :

•may be used for transport,

•provides water supply,

•provides defense on 3 sides, can be bridged easily

Relief:

•firm, flat land

•easy to build on Dry Point Site

Good farming land nearby

Forest and Rock outcrops nearby provide building materials.

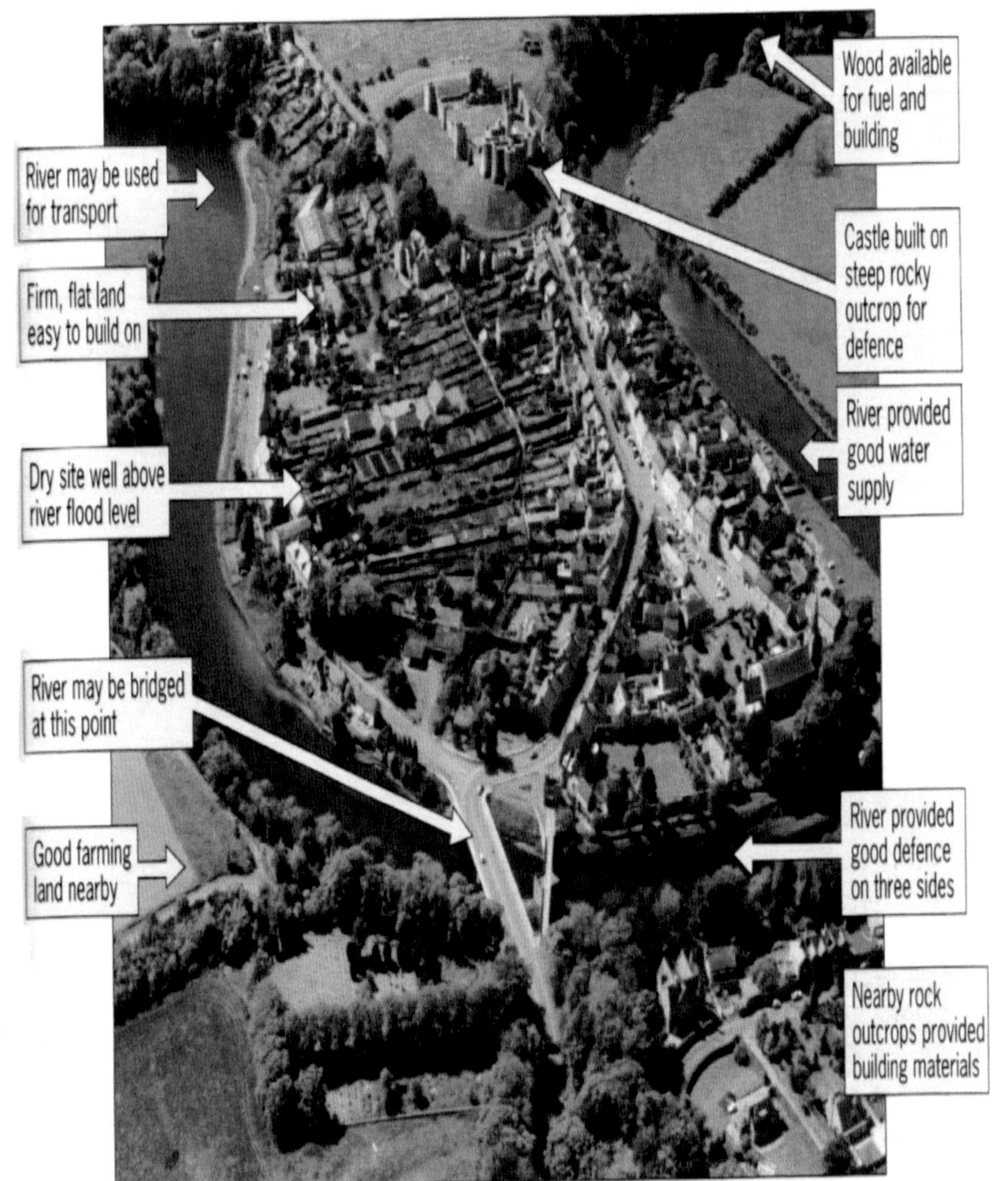

Wood available for fuel and building
River may be used for transport
Castle built on steep rocky outcrop for defence
Firm, flat land easy to build on
River provided good water supply
Dry site well above river flood level
River may be bridged at this point
River provided good defence on three sides
Good farming land nearby
Nearby rock outcrops provided building materials

SITUATION

Original advantages are not important today. Services and links to these services are not readily available here.

Example – **Rio de Janeiro, Brazil**

Settlement in LECDs

(Least Economically Developed Countries, "underdeveloped nations" or Developing Nations)
Previously referred to as "third world countries"

The world's fastest growing cities are presently in LEDCs

Growth of cities in South America is the result of Rural-Urban Migration

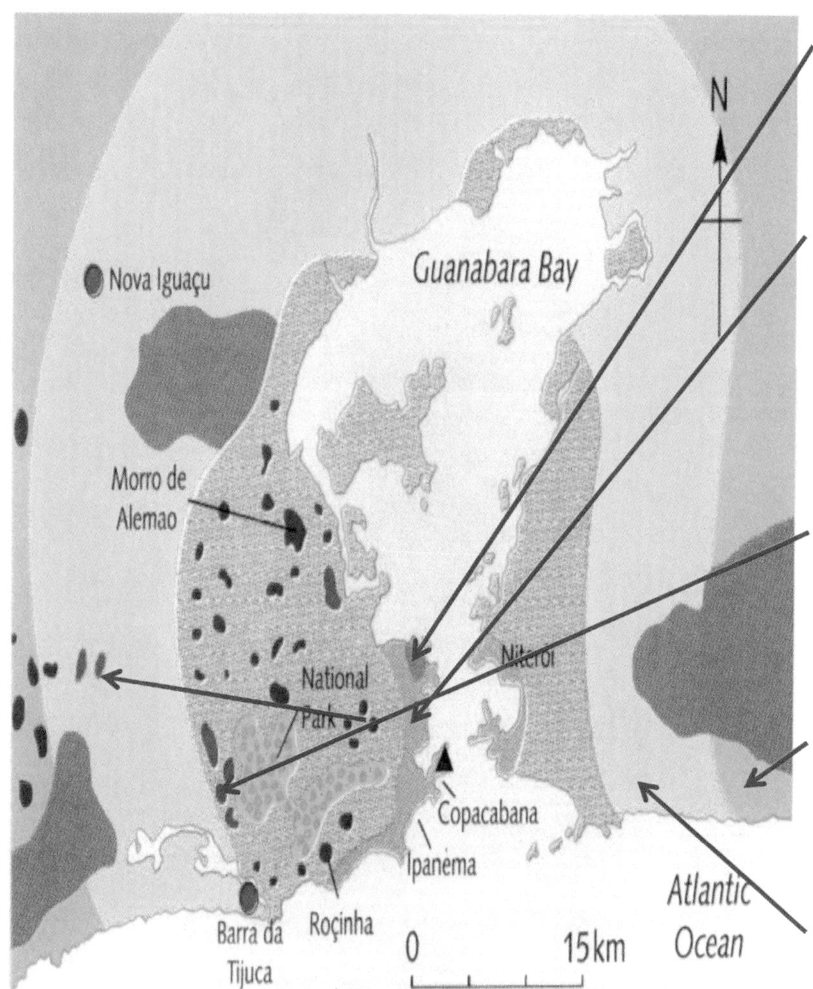

N
Guanabara Bay
Nova Iguaçu
Morro de Alemao
National Park
Niteroi
Copacabana
Ipanema
Barra da Tijuca
Roçinha
0
15km
Atlantic Ocean

CBD (Central Business District) focused in old, historical part of the city many shops, offices and company HQs - problems of crime, pollution, congestion – though still a 'vibrant' place to be.

Luxury Apartments close to city centre where people work and have fantastic views over bay; rich beginning to move to new towns on outskirts (Barra da Tijuca) which are safer, quieter, less polluted.

Favelas built 40-50 years ago and found closer to city center. Poor people move from the countryside; as there are no available homes they build their own from whatever material they can find.

(Newer Outer Suburbs) 'shanty towns' built on steep slopes where floods and landslides may occur.

(Older Inner Suburbs) improved homes, replacing shacks with brick houses; these have become towns in their own rights with approx. 100 000 inhabitants; these areas are located close to the factories where people work.

LECD Settlement
Rio de Janeiro - Population - Approx 12million
3 rd Largest City in Brazil; Situated around the huge natural harbor of Guanabara Bay

Sphere of Influence

(also Urban Field, Catchment Area, Market Area and Hinterland)

It is the area served by the goods, services, administration and employment of a settlement

Range is the maximum distance people are prepared to travel to use a service
* Goods bought frequently are called convenience goods è.g. - weekly shopping (people only travel short distances)
* Goods bought infrequently are called comparison goods è.g. - furniture (people travel greater distances)

Threshold is the minimum number of people needed to support a service
* Shops selling convenience goods have low threshold populations
* Shops selling comparison goods have high threshold populations

A Sphere of Influence Model

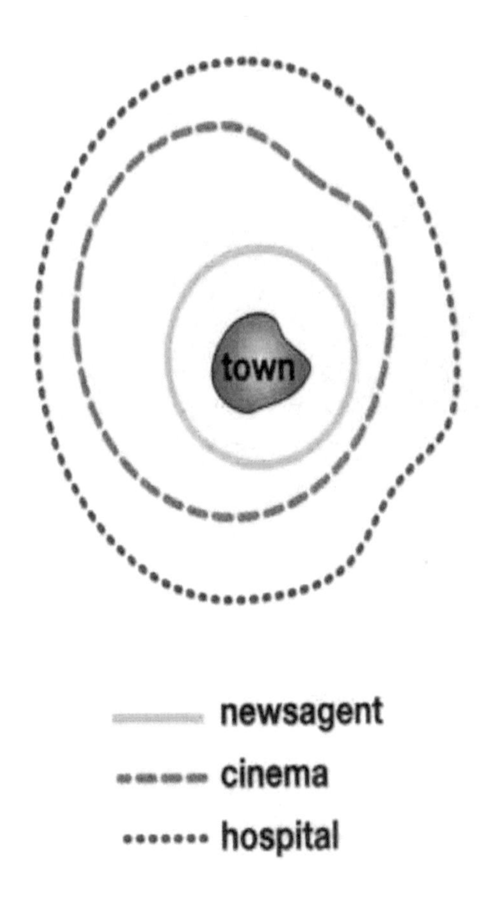
town
newsagent
cinema
hospital

The Functions of Settlements

On a basic level Settlement function can be described as: Residential;
Administrative;
Industrial; Commercial and Services
*The **function of a Settlement is its social and economic activities***
Most cities have more than one function:

TYPE OF FUNCTION	DESCRIPTION	WORLD EXAMPLE
Market Town	Originally collecting and distributing centers for surrounding farming area. Today they may service and process agricultural machinery and produce.	Winnipeg, Canada
Mining	Developed to exploit local mineral or fuels.	Prudhoe Bay, Alaska
Industrial Manufacturing	Where raw materials are processed into manufactured goods.	Pittsburgh, Pennsylvania
Ports	Located on coasts, rivers and lakes for the movement of goods and people from land to sea, or vice versa.	Thunder Bay, Canada
Route Centers	At the convergence of several natural routes or at nodal points (where communication links meet) resulting from economic development.	Paris, France
Commercial	Providing the needs of industry and business.	Hong Kong
Cultural/ Religious	Attracting people, perhaps for a short period, for educational and religious purposes.	Mecca, Saudi Arabia
Administrative	Developed to control areas which may vary from a small region (County Town) to a country (Capital City).	Brasilia, Brazil
Residential	Where the majority of residents live but do not work.	Rosslyn, Virginia
Tourist/ Resorts	Include spa towns, coastal and mountain resorts.	Orlando, Florida

Urbanizations in MEDCs

(MEDC) More Economically Developed Countries

- **Urbanization is an increase in the percentage of people living in cities.**
- **Urban Growth is the expansion of cities into the surrounding area.**

Urbanization affects RURAL and URBAN areas of a Country.

<u>Problems for the COUNTRYSIDE</u>	**<u>Problems for the CITY</u>**
-little rural investment	-overcrowding
-ageing population-young move out	-shortage of housing and jobs
-fewer extended families; changing social trends	-spontaneous settlements; shanty towns
-continued poverty	-young population (rapid increase in birth rate)
-continued reliance on agriculture	-sanitation and transport systems cannot cope
-economic stagnation	

Urbanization in LEDCs

(LEDC) Less Economically Developed Countries

- **Urbanization is an increase in the percentage of people living in cities.**
- **Urban Growth is the expansion of cities into the surrounding area.**

3 MAIN CAUSES OF URBANISATION IN LEDCs

1. Rural-Urban Migration has increased the relative proportion of people living in cities

<u>Rural 'PUSH' Factors</u>
-drought
-overgrazing by farm animals: (soil erosion)
-remoteness: lack of services
-pests eat crops and cause ill health
-farm machinery replaces workers; (unemployment)
-large families; not enough land for heirs
-poor seed; poor tools; little fertilizer; low output; insufficient food

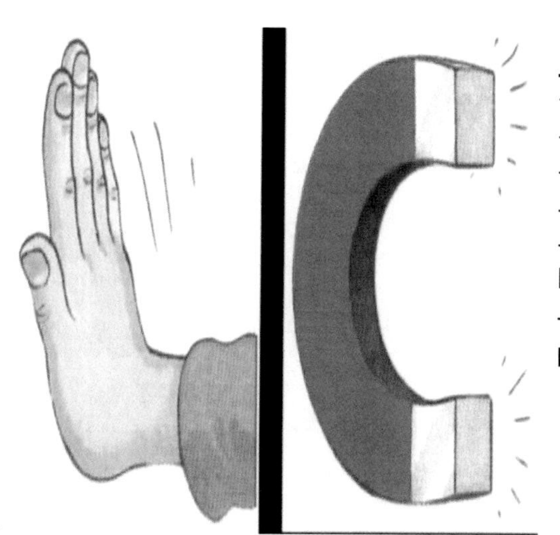

<u>Urban 'PULL' Factors</u>
-jobs in industry
-better housing, schools, hospitals
-more reliable sources of food
-higher salaries
-shops and entertainment ('bright lights')
-ability to carry out religious practices safely

2. Infrastructure of Cities in LEDCs is expanding faster than in rural areas, which attracts industrial investment (and people looking for work).

3. Population increase tends to be faster in urban areas because health care is better, so the death rate is lower. Also people moving to the cities are younger and have more children.

Urban Renewal

URBAN RENEWAL SCHEMES aim to attract industry back into older areas and encourage investment in new housing, amenities and employment. (e.g. - U Street Corridor - Washington DC)

Gentrification: old terraced houses and industrial buildings are converted to high-quality housing. (e.g. - Warehouse District, Minneapolis, MN)
Urban Regeneration: derelict factories and wasteland redeveloped with office blocks, shops and leisure
facilities. (e.g. - Camden Yards, Baltimore, MD)
Urban Redevelopment: old terraced housing replaced with tower blocks. (e.g. – Philadelphia, PA)
Integrated Transport Systems: new ring roads, light railways and trams relieve congestion. (e.g. - Hiawatha Lightrail, Minneapolis, MN)

Before

One of the biggest spots for gentrification in the country is the south Bronx. There's slowly more and more whites moving into the area. They're building on the vacant lots that once housed rubble from the buildings (from when the Bronx was burning). They're turning them into 2 family houses and luxury condos. There are a bunch of vacant lots, but new ones are springing up all over.

After

WHY GEOGRAPHY?

Never in history has a nation possessed more information, or been in command of more sophisticated means of acquiring, disseminating, and analyzing data than do contemporary Americans. Yet, given these potential means of enhancing geographic awareness and global understanding, most Americans – living in the Age of the Atom (or Satellite, or Computer, or cell phone or . . .) – continue to possess little more than a "Stone Age" awareness of the world in which we live and upon which we depend for our survival.

To individuals lacking a well developed "mental map" of Earth and its varied mosaic of physical and human features and conditions – the very heart and soul of geographic knowledge – the globe must appear as a fragmented and confusing hodgepodge of unrelated phenomena without pattern, rhyme, or reason. Theirs is a world inhabited by faceless people and cultures adrift without a proud heritage, unique institutions and customs, or revealing spatial dimensions. Places, to the geographic illiterate, lack the essential context of location, features, character, and relevance. Their world is composed of vague physical features and life sustaining environmental systems for which they lack appropriate terminology, valid mental images, or an understanding of causative agents or processes; they also lack sufficient knowledge of human use potentials to render reasoned decisions relating to wise human use of and care for Earth's abundant natural endowment.

To persons with no understanding of geography, temporal events occurred in a spatial vacuum, with "history" and "geography" being unrelated in space and time. Such individuals are confronted with a host of critical global problems and issues for which they lack reasoned criteria on which to base rational analyses, judgments, or attempts at resolution. To the geographically unaware, human differences can appear to be threatening and often constitute the basis for feelings of prejudice and acts of discrimination. Such individuals are prisoners of their own ignorance and provincialism. How poorly equipped they are to assume meaningful citizenship in the increasingly intra-dependent global community!

It stands as a rather sad and somewhat inexplicable indictment of this country's public priority and educational system that among the world's educated industrial societies, Americans rank among the least literate in geographic knowledge and curiosity. Examples of geographic "illiteracy" are numerous, as are the increasingly apparent and damaging consequences – be they social, economic, political, military, or environmental – of our failure to provide citizens with adequate geographic training.

In most countries of the Western urban-industrial world (and in many Third World countries as well), geography constitutes the "core" of the social science curriculum. The United States is somewhat unique among these nations in relegating geography to a very minor role in both elementary and secondary education. Although considerable progress has been made in terms of enhancing geography's position in the curriculum during recent years, it remains a sad and somewhat shocking reality that most

In an increasingly complex, troubled, and closely intertwined world community of cultures and nations, Americans simply do not know much about our global neighbors or, for that matter, we in a geographic sense. We have little understanding of, or feeling for, their lands and peoples, their resources, capabilities, or attainments; we are ignorant of their cultural similarities and difference, their hopes and dreams, and their problems and needs. Perhaps the greatest importance, we fail to understand how important they have become to us and we have become to them. How can Americans expect to maintain a position of leadership, strength, and respect within a world of nations about which we know – and seemingly care – so little?

Now more than ever, our citizens can ill-afford to remain ignorant of the world about us. The compression of time and space made possible by technological "explosion" has placed our most remote neighbors at our very doorstep. It is essential that all Americans know something about global community in which we reside. We must be aware of its fundamental physical and cultural patterns, its basic locations, divisions, networks, and systems; we must understand its basic interrelationships, including areas of production and need; and we must understand sources of conflict and promote reasoned means of resolution.

Geography is the ancient and time-honored field of study that can best provide the essential training needed to ensure that our citizens are prepared to assume responsible and enlightened leadership for the future.

T.S. Elliot wrote, "We shall not cease from exploration, and the end of all our exploring will be to arrive where we started and to know the place for the first time." We must think globally and act locally. By better knowing the world about us, we come to better know ourselves.

//TYRELL HEATON//

http://www.tyrellheaton.com/sense-of-place
http://www.tyrellheaton.com/sense-of-place/europe
http://www.tyrellheaton.com/sense-of-place/south-asia
http://www.tyrellheaton.com/sense-of-place/east-asia
http://www.tyrellheaton.com/sense-of-place/southeast-asia
http://www.tyrellheaton.com/sense-of-place/austral-realm-australia-new-zealand
http://www.tyrellheaton.com/sense-of-place/sub-saharan-africa
http://www.tyrellheaton.com/sense-of-place/north-africa-southwest-asia-to-include-the-middle-east
http://www.tyrellheaton.com/sense-of-place/middle-america-mexico-to-panama-and-the-caribbean
http://www.tyrellheaton.com/sense-of-place/south-america